WILDLIFE MANAGEMENT:

Science & Technology

Second Edition

CHARLES D. STUTZENBAKER

Certified Wildlife Biologist
Former Biologist, Texas Parks
and Wildlife Department
Port Arthur, Texas

BRENDA J. SCHEIL

Agriculture Teacher
Prairie Farm, Wisconsin

MICHAEL K. SWAN

Agricultural Educator
Washington State University
Pullman, Washington

JASPER S. LEE

Agricultural Educator
Adjunct Professor
North Carolina State University

JERI MATTICS OMERNIK

Agriculture Writer
Rocky Mountain Marketing Communications, Inc.
Montrose, Colorado

WILDLIFE MANAGEMENT:
Science & Technology

Second Edition

AgriScience & Technology Series

Jasper S. Lee — Series Editor

Interstate Publishers, Inc.
Danville, Illinois

Cover design by Jody Mattics, Rocky Mountain Marketing Communications, Inc., Montrose, Colorado

ISBN 0-8134-3244-8

1 2 3 4 5 6 7 8 9 10   06 05 04 03 02

128269

Preface

How important are wildlife? Sometimes we fail to consider all of the important contributions they make. Wildlife provide many benefits in assuring a good environment for people. The interactions of wildlife with each other, with humans, and with non-living things make our world a better place to live.

Every person needs basic knowledge of wildlife science and management. Better citizenship and the ability to participate in society's decisions result from wildlife education. Knowing that wildlife are far more than hunted game species is important. Further, emphasizing the well-being of animals in managing and using wildlife resources is essential.

Wildlife Management Science & Technology, 2nd Edition, is the perfect book for introductory classes in wildlife. It carefully defines and presents important concepts. All aspects of wildlife are built on a science-based foundation. Biological science has a major role. Earth science and environmental science are important areas that support wildlife. People without interest in hunting game animals can derive considerable benefit from the study of wildlife.

An integrated approach to the study of wildlife is used in this book. State education standards have been considered in the overall content of the book. Further, a broad approach to wildlife is taken. Wildlife species include all living things that have not been domesticated. Emphasis is on animals. Plants, algae, and other living kingdoms are included to a lesser extent. Relationships between all species are stressed.

This book is also the perfect introduction for students interested in hunting, fishing, and other uses of wildlife. Safety is emphasized. Being responsible citizens is stressed. Making good decisions is an undergirding principle. Relating to individuals with different opinions about taking wildlife is carefully integrated throughout the book. Further, human interests have been included throughout the book with wildlife connections and career profiles.

The 1st Edition of this book was exceptionally well received by students and teachers. They found that no other book matches this book for an introductory wildlife class. The solid foundation of authors, reviewers, resources, and support make the *Wildlife Management Science & Technology*, 2nd Edition, even better.

Begin your study today.

Acknowledgments

The authors are indebted to many people who helped make this book possible. A number are acknowledged throughout the book as photographs and other resources are presented. Several are recognized here for their important contributions.

The teachers and students who used the 1st Edition were valuable sources of input for the 2nd Edition. These individuals are acknowledged and thanked for their helpful suggestions.

Two individuals who initially made strong contributions to the book are Clyde Gottschalk of the Association of Texas Soil and Water Conservation Districts and Charles Thoits of the New Hampshire Fish and Game Department. These individuals carefully reviewed the draft manuscript and offered many useful suggestions.

Marion Fletcher, state supervisor of agricultural education with the Arkansas Department of Education, reviewed the revised manuscript.

Michael Melgaard, wildlife biologist with Cooper Engineering of Rice Lake, Wisconsin, is acknowledged for his assistance in providing resource materials.

Jody Mattics of Rocky Mountain Marketing Communications, Inc., Montrose, Colorado, is acknowledged for her assistance in designing the cover.

Other individuals are acknowledged here. George Hurst, professor in the Department of Wildlife and Fisheries, Mississippi State University, is acknowledged for his assistance with illustrations. LaVonda Walton of the U.S. Fish and Wildlife Service is acknowledged for valuable assistance in locating and providing illustrations. Betty Branch and Stanley Harrison of the U.S. Department of Agriculture are acknowledged for their assistance with illustrations. Dale Payne, Tracy Westrom, and Amanda Patrick of Piedmont College are recognized for their assistance with photographs, nature settings, and wildlife information.

The authors are most grateful to the staff of Interstate Publishers, Inc., for their assistance. Kim Romine and Rita Lange are acknowledged for their assistance in design and graphics in the book. Mary Carter is acknowledged for assistance in preparing line art. Vernie Thomas is acknowledged for his enthusiastic support and help in all phases of producing the book. Dan Pentony is acknowledged for his assistance in refining the outline and conceptualizing the final product.

Each author acknowledges the important roles of family members and close associates in helping this book become reality.

Contents

PART ONE—IMPORTANCE OF WILDLIFE AND ITS INDUSTRY

PART TWO—SCIENCE AND TECHNOLOGY IN WILDLIFE MANAGEMENT

PART THREE—ANIMAL WILDLIFE MANAGEMENT

PART FOUR—PLANT WILDLIFE MANAGEMENT

PART FIVE—ENJOYING WILDLIFE: CITIZEN RESPONSIBILITIES

APPENDIXES

Importance of Wildlife and Its Industry

CHAPTER 1

Importance of Wildlife

OBJECTIVES

This chapter introduces the importance of wildlife and how wildlife species are classified. The objectives of the chapter are:

1 Explain the importance of wildlife resources.

2 Explain wildlife conservation, management, and recreation.

3 Describe how wildlife species are classified.

4 Identify impacts on wildlife populations.

5 Explain biodiversity as related to wildlife populations.

TERMS

aesthetic value	fisheries	renewable natural resource
aquatic wildlife	game	scientific value
biodiversity	game value	terrestrial wildlife
commercial value	habitat	wildlife
consumptive use	mortality	wildlife animal
domestication	natality	wildlife conservation
ecological value	nonconsumptive use	wildlife management
ecology	overpopulation	wildlife plant
ecosystem	population density	wildlife population

1-1. Wildlife must sometimes be captured and moved to expand populations. This shows a sedated gray wolf being prepared for moving to a new area by helicopter. (Courtesy, U.S. Fish and Wildlife Service)

MANY living things are found on Earth. Scientists have identified about two million different species. These organisms help people enjoy life on a wonderful planet! They make our lives fun and provide for a near balance in nature so life-giving processes can occur.

What would our lives be like without wildlife? Wildlife species add to the enjoyment of living in many ways. As you travel from your home, you may see birds, rabbits, wildflowers, and many other forms of wildlife. Each has an important role in maintaining a quality planet on which humans can live.

Sometimes, people fail to treat wildlife properly. Some species have been wiped out forever by human actions. Other species are in danger of becoming extinct—gone from the earth. Fortunately, people can learn to wisely use and protect wildlife.

WILDLIFE RESOURCES

Most of the living things on Earth are wildlife. **Wildlife** includes all plants, animals, and other living things that have not been domesticated. Wildlife biologists sometimes restrict the definition to animals. That is not the case in this book.

Domestication is the process of bringing living things under the control of humans. These organisms are grown by humans—often in a controlled environment. Common domesticated organisms include animals, such as dogs, cats, sheep, and horses, and plants, such as tomatoes, cotton, beans, and petunias. Domestication is important in producing the food and clothing people need. For example, dairy cattle are kept in carefully controlled conditions and milked to assure a quality food product.

1-2. Mountain sheep are appealing wildlife. (Courtesy, U.S. Fish and Wildlife Service)

Wildlife touch our lives in many ways. Most people admire at least some forms of wildlife. Who doesn't appreciate a spotted fawn or a beautiful wildflower? We need to take a closer look. We will see many ways wildlife influences our lives. The influence often goes unnoticed.

Uses OF WILDLIFE

As users, humans are said to be consumptive or nonconsumptive. This refers to how wildlife or other natural resources are used.

A **consumptive use** is taking or harvesting wildlife. This includes hunting, fishing, trapping, or otherwise harvesting wildlife. Problems in maintaining certain wildlife populations have occurred when people made too great a consumptive use.

A **nonconsumptive use** is watching or using so the wildlife is not destroyed or taken. Bird watching and wildflower watching are examples of nonconsumptive use. Nonconsumptive use leaves wildlife for people to enjoy later. Parks are popular places for nonconsumptive use.

VALUES OF WILDLIFE

Wildlife has value in the lives of people. These values are often known as benefits or uses. Wildlife has five basic values:

1-3. A king salmon has been harvested—a consumptive use of wildlife. (Courtesy, U.S. Fish and Wildlife Service)

- Commercial value—**Commercial value** is the money realized from wildlife, including fish. This ranges from aquatic species, such as seafood, that are sold in markets to the sale of exotic animals such as bison. Wildlife also has commercial value in other ways. Travel agencies benefit from taking people on trips to enjoy wildlife. Magazines feature wildlife to create appeal in sales. In some cases, wildlife has been exploited for commercial value. The desire for hides, horns, tusks, and other products helps create value.

- Game value—**Game value** is the value placed on wildlife that is used as game. Sport hunters and fishers enjoy taking wildlife. This includes those who hunt for mushrooms, wild berries, and nuts, as well as the animals that are taken. Some individuals spend considerable money on their sport. They buy supplies, equipment, clothing, and other items. Revenue from hunting and fishing licenses provide funds for improving wildlife management. Game farms and shooting preserves are attractive to some hunters. Tourism is built around wildlife in some communities.

- Aesthetic value—**Aesthetic value** is the value people place on wildlife for its beauty and appeal. No price tag is used. State and national parks and forests feature many kinds of wildlife. People drive long distances for a chance to view wildlife. Yellowstone National Park is a popular destination. Thousands of tourists visit Yellowstone each year to see its natural wonders. Moose, bear, elk, trees, wildflowers, and other species have special appeal to park visitors. Many organizations are involved in the aesthetic value of wildlife. These organizations are supported with private funds.

- Scientific value—**Scientific value** is the value of wildlife for research and study. Many plants and animals are used in helping us better understand the environment. One example is the use of deer antlers to measure radiation levels in the environment. Another example is the use of lichens to determine the nature of air pollution. Some studies help cure human disease. A good example is the armadillo. The armadillo can

1-4. A bull frog sits on a lily pad as part of an aquatic ecosystem.

carry leprosy, and is being used to study ways of curing human leprosy. Rhesus monkeys have been most beneficial in blood research as related to humans.

• Ecological value—***Ecological value*** is the value realized from the role of each species in nature. This deals with ecology. ***Ecology*** is the study of ways organisms interact with their environment. Further, wildlife interaction with nonliving things, such as rocks and climate, is studied. The living and nonliving features of an environment comprise an ***ecosystem***. Understanding ecosystems is a major goal in successful wildlife management. Complex relationships exist. These help make our planet a desirable place for humans to live.

WILDLIFE CONSERVATION AND MANAGEMENT

Wildlife conservation is the wise use of wildlife resources. It involves maintaining a habitat that supports a species or community of species and protecting wildlife from destruction. Emphasis is on people making good decisions.

Wildlife conservation is closely related to land use. Most people recognize the importance of maintaining wildlife and preventing waste. Many people, however, fail to realize what is involved.

AREAS IN WILDLIFE CONSERVATION

Four areas are important in wildlife conservation. These are:

• Research—Research helps us understand wildlife and the habitat it needs. Wildlife research is a systematic way of seeking answers to questions about wildlife. It is carried out by industry as well as associations and government agencies. Research helps in understanding habitat needs and how to promote good habitat growth.

- Education—Education informs people about the roles they have in wildlife conservation. The education may be provided by schools, organizations, the media, and other sources. All citizens need a general knowledge of wildlife. Those who hunt and otherwise consume wildlife need to know even more about wildlife conservation.

1-5. White-tail deer populations have increased with the use of research findings. (Courtesy, Agricultural Research Service, USDA)

- Law Enforcement—Law enforcement ensures that laws related to wildlife are followed. This includes laws in all areas—research, education, and use. Much of the focus of law enforcement is often on hunting. This is to reduce violation of hunting laws.

- Management—**Wildlife management** is an important part of wildlife conservation. It is the art and science of manipulating a wildlife system to achieve a desired goal. This includes habitat production and human use of wildlife. In some cases, the practices involved are complex. Specific work related to fish is known as fishery management. Wildlife management receives much attention from hunters and others who enjoy nature.

Benefits of Wildlife Management

As the human population continues to grow, demand for space will reduce or eliminate wildlife populations. Simply, new roads, airports, power transmission lines, pipelines, homesites, schools, shopping centers, and other human activities will threaten wildlife. Smaller areas will be available for wildlife. Making good use of these areas is essential. Improving habitats is the key to having adequate wildlife populations.

Wildlife management helps to maintain wildlife populations. This will provide adequate wildlife for human enjoyment. Good wildlife management promotes hunting and non-hunting activities. Money spent on sport fishing is a welcome part of the economy of many towns and cities. Sales of hunting equipment, hunting leases, food, lodging, gasoline, and guide services are important sources of income to landowners and residents of many rural areas.

1-6. Construction activity often destroys wildlife habitat. (Courtesy, Lynn Porter, Hinds County Soil and Water Conservation District, Mississippi)

RECREATION

Wildlife provide many recreational opportunities. The nature of the activities varies widely. Some people enjoy viewing wildlife, such as observing the grandeur of a bald eagle or the detail of a ruby-throated hummingbird. Other people take canoe trips to observe wildlife along waterways. A walk through a park or zoo can provide up-close encounters with wildlife. Still other people enjoy hunting, fishing, and related activities. Searching for mushrooms, deer, berries, or other wildlife products is important to many people.

The intensity of the recreation varies. Some sport fishers enjoy hooking a trout in a crystal-clear stream. Others enjoy the challenge of hunting for moose or elk. People may travel long distances and spend considerable money on some kinds of recreation associated with wildlife.

Guide services are available to help people find and enjoy wildlife. These are found throughout the United States. Deer, moose, elk, pheasant, and other hunts may be carried

Wildlife Connection

THE NATIONAL PARK SYSTEM

The U.S. Government has set up some 355 parklands. These areas are for the benefit and enjoyment of people. Parklands often have many kinds of wildlife. All of the parks comprise the National Park System.

The first national park in the world was Yellowstone National Park, established in 1872. The purpose was to protect wildlife as well as the physical wonders, such as geysers. Today, Yellowstone and the other parks, such as Yosemite, provide great opportunities for people to explore and learn about nature.

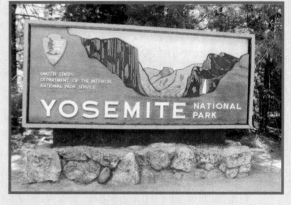

The National Park System is administered by the National Park Service, which is in the U.S. Department of the Interior. Each year, Congress appropriates money for the National Park Service. National parks are very popular. The Great Smoky Mountain National Park in Tennessee and North Carolina has the most visitors.

Career Profile

PARK RANGER

A park ranger works in a national or state park. The duties include giving tours and lectures, enforcing laws, and assisting with information and safety. Park rangers often operate boats, snowmobiles, trucks, and automobiles.

Most park rangers have a college degree in biology, wildlife science, or a closely related area. They need a good knowledge of biology and earth science. They need to be good communicators and enjoy working with people.

Most jobs are with national and state park systems. In some cases, the jobs are in remote areas far away from large cities.

out by qualified guides. Canada has many popular fishing destinations available through guide services.

WILDLIFE ORGANISMS

Wildlife can be classified in a number of ways. One method is to use a scientific approach based on the similarities and differences in wildlife. Another approach is to classify based on where wildlife species live—habitat. Other ways of classifying can be used, such as game or non-game wildlife.

SCIENTIFIC CLASSIFICATION

All organisms (living things) can be classified into one of five scientific kingdoms: animals, plants, fungi, Protista, and Monera. Each kingdom has many species, which have been identified by scientists.

Animals

A **wildlife animal** is an animal that has not been domesticated. These animals are relatively free to roam about on land or in the air or water. They live on their own and must find their food. Animals do not make their food as do plants.

Exotic wild animals found in zoos are not domesticated. They retain much of their natural behavior. Taming wild animals does not turn out well. Many will quickly attack a person who comes near or threatens them.

Some wildlife animals are used as game. **Game** is any animal hunted for sport or food. Common game animals include deer, squirrel, quail, fish, elk, and rabbit. Many game animals are protected by law. Sport hunters must follow the laws or risk being fined or sent to prison.

1-7. The rhododendron is an appealing wildlife plant. (Courtesy, Dan Pitillo, U.S. Fish and Wildlife Service)

1-8. Leaf-eating beetles are being released in this wetland area with an infestation of purple loosestrife. (Purple loosestrife is an undesirable wetland herb that can overtake a wetlands area.)

Plants

A **wildlife plant** is a plant that has not been domesticated. These plants are found on land and in water. They grow in natural environments without human effort. Examples include vines, grasses, trees, and shrubs. Plants planted and cared for on farms are usually domesticated species. Plants make their food. This is in contrast with animals, which obtain their food from other sources.

Wildflowers are popular kinds of wildlife plants. Most grow wild but some are planted along highways or in parks to beautify the area. Many plants are admired for their blossoms. Others are desired for the color of their leaves, bark, or fruit.

Some wildlife plants are pests. They can grow where they are not wanted in crops or lawns. A few wildlife plants cause allergies. Poison ivy is an example of a plant that causes a miserable itch on human skin.

Fungi

Fungi are not often viewed as wildlife. Most grow wild without human intervention. Some are grown in laboratories, such as those used in producing human medicine. Penicillin is produced from fungi.

Other fungi are also grown, such as the shiitake and portabella mushrooms. Some fungi are cultured in making cheese and yeast bread.

Fungi are organisms that absorb food from their surroundings. Many fungi are quite small and must be viewed with magnification. An example is the mold that forms on bread. Other fungi are larger, such as the mushrooms that grow in a forest. Some fungi cause disease on plants. Other fungi, known as mildew, attack property.

Many fungi perform valuable roles in the environment. They help decay dead plants and animals. This returns nutrients to the soil and releases carbon dioxide into the air. Plants use the carbon dioxide.

1-9. Mushrooms are important fungi in nature.

Monera and Protista

Monera and Protista are two kingdoms of small, single-celled organisms which are not often viewed as wildlife. They perform important functions in the environment.

Monera are found in the environment as bacteria. Most have useful roles. Some help decay plant and animal material. Other bacteria provide nutrients for plants and food for aquatic animals, such as oysters and shrimp.

Protista includes several groups of one-celled organisms. The most common are algae. Some form into groups that resemble plants, with seaweed being an example. Protista includes protozoa, amoeba, and paramecium.

HABITAT

Habitat is the physical area in which a wildlife species lives. Factors influencing habitat are climate, topography, soil, water, and presence of other living organisms. Habitats vary among the species. Some prefer wooded areas with much rain. Others prefer dry areas, steep mountain cliffs, and cool temperatures.

A major factor in classifying a wildlife species is whether the dominant feature of its habitat is on land or in water. Most are classified as terrestrial or aquatic.

1-10. Grizzly bears are terrestrial wildlife. (Courtesy, Bob Stevens, U.S. Fish and Wildlife Service)

Terrestrial Wildlife

Terrestrial wildlife is the term applied to species that live on land. Many species of plants, animals, and other kinds of wildlife fall into this category. They must have water and other nutrients to live. A wide range of climates and other conditions may be a part of a terrestrial habitat. Some species live in trees, while others live in the ground, on the surface of the ground, at high elevations, and in places with varying rainfall.

Many of the common species we see are terrestrial wildlife. Rabbits, deer, squirrels, fox, elk, and opossum are a few examples of terrestrial wildlife.

1-11. Snapping turtles live in close proximity to water. They have light brown to black shells that are spiked when young but flatten with maturity.

Aquatic Wildlife

Aquatic wildlife refers to species that live in water. Some species may spend a part of their time on the land, such as alligators and turtles. Other aquatic wildlife species spend all of their time in water, such as whales and dolphins. Seaweed, fish, mussels, clams, and many others are included.

The study of aquatic wildlife animals is often referred to as fisheries. **Fisheries** is the study of the fish and related species in an area of water. It includes a wide range of species, such as trout, bullfrogs, crawfish, snails, and turtles.

An aquatic habitat may be further classified on the basis of salt content of the water. Freshwater has little or no salt. Brackish water is common where freshwater and saltwater flow together, such as where a river flows into an ocean. Saltwater has a high salt content—often 33 to 37 ppt. in the oceans. (Salt in water is measured as parts per thousand, or "ppt.")

Most species have specific water requirements. Freshwater species cannot usually survive in saltwater, and vice-versa. Most species of trout, for example, prefer freshwater. Sharks and whales prefer saltwater. Oysters may be found in saltwater where salinity is low.

1-12. Manatees are aquatic wildlife. (This shows a female with a young manatee, known as calf.) (Courtesy, U.S. Fish and Wildlife Service)

Providing a good habitat for aquatic species is obviously different from terrestrial species. Water quality is a major factor. Keeping water free of pollution so it remains in its natural state is essential for aquatic wildlife.

Wildlife Connection

BEWARE PIT VIPERS

Snakes are long, legless wildlife animals that often cause fear. Many snakes are harmless and have useful roles, such as preying on pests. Some snakes are poisonous and should be treated with respect.

Poisonous snakes usually have fangs that can be extended to inject poisonous venom. These snakes are known as vipers. We cannot usually get close enough to a snake in the outdoors to see all of its characteristics. Head shape, body structure, color, and pattern of scales are important in identification. It is best to learn the overall characteristics of snakes in your area so you can make a quick identification.

Most all poisonous snakes in the United States are pit vipers. This is because the snake has a small pit organ for detecting heat. The pit helps the snake "zero-in" on warm animals it wishes to attack. Most vipers have only one pit organ on each side of the head between the nostril and eye. Pits should not be confused with nostrils. A few species have several pits.

Snake Head Comparisons

Pit Vipers

Other Snakes

Flat triangular head

Usually oval elongated head

Eye

Nostril

Pit

Facial pit; vertical pupil

No pit; round pupil

WILDLIFE POPULATIONS

1-13. Populations of purple martin birds can be attracted with the proper house. (Courtesy, U.S. Fish and Wildlife Service)

1-14. Biologists are moving eggs of the nearly-extinct whooping crane in an incubator. (Extra care is needed to assure hatching.) (Courtesy, Luther Goldman, U.S. Fish and Wildlife Service)

Some streams, woods, and meadows have many species of wildlife. Others have few wildlife species. Why is there a difference?

Many factors impact the number of wildlife in a location. **Wildlife population** is the number of individuals in a group of organisms that occupy an area. The population may be stated to include all of the same species or a combination of species.

POPULATION DENSITY

Populations are described as having density. **Population density** is the number of organisms in an area. An example of density is five beavers per one acre of lake.

Animal populations are influenced by natality and mortality. **Natality** is the number of new animal organisms born in an area each year. Natality is sometimes known as birth rate. It is given as the number of births per 100 or 1,000 animals. Good food and shelter support animal reproduction and higher natality.

Mortality is the death rate of animals. It is usually given as the number of deaths per 1,000 animals each year. Adequate food and shelter reduce mortality. Overpopulation and a shortage of food and shelter increase mortality. Disease outbreaks or weather-related disasters can have major effects on mortality.

RENEWABLE NATURAL RESOURCE

Wildlife is a **renewable natural resource**. This means it can produce more of itself if conditions are favorable. Unfavorable conditions can result in the decline of a population. Long-term unfavorable conditions can result in extinction. Proper management of wildlife supports renewability.

Here are a few examples of past efforts in renewing wildlife.

- Beaver—In the 1800s, the beaver was nearly exterminated in some locations by trapping. Now, with favorable practices, the beaver population has been renewed. It is common to see beaver dams, cut trees, and other evidence of the return of a beaver population.

- Bison—The American Bison was reduced to a population of only a few hundred in 1905. These were located in Yellowstone National Park, on a few ranches, and in selected zoos. The great herds that once roamed the Plains states had been eliminated by over-harvesting and destruction of habitat. Restocking efforts and laws protecting bison have led to restoration of the large animals.

- Passenger pigeon—Passenger pigeons were once believed to be the most numerous birds on earth. Shooting and trapping for market brought a decline in their numbers. Also, a part of the decline was the cutting of oak and beech forests where pigeons obtained food and nested. Disease also impacted the population. Storms and fog during migration further reduced passenger pigeon numbers. The "critical mass" required for successful nesting colonies was no longer present. The species became extinct in 1914 when the last surviving passenger pigeon died in the Cincinnati Zoo.

Measures to protect wildlife can result in too much wildlife. **Overpopulation** results when excessive numbers of wildlife exceed the carrying capacity of their habitat. The density of the population is too great for the available food. The wildlife may then attack valuable crops, property, and people. Farm crops may be destroyed when there are too many deer. Squirrels can damage property and be a nuisance. Beaver can build dams that flood meadows and woodlands. This may kill trees and other wildlife. Wolves can attack farm animals and people. Birds can attack crops and damage buildings, as well as carry disease. Overpopulation may result in stunted growth and disease. Starvation and death often result.

A balanced approach to maintaining wildlife populations is needed. This requires continual monitoring of wildlife. Adjust-

1-15. Some snakes are useful in controlling pests. (This shows a black rat snake swallowing a mouse.)

ments can be made to control population density. With some species, hunting is used to control density.

WILDLIFE AND BIODIVERSITY

Biodiversity has become an important concept among wildlife specialists and scientists. **Biodiversity** is the variety of living things that naturally exist in an area. It is short for "biological diversity."

The diversity of living things affects the ecology in an area. Biodiversity is essential in having a healthy environment and relatively balanced ecosystem. The loss of a species from an area reduces biodiversity and alters the natural environment.

KINDS

Biodiversity is based on one or more of three factors: species, genetics, and ecosystem.

Species diversity refers to the number of different species found in a place or in a group of living things. It is the most common kind of biodiversity. Species diversity varies with climate. Warm climates have greater diversity of species than cold climates.

Genetic diversity refers to the variety of genes within members of species found in a location. When only a few members of a species breed to establish a population, the genetic diversity is narrow. If a large number of individuals breed to create a population, the genetic diversity would be greater.

1-16. Biodiversity in this scene shows a bison and plant materials supported by several ecosystem factors. What insects, rodents, and other animals might be present and not seen?

Ecosystem diversity refers to the variety of living and nonliving things found in a location. The nonliving things support life processes of the living organisms. If these nonliving things were removed, the living organisms would likely be unable to survive.

All three factors influence the diversity in a location. They are closely related. Human actions sometimes threaten the factors in biodiversity.

1-17. Biodiversity is influenced by the ecosystem (in this case, a beach).

MAINTAINING

Biodiversity in an area is maintained by paying careful attention to the woods, water, or land. Managing wildlife is often needed to achieve superior biodiversity. Long-term planning may be required. Planning begins with understanding the needs of wildlife species.

Most of the attention on biodiversity has been on animals. Scientists now recognize the importance of plants and other wildlife in maintaining biodiversity. The loss of just one species could change the ecosystem so that other species are threatened.

What about biodiversity near your home? Select an area of woods, meadow, pond, stream, or desert. Observe the area for the organisms that are present. Cluster the species by plant, animal, fungi, and other groups. Within each of these, further classify the species. In some cases, you may need the help of a trained wildlife biologist.

REVIEWING

MAIN IDEAS

The term, wildlife, is broadly defined as all living things that have not been domesticated. These organisms have value to people. Some values are consumptive; others are nonconsumptive. The major values relate to commercial, game, aesthetic, scientific, and ecological uses.

Wildlife conservation is the wise use of wildlife resources. Four areas are a part of wildlife conservation: research, education, law enforcement, and wildlife management.

Wildlife organisms can be classified in many ways. In most cases, scientific classification and habitat classification are used. With scientific classification, there are five kingdoms: animal, plant, fungi, Monera, and Protista. Wildlife can be classified by habitat into two broad categories: terrestrial and aquatic. These can be further divided based on differences within terrestrial or aquatic needs.

Maintaining adequate wildlife numbers involves using wildlife population information. Population density is the number of wildlife in an area. Population is influenced by natality and mortality. As a renewable natural resource, wildlife numbers can be protected and kept in proper balance.

Biodiversity is an important concept involving wildlife. Having a variety of living things is essential in maintaining an ecosystem. The loss of one species can have a major impact.

QUESTIONS

Answer the following questions using correct spelling and complete sentences.

1. What is wildlife?

2. How does domestication change the nature of wildlife?

3. What are the basic values of wildlife? Explain each in one sentence.

4. What is wildlife conservation?

5. What four areas are part of wildlife conservation?

6. What are the five kingdoms of wildlife? Give one example of each.

7. What is habitat?

8. What is the distinction between terrestrial and aquatic wildlife?

9. What is a wildlife population? Explain how natality and mortality affect population density.

10. Why is wildlife said to be a renewable natural resource?

11. What is overpopulation?

12. What is biodiversity? Name and briefly explain the three kinds of biodiversity.

EVALUATING

Match the term with the correct definition.

a. domestication
b. game
c. ecology
d. ecosystem

e. habitat
f. terrestrial wildlife
g. aquatic wildlife
h. population diversity

i. consumptive use
j. natality

_____1. Number of wildlife in an area.

_____2. Bringing living things under the control of humans.

_____3. Rate at which new animals are born.

_____4. Ways organisms interact with their environment.

_____5. Any species hunted for food or sport.

_____6. The living and nonliving features of an environment.

_____7. Organisms that live on the land.

_____8. Physical area in which a wildlife species lives.

_____9. Destroying organisms for human use.

_____10. Organisms that live in water.

EXPLORING

1. Take a field trip to a game preserve or park to observe wildlife and its habitat. Have a guide provide information on the kinds of wildlife and how they relate to each other. Take notes on what you learn. If possible, take photographs and prepare a poster or bulletin board on your field trip. Prepare a written report to summarize your observations.

2. Interview a local wildlife official, such as a biologist or game warden. Ask the individual about important wildlife species in the local area, especially those that are endangered.

3. Make an inventory of the wildlife found on the school grounds or in an area near your home. Classify the wildlife species you observe as to animal, plant, fungus, Protista, or Monera and if they are terrestrial or aquatic. Prepare a written report on your observations.

CHAPTER 2

Wildlife Industry

OBJECTIVES

This chapter introduces the wildlife industry and provides direction in learning more about it. The objectives of the chapter are:

1 Identify career and entrepreneurship opportunities in wildlife management.

2 Develop appropriate leadership and interpersonal skills.

3 Identify sources of information on wildlife management.

4 Describe the role of research in wildlife management.

5 Identify employer expectations, including work habits and citizenship skills.

6 Demonstrate appropriate occupational safety skills.

7 Use supervised experience to develop job skills.

TERMS

career	hazard	research
career pathway	leadership	safety
citizenship	personal skill	scientific method
entrepreneur	personal trait	supervised experience
follower	PPE	work habits

2-1. A hunting guide enjoys wildlife and helps sport hunters find game.

HAVE you thought about a career in the wildlife industry? If not, you might want to give it some thought. Begin by relating your interests in wildlife to a job that you would enjoy (and could earn money). Next, gather information to help you in making a wise choice.

There are many important things to consider when making decisions about careers. Education is often needed. A job must be available where you want to live. Your goals must be realistic in terms of your situation. It may be a little impractical to dream about being a safari tour guide when the jobs are thousands of miles away.

Even if you don't pursue a job in the wildlife industry, you most likely still have a strong interest in wildlife. You may interact with people in wildlife jobs. You may need to read information about the industry. Begin with this chapter because it provides background information on achieving career success.

CAREERS: WORK FOR OTHERS OR YOURSELF

A *career* is the general direction or sequence that a person takes as related to work. Careers in wildlife are often comprised of several stages. Young people start with entry level work and, with good effort, advance to more responsible work. Thus, a career is made up of a series of occupations and jobs.

2-2. A marine biologist is studying the growth of blue crab in brackish water. (Courtesy, Agricultural Research Service, USDA)

Choosing a career is an important decision. It affects so many areas of your life—where you live, how much money you make, the nature of your work, and many more areas. Most people can be successful in a range of career areas. Begin by setting worthy goals and taking the steps to achieve them.

CAREER PATHWAYS

The area of wildlife is broad and has a wide range of career possibilities. These are a part of the natural resources and conservation pathway. A *career pathway* is a grouping of occupations involving similar

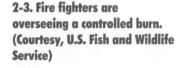

2-3. Fire fighters are overseeing a controlled burn. (Courtesy, U.S. Fish and Wildlife Service)

education and interests. Individuals taking education in the pathway may be able to meet general requirements for changing from one career area to another within wildlife occupations.

Several areas in the career pathway are:

- Wildlife management—More jobs are found in wildlife management than other areas of wildlife. The jobs range from entry level to advanced levels. The work involves studying habitat and wildlife and developing strategies to achieve desired goals. On a wildlife refuge, emphasis is on promoting the well-being of wildlife, particularly those that are threatened. In a forest, the goal is to assure wildlife growth and wise harvesting. A college education is usually needed.

- Wildlife recreation—Wildlife recreation jobs are quite diverse. They range from serving as a hunting or fishing guide to operating a tackle shop, running a fee lake, and managing a hunting preserve. The general nature of the work is to help people enjoy wildlife. Some people are outside in forests and on lakes. Others are inside and may involve marketing wildlife supplies and services or in providing customer assistance. Some college education is useful and may be required.

- Wildlife rehabilitation—Jobs in wildlife rehabilitation involve treating and temporarily caring for injured and/or diseased wildlife. Once restored to good health, the animals are returned to the wild. The work may involve restraining injured animals, bandaging wounds, administering fluids and medications, feeding, cleaning cages, and

Wildlife Connection

BEING IN THE ORANGE

Be safe when enjoying wildlife. If you hunt or go out into a forest during hunting season, it is wise (and may be legally required) that you wear a bright, easily seen color. Most often the color is known as "hunter orange." It is also known as international or fluorescent orange.

The "orange" may be the color of a vest, jacket, shirt, hat, or other clothing. In some cases, laws set the minimum amount that must be worn such as 500 visible square inches. Some states require a hunter orange hat in addition to a vest or other clothing. The laws are to assure that you are seen and not mistaken by a hunter as an animal and shot. This shows a hunter putting on a hunter orange vest and wearing a stocking cap.

Always practice safety. It will help prevent hunters from needless accidents.

otherwise caring for animals. Jobs are with associations, government agencies, and other groups. Some are with nonprofit foundations. A college education and experience with wildlife are typically needed.

- Wildlife research—Jobs in wildlife research involve using scientific methods to develop a greater understanding of wildlife and to solve problems. The work may be on game preserves, with large forest companies and government agencies, and experiment stations of colleges and universities. The researchers typically have masters and doctors degrees. Technicians may have high school diplomas, post-secondary education, or college degrees in wildlife or a related area.

2-4. A game management technician prepares to make his rounds.

- Wildlife education—Wildlife education involves developing materials or conducting programs to educate hunters, fishers, the general public, and other special interest groups. Some of the jobs are with departments of wildlife and fisheries; others are as teachers in schools or with law enforcement agencies. A college degree with a background in wildlife and emphasis in communication and teaching is typically required.

- Wildlife law enforcement—Law enforcement jobs involve enforcing laws about wildlife. Some are as game wardens or conservation officers who have the

Table 2-1. Occupations in Wildlife

Area	Examples of Occupations
wildlife management	game farm operator, wildlife refuge technician, wildlife biologist,
wildlife recreation	fly fishing instructor, gun safety instructor, hunting guide, hunting and fishing supplies store operator
wildlife research	wildlife biologist, aquaculturist, fishery scientist, hatchery operator, fishery biologist,
wildlife education	college or high school wildlife teacher, gun safety instructor, birding instructor, park service naturalist,
wildlife law enforcement	game warden, wildlife refuge guard, park service ranger

authority to arrest people who break the law. The work may involve informing the public about game laws and how to be good stewards of wildlife resources. Some college education is typically needed. On-the-job training is often provided.

ENTREPRENEURSHIP

An **entrepreneur** is a person who starts and owns a business to meet a particular consumer demand. The focus is often on a unique market opportunity. The individual takes a great deal of risk. If the business fails, the individual can lose all that has been invested. They must also be able to get the needed finances to go into a wildlife business. Most entrepreneurs begin small and grow by expanding their business.

Entrepreneurs have a lot of responsibility. They often oversee other workers and greet the public. They must keep careful financial records and comply with all laws related to running their business.

Several examples of entrepreneurship opportunities in wildlife are: fishing guide, bait and tackle shop owner, hunting supplies store owner, game processing business, and game preserve owner.

LEADERSHIP AND PERSONAL SKILLS

Success in a career often requires leadership and personal skills. These can be developed through study and practice.

LEADERSHIP

Leadership is the ability to influence others to achieve worthy goals. Often, a leader must help others set goals. Sometimes the goals are for a group; other times goals are for individuals. Goals are sometimes tied to a specific time for completion.

An important part of leadership is communication. Individuals need the

2-5. Important leadership and personal skills can be learned in student organizations.

ability to exchange information. This requires listening as well as expressing thoughts on a subject.

Leaders have qualities that help them serve in their roles. They must inspire and motivate followers. A **follower** is an individual who adopts the ideas, goals, or tasks of a leader. A follower helps a leader in being successful. Followers are loyal to their leader. In turn, leaders are loyal to their followers.

Leadership is viewed differently. The varying views help understand the meaning of leadership. Some views of leadership are:

- A relationship—Relationship is the bond or trust that exists between a leader and the followers. It involves caring and motivation to do certain things. Loyalty and trust are essential parts of understanding leadership as a relationship.

- A process—Credibility among the followers in a group is essential for an individual to be a leader. Group members must respect and rely on the judgement and skills of the leader.

2-6. The ability to speak before groups is important in some wildlife occupations. You can develop these skills while in school.

- Influence—An important part of leadership is the ability to motivate people to use their energy to do certain things. Incentives and rewards sometimes work.

- Service—Leaders put the welfare of others above their own. They must usually put forth more effort than group members. Some say that a leader is the servant of the group being led.

PERSONAL SKILLS

Success requires that people have personal skills. A **personal skill** is a quality of an individual that helps him or her relate to other people. This allows the individual to work more efficiently. Most all jobs involve relating to other people in some way.

Personal skills can be developed. We are not born with them. Young people need to strive to develop the needed skills. In order to develop the skills, we need to know what they are. We can identify with people who appear to have the skills and, to some extent, model our behavior after them.

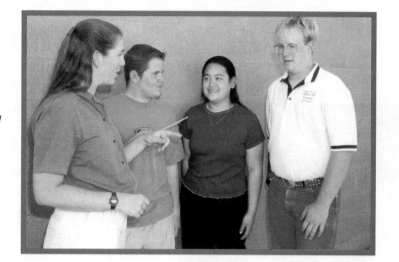

2-7. The ability to listen and follow instructions is essential in being successful.

Important personal skills include the following traits:

- Communicate clearly with others orally and in writing.
- Listen effectively to what others have to say.
- Respect the rights of other people who have views different from yours though you may not personally agree with them.
- Assume responsibility—do what you said you would do when you said you would do it!
- Have a positive attitude toward people, events, work, and employer.
- Be trustworthy.
- Have appropriate moral standards.
- Be honest and fair.
- Analyze situations and make decisions; involve others in the process if the decision influences them.
- Organize events.
- Plan and conduct meetings.
- Have discussions with others.
- Dress and groom appropriately.
- Regularly bathe and follow good personal hygiene.
- Be courteous to other people.
- Frequently use "please" and "thank you" when speaking with others.
- Strive to be competent and productive in all that you do.

WILDLIFE INFORMATION

People often need information about wildlife. Those working in wildlife areas need to keep up with the latest trends and new issues or problems that have emerged. Those who are wildlife watchers, hunters, fishers, and other users also need to know the rules that apply.

Three things to consider with wildlife information are how to locate what you need, how to assess its quality, and how to use the information once you have found it.

Locating information

In locating information, there are two considerations: format and source.

Format

Format refers to how the materials are presented. Some are as brochures and books while others are as video tapes or CDs. Information needs to be in a format that you can readily use.

The common formats are summarized in Table 2-2.

2-8. Good information about wildlife is widely available.

Source

Information is available from a number of sources. These sources may require making requests via Postal Service mail, the Internet, by telephone, or with personal visits to offices or with individuals.

A few general sources of information are:

- Associations—Associations dealing with wildlife often have good information. The information may be available from the office of the association or through the Internet.

- Government agencies—Federal, state, and local government agencies often provide useful information. Federal agencies include the U.S. Fish and Wildlife Service, the National Park Service, and the U.S. Forest Service. State agencies vary but most all

Table 2-2. Common Wildlife Materials Formats

format	characteristics
books	Provide basic information; most are carefully written to assure accuracy; illustrations help understand concepts; size is great enough to provide adequate details to understand a subject; the most widely used source for detailed information.
bulletins	Small publications that provide information on only one narrow topic; often available free of charge; used to provide information, regulations and laws; check the date to be sure a bulletin is up-to-date.
newspapers	Published regularly (daily or weekly) in a throw-away format; information should be up-to-date; details may be lacking.
magazines	Published on a weekly, monthly, quarterly basis; articles focus on a narrow topic; should be up-to-date; assess for writer bias.
video tapes	Provide both visual and audio information; should be of professional quality; filming on location should add reality; equipment is needed to use the information.
audio tapes	Provide sounds of nature, such as bird calls; quality recording and play-back is essential; a player is needed to hear the information.
CDs and DVDs	Provide audio and visual information; should be up-to-date; equipment is needed to have access to the information.
the Internet	Many sites have information but must assess its usefulness; web sites vary in terms of quality; computer and Internet provider are needed.

states have agencies that deal with fish and wildlife by providing information as well as enforcing regulations. Local governments may also have information. The extent of such information is often more limited than state and Federal agencies. Some Federal, state, and local governments operate museums that can provide a wide range of information.

• Private businesses—Businesses and industries that involve forestry and related areas often have information on wildlife. Large companies with extensive land holdings often employ wildlife biologists who can provide information.

• Colleges and universities—Some colleges and universities have programs or departments that have information on wildlife. The land-grant universities in each state usually have an extension service with numerous bulletins and other materials on wildlife. These same universities may have experiment stations that conduct research about wildlife.

• Clubs and preserves—Hunting and fishing clubs often have local information about wildlife conditions. Private animal preserves may also have information on wildlife problems, populations, and other conditions.

2-9. Parks and preserves may have displays that provide useful information, such as this wetlands area in Illinois.

ASSESSING INFORMATION

In using information, be sure to assess its quality. Some information is accurate and free of bias. Of course, you want to use the best possible information.

A few factors to consider in assessing information are:

- Source—You will want to know if the source is reliable. Look for the name of the agency or business who produced the material. Determine who wrote the material. See if reviewers were used to assure accuracy of the information.

- Date—You will want to use only information that is current and up-to-date. Look for a date printed on the material. If the date is several years back or if there is no date, use the material with caution or discard it.

- Safety—You will want to read and see examples that depict safety. Using materials that do not reflect safety could result in your failure to recognize potential hazards.

- Illustrations—You will want to see photographs or line drawings that help explain concepts. Determine if they are modern and reflect appropriate practices.

- Availability—You can only use materials that are available to you. Identifying a material that is unavailable is of little benefit. Cost may also be a factor to consider.

USING INFORMATION

Good information is of little value if it is used in the wrong way. Determine how the information applies in your situation.

- Geography—Information must relate to the location where you will use it. For example, people in mountain areas may not find information prepared for coastal areas useful.

- Relevance—Information must be relevant in terms of your situation. See if the information relates to your needs. For example, information about wildlife habitat in hardwood areas may lack relevance in areas with pine trees.

- Get the details—Read or view materials in their entirety as

2-10. States often publish a range of materials about wildlife. The Texas Hunter Education Manual provides details on how to legally and safely enjoy wildlife.

related to your needs or interests. Stopping before the details are fully known may create problems. For example, read a brochure on fishing laws in its entirety. The information not read could result in breaking a law.

- Advice of others—Information gives background that may allow you to make better use of resource persons in the local area. Reading or viewing beforehand helps ask the "right" questions and understand the answers you get.

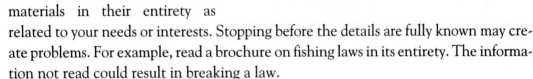

THE ROLE OF RESEARCH

Research is the investigation of problems related to the well-being of wildlife. Scientific methods are used to assure research that is reliable and valid. Those who do research are known as scientists or researchers.

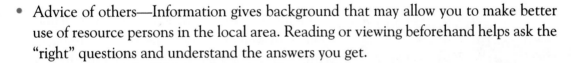

DOING RESEARCH

People who do research should be well trained in the methods of research. Many have doctoral degrees in wildlife biology or a related area. They often have technicians to assist in the work.

Researchers use the scientific method. The **scientific method** is an organized way of asking questions and seeking answers. It involves several procedures to assure quality research. The steps in scientific method are listed in Table 2-3.

Table 2-3. The Scientific Method

procedures*	meaning
1. Identify the problem	The researcher must know the problem that is to be investigated; avoid researching symptoms of problems; Example: death of deer is a symptom; the cause of death is the problem to researched.
2. Gather information	Background reading and interviewing informed people helps get needed information to design a good research project.
3. Suggest an answer	A suggested answer is often stated as an hypothesis; an hypothesis is a statement that can be tested; Example: Feeding newly-hatched fish in a hatchery each hour will result in faster growth than with twice daily feedings.
4. Experiment	Trials or tests are used to determine if the hypothesis is accepted or rejected; the procedures used must control "things" that could make research invalid; careful measurements are needed to have good data for analysis.
5. Reach a conclusion	Once an experiment has been completed, a judgement of the findings is needed; data are studied and inferences are made.

* Five procedures are listed here. Some scientists include other steps such as prepare a report on the findings. The sequence in doing the procedures may vary somewhat.

2-11. Students can often do research in their school labs.

Wildlife research is carried out by Federal and state agencies as well as associations and private businesses. Many states conduct wildlife research through the land-grant universities and experiment stations.

The problems studied often focus on improving habitat, investigating wildlife biology, and developing ways of promoting wildlife populations and health.

In fisheries areas, the research often deals with water quality, disease control, nutrition needs, and improving stocks to assure survival and growth. The work may relate to improving populations in streams and lakes. Some fisheries research is used to promote aquaculture, or the farming of fish and other aquatic species.

USING RESEARCH

The findings of research must be useful in some way. If not, the effort given to the research has no value.

Some ways of using the findings of wildlife research are:

- improve habitat
- provide better nutrition
- control disease
- determine species to introduce
- determine wildlife population trends
- identify species to protect
- make regulations on wildlife harvest

JOB SUCCESS: WHAT EMPLOYERS WANT

People want to be successful with their jobs. They want to do the right things and help employers achieve their goals. Overall, employers are interested in two areas: work habits and citizenship.

WORK HABITS

Work habits are the traits of an individual as related to job performance. Success or failure of an employee is often related to how well the work habits are carried out.

Two major areas are included in work habits: employer expectations and personal traits.

Employer Expectations

Employers have goals they wish to achieve. In a private business, the goals relate to serving customers so that the business makes a profit. In an agency or

2-12. Employers want employees who have job skills, can get along with other people, and are productive.

association, the goals may involve carrying out certain activities to serve the public or needs of wildlife.

Common expectations include:

- Communication—This is the ability to receive and share information. It includes speaking, listening, and non-verbal areas such as dress, eye contact, and posture. Good language skills are very important in some occupations.

- Responsibility—Employers want employees who are responsible. They use care in their work and strive to do it right. Employers want employees who are reliable and can be counted on to do their jobs.

- Performance—Job performance is carrying out work with skill and competence. It includes being productive and getting as much done during work hours as possible. Each person has an obligation to stay up-to-date with their job skills and knowledge.

- Team ability—People work with other people. They need to get along, support each other, and share in the work to be done. The work setting is much like the setting for an athletic team event. People who work together well will get more done.

- Honesty—Telling the truth is essential. This includes being truthful to the boss as well as fellow employees and customers. Honesty includes using time well, using materials to be productive, and not stealing from the employer.

- Customers—Dealing with customers is important. This is true with businesses as well as agencies and organizations. Using a positive, friendly approach in greeting customers is needed. Always do what you say you will do. It is a good idea to remember that "the customer is number one." Without customers, businesses, associations, and agencies will be unsuccessful. Good attitudes toward customers are essential.

2-13. Jobs in wildlife often require people to assume responsibility for the well-being of animals. This photo shows a falcon being released.

Personal Traits

A ***personal trait*** is a quality of an individual that expresses the nature of the person. Personal traits include how we relate to other people as well as how we present ourselves. They are important in job success.

Examples of personal traits are:

- Life style—People need wholesome lifestyles to help them to be good workers. After hours activities can influence job performance. Substance abuse is often a problem. People need to have adequate sleep and rest to be able to focus their minds and energies on their work.

- Respect for others—An individual should respect other people and value their ideas. Strive to solve differences by discussion. Violence is never the answer. Physical abuse of others has no place in our work or personal lives. Always properly greet other people when you see them. A friendly "hello" builds goodwill.

- Loyalty—Loyalty is being faithful to another individual or group. Employers want employees who are loyal. Loyalty involves never being critical of an employer and upholding the employer. Say good things about your employer or say nothing at all.

- Learn—People have to learn new things to stay current. Always be enthusiastic about learning new job duties. Use a positive approach. Never be negative about new things or avoid learning just because something is new.

- Happiness—Be happy and demonstrate a sense of humor. Be able to laugh at a mistake you make and strive to do better in the future. Keep a smile on your face. Speak with enthusiasm.

- Assume personal responsibility—Many things are a part of personal responsibility. Pay your bills on time. Be honest and truthful. How you go about your personal life reflects on the employer because you represent the employer.

CITIZENSHIP

Citizenship is the role of people in support of their government and the ideals for which it stands. It is how we conduct ourselves as citizens. Citizenship involves certain duties and responsibilities.

Some people are said to be good citizens. What does that mean? Most likely it means that they conduct themselves in ways that show good citizenship attributes. They fulfill responsibilities in their communities. They promote community well-being and development.

Some of the traits associated with citizenship are:

- Law abiding—Good citizens know the law and how it applies to them. They are careful to obey laws. This applies to operating a motor vehicle as well as paying taxes and being honest in business dealings. In wildlife, it includes following hunting and fishing regulations as well as striving to protect wildlife species.

- Voting—Voting is participating in selecting government leaders and setting policy, such as general guidelines on taxation and other matters. A person must be 18 years of age, a citizen of the United States, and not have lost the right to vote because of a criminal conviction. Voters must register at the appropriate local government office.

- Taking pride—Good citizens promote their communities and strive to make them better places in which to live. Sometimes simple things can make important improvements. Picking up trash, helping build a park, and providing activities for children are included.

- Demonstrating patriotism—Loyalty to and admiration for the United States are major ways we demonstrate patriotism. Saying the pledge to the flag and showing respect for government actions to defend the Nation are a part of patriotism. Abiding by laws is another part of patriotism.

- Supporting the well-being of others—Good citizens respect other people and extend equality to them. They are inclusive of all people regardless of differences.

- Contributing to worthy causes—Good citizens help support other people, especially those have had losses or who lack money to provide for themselves.

SAFETY

Hazards are often present in wildlife work. A **hazard** is something that causes danger or risk. Hazards can potentially cause injury or, in severe situations, death. Fortunately, the risk we take can be reduced.

Practicing safety reduces the likelihood of an accident. **Safety** is taking steps to be free of harm and danger. The steps vary with the nature of the hazards that are involved. For example, live animals pose hazards that are quite different from those in operating power equipment.

2-14. Safety in hunting or shooting sports may require shooting glasses and shooting muffs.

People need to make safety a habit. When they do, safe practices become routine. This helps prevent injury and loss.

HAZARDS

The hazards in a work place should be identified and steps taken to correct them. People need to take extra care in working around hazards.

Examples of hazards in wildlife work are:

2-15. Use caution with dead animals as they may have a disease that can be transmitted to you. A dead bird may be a sign of West Nile Virus disease.

- Animals—Wildlife work may involve live or dead animals. Live animals pose hazards of biting, kicking, scratching, butting, and otherwise harming a person. Precautions involve understanding the nature of the animal. Knowing how to properly restrain and handle an animal may be needed in some jobs. Frightened animals behave differently from those that feel no threat. Some animals are quite aggressive; others are more inclined to run away. Dead animals may transfer disease to a human or create unpleasant odors or sights.

- Plants—Plants may pose hazards in several ways. Some plants are poisonous, such as poison ivy. Other plants have thorns or prickers that can puncture the skin and cause injury. Falling limbs or trees also pose hazards.

- Power equipment—Wildlife work may involve using equipment. Chain saws, tractors, motor boats, and water pumps are examples. These often have powerful engines and can inflict serious injury. Knowing how to properly operate the equipment is essential. Using safety equipment helps reduce the chance of injury.

- Restraints, guns, and traps—Some wildlife work involves restraining, shooting, or trapping animals. The equipment should be properly used. This helps protect the user as well as those around the user. Proper use also helps assure animal well-being. Many states require hunter safety education before a license can be issued.

- Hand tools—Wildlife work may involve using common wrenches, hammers, and similar tools. These should be properly selected, used, and maintained.

- Chemicals, fuels, and medications—Chemicals are sometimes used to control pests, such as weeds or insects. Use only as approved and follow all safety practices. Engines often require fuel and lubricating oil. These should be handled properly to protect people as well as the environment. Animal medicines are sometimes used. These include chemicals in which animals are dipped to control parasites as well as injected materials such as antibiotics or vaccines.

- Fire and explosion—Work may sometimes involve using or controlling fires. Always follow appropriate actions with fire. Explosion may result from fires or from the improper use of some materials.

- Weather—Exposure to sunlight, wind, cold or hot temperatures, and other conditions is hazardous. Wear proper clothing. Use sun screen. Eat and drink properly.

2-16. Use sun screen to protect the skin from blistering and future skin cancer associated with excessive sunlight. (SPF is the sun protection factor. It is measured in numbers from 2 to 45. The higher the number, the greater the protection.)

Ppe

A part of practicing safety is using personal protective equipment (PPE). *PPE* is equipment that can be worn or used to protect the human body from injury. The kind needed varies with the nature of the hazard.

Eye protection is needed when tiny objects, liquids, or light may cause injury. Appropriate goggles, safety glasses, face shields, or helmets should be used. In most cases, goggles offer greater protection than safety glasses. In addition, eyewash bottles or eyewash fountains should be available where the greatest risk for eye injury is present.

Hearing protection is needed in areas with loud noise. Engines, sirens, and other equipment may produce noise that can cause damage to hearing. Hunters and people in target practice should wear ear plugs or ear muffs to reduce the shock of loud and sudden gunfire. Without hearing protection, hearing loss may be gradual going unnoticed and end in being hard of hearing or deaf.

Foot and leg protection may be needed. If hazards for foot and leg injury are present, wear appropriate shoes or boots and protect the legs with leggings or other safety equipment.

2-17. Examples of PPE that may be needed in working with wildlife.

Steel-toed shoes help protect feet from injury by heavy objects. Waders may be used in water several feet deep in working with fish or other aquatic species.

Gloves are often needed to protect hands. Some gloves protect from sharp spines of fish, teeth of small animals, and claw scratches from birds. Select gloves designed to offer protection from the hazard you have.

A hardhat may be needed in some work. Any work in a forest where limbs or other objects may fall usually requires a hardhat.

Life vests may be needed in working around water. Throw-rings should also be available to help rescue a person who is stressed in water.

Colorful vests, hats, or other clothing may be needed in some occupations or when hunting. The bright orange color makes it easier to be seen. This helps prevent being mistaken for

2-18. Water safety involves two types of PPE—life jackets and throwable flotation devices. Everyone enjoying water recreation should wear a life jacket especially children and non-swimming adults.

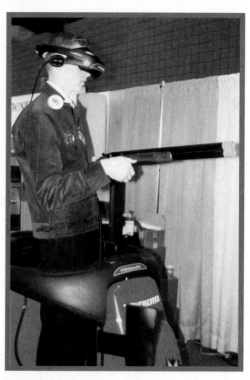

2-19. Virtual reality systems are now used to train in gun use and hunter safety.

wildlife and shot by a sport hunter. Some states have laws that require a certain color and amount of color to be worn by a hunter.

Always know the hazards associated with work or recreation involving wildlife. Take the appropriate steps to reduce the risk of an accident occurring.

GAINING EXPERIENCE

Practical experience in an occupation helps develop job skills. It also allows an individual to explore his or her personal interests. Supervised experience helps explore possibilities and find interests.

Supervised experience (SE) (also known as supervised agricultural experience—SAE) is the planned application of skills learned in classes. Students carry out projects or have part-time jobs related to their school studies. It is important to keep good records of the skills gained as well as the income received. An adult is responsible for overseeing the work of the student.

Students are counseled about supervised experience (SE) by their wildlife or agriculture teacher. Each student's SE program is individually planned. Students, parents, employers, and others may be involved.

Supervised experience is important in progressing in the FFA organization. Most schools have an FFA chapter. The chapter has activities that lead to participation beyond the local school. These advanced levels may include district, state, and national activities.

2-20. A California student is discussing supervised experience plans and records with his teacher.

WHERE SE IS CARRIED OUT

Supervised experience is carried out in a wide range of settings. The most common places are:

- School—Students may have SE in school labs after their regular class time. This is particularly useful for students who cannot leave school or travel to another location. School facilities may be used that are not otherwise available.

- Home—Some students may have opportunities at their homes. This is particularly useful if the homes are on farms or in rural areas where land is available for wildlife. Students may also have ponds, pens, or small areas for urban wildlife.

- Agencies—Agencies or organizations dealing with wildlife may have SE opportunities. For example, a state park, animal refuge, or preserve may have good learning situations. Zoos could be included as well.

2-21. Students may work together in school lab supervised experience.

- Businesses—Some businesses are involved with wildlife and may be good places for SE. Fee lakes (places where people pay to fish), forest areas that protect wildlife, and utility companies that own or control water reservoirs are examples. In some cases, opportunities may exist with wildlife rehabilitation organizations.

2-22. Students collecting a water sample from a stream in their community.

- Community—A wide range of community facilities may be used for supervised experience. These include parks, museums, playground areas, forests, and school grounds.

TYPES OF SE

Four types of supervised experience are generally used. These are based on the level of the SE and the role of the student. Opportunities are available in most communities in wildlife areas for either of the four types.

The types are:

- Exploratory—Exploratory SE is often for young students and those who are enrolled in wildlife or agriculture classes for the first time. Students who are unsure about their future careers in wildlife, and the SE they would like to have, can benefit from exploration. It allows students to investigate different areas of wildlife work. It may involve observing others at work such as in a wildlife refuge, research facility, or zoo. Exploratory SE may have students investigate topics or areas to determine potential interests.

- Ownership/Entrepreneurship—Ownership/Entrepreneurship SE involves starting a project or business that is owned by the student. It is often based on unique market situations or other opportunities in the local area. The student is an entrepreneur. Good records are essential. A parent or other adult individual supervises an ownership/entrepreneurship SE.

- Placement—Placement SE is working for another individual, business, or agency. Students typically receive pay for their work. Laws relating to employment must be observed. Careful records of experiences gained and income are kept. Supervision is provided by the employer.

- Research—Research SE allows students to apply scientific methods in investigating a problem. Carefully planned procedures are followed. Local problems may be investigated. Facilities may be the school lab, a local park or refuge, a preserve, or other facility. The outcome may be a project that the student can enter in the school science fair

2-23. Students are examining a jawbone to better understand anatomy and physiology.

or the agriscience fair sponsored by the FFA organization. A teacher supervises a research SE.

PLANNING AND MANAGING SUPERVISED EXPERIENCE

Supervised experience usually involves developing a training plan. This is a list of the experiences to be gained from the SE. Placement SE may also involve a training agreement, which is a written agreement between the school, employer, student, and others related to the SE.

Good records are essential. The records are of the activities carried out, skills learned, hours worked, and/or income. Records are useful in applying for FFA awards. Records allow an individual to see the progress they are making and determine if they are making a profit from ownership ventures. Most states have specific recordkeeping systems. Some use printed record books while others use computer-based programs.

REVIEWING

MAIN IDEAS

A career is the general direction of a person's life as related to work. Numerous opportunities are available in areas of wildlife. These include wildlife management, wildlife recreation, wildlife rehabilitation, wildlife research, wildlife education, and wildlife law enforcement. Some people work for others; some are entrepreneurs and own their businesses.

Leadership and personal skills are important in career success. Skills in both areas can be developed through study and practice. Being a caring, considerate, and moral person are qualities that summarize the important personal skills and traits.

Good information is often needed. Several sources are available. Assess the quality of information by looking at its source, date, safety inclusions, illustrations, and availability. Information is in several formats: books, brochures, newspapers, video tapes, audio tapes, and CDs and DVDs.

Research is important in wildlife. Problems are studied to seek solutions resulting in improvements in wildlife and their well-being.

Employers have expectations of their employees. These are intended to assure job productivity. Among the needed skills are good communication, ability to assume responsibility, carry out job with skill and competence, be able to work as a team member, be honest, and deal with customers to assure their happiness. Citizenship skills are also important.

Hazards may exist in wildlife jobs. Safety should become a habit in all work. This includes identifying the hazards and taking steps to reduce the risks involved. Using PPE is essential in some activities.

High school students can gain needed experience with supervised experience. The activities are planned to apply skills learned in the classroom. They can be carried out at school, at home, with agencies, or with businesses. SE types are exploratory, ownership, placement, or research. Good planning is essential in having quality SE.

QUESTIONS

Answer the following questions using correct spelling and complete sentences.

1. What is a career?
2. How are wildlife careers often in stages?
3. What are three areas in the wildlife career pathway? Briefly explain each.
4. Why is entrepreneurship risky?
5. What are the important qualities of leaders?
6. What are the important traits in personal skills? List four.
7. What are the major sources of information about wildlife?
8. Name and briefly explain two sources of wildlife information.
9. What criteria should be considered in assessing information?
10. What is the scientific method? What steps are in the scientific method?
11. How are the findings of research about wildlife used?
12. What are the important expectations employers have for employees?
13. What are the important personal traits associated with job success?
14. What are the attributes of an individual that demonstrate citizenship?
15. Why is practicing safety important in work?
16. What are the potential hazards in wildlife work? Name and explain at least three.
17. What is PPE? Name three examples.
18. What is the role of supervised experience?
19. What are the types of supervised experience? Explain each.
20. Where is supervised experience carried out?

EVALUATING

Match the term with the correct definition. Write the letter of the term in the blank provided.

a. hazard	e. research	i. career
b. leadership	f. safety	j. personal skill
c. citizenship	g. work habits	
d. PPE	h. supervised experience	

_____1. General direction or sequence of a person's work.

_____2. The ability to influence others to achieve worthy goals.

_____3. The quality of an individual that helps him or her relate to other people.

_____4. The systematic investigation of a problem.

_____5. Traits of an individual as related to job performance.

_____6. The planned application of skills learned in classes.

_____7. Role of people in support of their government and way of life.

_____8. Something that poses a danger or risk.

_____9. Taking steps to be free of harm and danger.

_____10. Items of equipment that can be worn to protect from injury.

EXPLORING

1. Interview a local leader, business person, or government official about the qualities needed to be a leader. Determine qualities they have observed in leaders. Prepare a written report on your findings.

2. Arrange to visit a local wildlife preserve, zoo, or similar facility where you can job shadow an employee. Do so for one day. Prepare a written report on your experiences.

3. Determine the safety and license requirements for hunting a species in your state. Obtain information from a local game warden or conservation officer. Prepare a written report on your findings.

4. In collaboration with your teacher, plan and initiate appropriate supervised experience. Develop a training plan and, if needed, a training agreement. Be sure to keep careful records of your experiences.

CHAPTER 3

History of Wildlife Conservation

OBJECTIVES

This chapter introduces the meaning and importance of wildlife conservation. It describes how management is a part of conservation. The objectives of the chapter are:

1 Trace the early history of wildlife conservation.

2 Identify national policies impacting wildlife conservation.

3 Name past leaders in wildlife conservation efforts.

4 Explain the relationship between game management and productivity.

TERMS

banding
Forest Service
Lacey Act

National Park Service
vegetation survey
wasteful exploitation

wildlife population survey
wildlife productivity
Wildlife Refuge System

ALL PEOPLE share in owning wildlife. The species belong to all citizens—the public—in the United States. Unfortunately, a few people have sometimes abused wildlife. This resulted in laws to regulate how wildlife may be used. Early efforts in wildlife conservation in the United States were much like those in Europe.

People have united to develop programs that benefit wildlife. These programs occur at local, state, and national levels. Your local community probably has at least one park or other location where wildlife is protected. If nothing more, communities may designate themselves as bird sanctuaries!

People often have questions about wildlife conservation. What were the major events in wildlife conservation? Who were the early leaders in wildlife conservation? What are some examples of wildlife conservation? You probably have many more questions.

3-1. Research on stream water quality is important in aquatic wildlife conservation. This shows a biologist collecting small wildlife samples from water. (Courtesy, Agricultural Research Service, USDA)

THE BEGINNING

Organized wildlife conservation was first practiced in England during the Middle Ages. The earliest attempts to manage wildlife involved setting aside lands and restricting hunting. During this era, all wildlife belonged to the ruling classes.

Fish were among the first species moved to special locations for growing. Motes (water barriers around estate homes) often had fish placed into them. These fish grew and reproduced. Some were harvested for food; others found their way into local streams.

Severe restrictions were placed on people in the lower or working classes. They were forbidden to take wildlife for food. The storybook character, Robin Hood, clearly shows the issue of people being punished for taking deer that belonged to the king!

ARRIVAL OF PILGRIMS

When the Pilgrims arrived in North America in 1620, they found a wilderness of vast forests, broad prairies, and abundant waters. Rivers, lakes, creeks, bayous, swamps, and marshes provided habitats. Explorers and settlers who followed encountered American Indians. Wildlife was important to the Indians.

Indians were scattered across the land. They did not live in large cities. Their lives had little negative impact on the land and wildlife. Large-scale farming had not developed. Factories had not been constructed. Since the Indian tribes tended to be nomadic, they did not stay in one place long enough to cause severe damage.

IMPACT OF EUROPEAN SETTLERS

The European settlers created an almost immediate impact on the land. They brought livestock and farming techniques and created towns and cities similar to those in Europe. Many settlers feared the wilderness. There was little sentiment for protecting the environment because of a seemingly endless supply of land. The land typically had abundant trees, water, and wildlife. As the human population increased in North America, the people moved west from the Atlantic shores.

3-2. Some people view taking wildlife for fur as wasteful exploitation; others disagree.

The earliest signal of environmental stewardship came from George Washington, the first President of the United States. Washington wrote of his concern for soil fertility and erosion on his Virginia farm. His voice was lost in the progress and development of a new nation. As the United States developed, wasteful exploitation was far too common. **Wasteful exploitation** is making unwise use of resources. It includes killing too much game and not eating it or cutting trees and not using them. Much of the nation's wildlife was destroyed by wasteful exploitation.

By the late 1800s, opinions were beginning to change. People were seeing wildlife numbers being reduced and some nearing extinction. In 1870, the first game refuge was created in California. Two years later, land was set aside to create Yellowstone National Park. Our nation was beginning to address wildlife conservation.

POLICIES IMPACTING WILDLIFE

Policies about wildlife are made by local, state, and the federal governments. The laws relate to conserving and managing wildlife. Most sport hunters are well aware of the game laws. Government agencies have been set up to aid in carrying out the laws. States have agencies that deal with game and fish, including enforcement officers who are often known as game wardens. Over the years, wildlife conservation and environmental protection tended to merge into one major initiative.

International programs also apply to wildlife. The United Nations helped set up the International Union for the Conservation of Nature and Natural Resources in 1948. One role is to gather information on wildlife that may be endangered. The World Wildlife Fund raises money to support wildlife conservation.

FEDERAL ACTIONS

A number of federal laws have been enacted to conserve and manage wildlife. Wildlife conservation received little attention in the early years of the United States. The supply of wildlife was ample for the needs of the people. Attitudes began to change in the late 1800s.

3-3. Laws about wildlife have been made by the United States Congress.

3-4. Millions of visitors enter Yosemite National Park each year.

In 1872, land that later became Yellowstone National Park was set aside in Idaho, Montana, and Wyoming. This was the first effort in the world to have a park that protected wildlife. It was not until 1916 that the **National Park Service** was established. In the early years, Yellowstone was inadequately protected from illegal hunting. Some species of wildlife continued to be damaged.

Today, the National Park Service has 330 protected areas. Yosemite and Sequoia in California, the Great Smoky Mountains in North Carolina and Tennessee, and Carlsbad Caverns in New Mexico are among the most popular national parks. The National Park Service also oversees monuments and parkways, such as the USS Arizona memorial in Hawaii and the Natchez Trace Parkway in Tennessee, Alabama, and Mississippi. A few areas are outside the United States in territories and possessions, such as the American Samoa National Park and Buck Island Reef in the Virgin Islands.

In 1900, the U.S. Congress passed the Game Bird and Wild Bird Preservation Act. Known as the **Lacey Act**, the law regulates the shipment of illegally killed animals. The Act also regulates international trade of protected wildlife. The Lacey Act was helpful to states in enforcing laws.

The Migratory Bird Conservation Act of 1929 was the first major step in protecting migratory birds such as ducks and geese. No money was appropriated to buy wetlands or other areas for wildlife protection.

In 1934, the Migratory Bird Hunting Stamp Act was passed. This law obligated all waterfowl hunters to buy a special hunting stamp in addition to the cost of state hunting license. Migratory game bird hunting stamp revenues raised since 1934 have been used to fund activities to promote

3-5. A trumpeter swan in Yellowstone National Park.

the well-being of migratory game birds. These stamps are often known as "duck stamps." At first the stamps cost $1 each; today they are $15. Since inception, the duck stamp program has raised nearly $1 billion for waterfowl protection. The stamps are sold at post offices, selected sporting goods stores, and the Federal Duck Stamp Office in Washington, DC.

The design on duck stamps reflects competition among artists each year. The U. S. Fish and Wildlife Service annually holds a contest to determine the best design submitted. A junior duck stamp design program is held each year. Students throughout the U.S. prepare and submit designs. For additional information and to view proposed designs, use the web site: http://duckstamps.fws.gov.

In 1937, Congress passed the Pittman-Robertson Act. This law placed an excise tax on all hunting equipment and ammunition. The money is collected by the federal government and made available to the states on a matching fund basis. Funds from this Act are the mainstay of state conservation agencies and have supported wildlife management programs.

The Endangered Species Act was passed by Congress in 1966. This Act protected endangered and threatened wildlife species. Money was appropriated to identify rare, threatened, or endangered species and to manage those populations so they might increase in numbers.

In 1966, a **Wildlife Refuge System** was organized as part of the U.S. Fish and Wildlife Service. Today, there are more than 400 refuges in the United States. These contain vast land areas. Some are occasionally open for hunting and other uses. Both the National Park Service and the Fish and Wildlife Service are part of the U.S. Department of the Interior.

The U.S. **Forest Service**, an agency in the U.S. Department of Agriculture, has 156 national forests throughout the nation. These vast areas were originally set up to protect timber and water as part of the federal forest conservation policy of 1891. The lands were ini-

3-6. Wildflowers, such as Canterbury bells, are protected within Yellowstone National Park.

3-7. Federal duck stamps in 1934 and 1996.

3-8. Wildlife is protected in habitats provided by the National Wildlife Refuge System.

3-9. National forest areas are carefully marked by signs, such as Prescott National Forest in Arizona.

tially managed to produce a variety of wildlife species and protect them for future generations. It has been estimated that the national forests contain 60 percent of the nation's wildlife. Today, the Forest Service manages 191 million acres of forest and grass land.

In addition to setting up land areas for the well-being of wildlife, the federal government has other laws. Some of these laws specifically protect wildlife. Other laws relate to research and education programs. These programs focus on solving problems associated with wildlife and educating the general public about the importance and use of wildlife. Some of the work is done in collaboration with the states.

Career Profile

WILDLIFE BIOLOGIST

Wildlife biologists work in many areas to conserve wildlife and protect the environment. They study wildlife habitat and health, conduct educational programs, and build or re-generate habitat areas. They may improve streams and other structures for aquatic wildlife.

Most wildlife biologists have a college degree in biology, wildlife management, or a related area. Advanced study at the graduate level is most beneficial to wildlife biologists. Many have practical experience working with wildlife. The work is often outdoors and may involve operating vehicles, capturing wildlife, and conducting educational programs.

Jobs for wildlife biologists are with parks, forestry companies, government agencies, and others that deal with nature and wildlife. This shows a wildlife biologist examining the paw of a wolf. (Courtesy, U.S. Fish and Wildlife Service)

Table 3-1. Summary of Federal Actions to Protect Wildlife

Year	Action
1872	President Grant set aside land that would later become Yellowstone National Park; helped protect wildlife
1900	Lacey Act (Game and Wild Bird Preservation Act); prohibited transporting certain killed game across state lines and required permits to have exotic animals
1903	Pelican Island Refuge established in Florida; first wildlife refuge
1913	Weeks-McClean Act; protected migratory waterfowl and song birds from being hunted during closed season
1918	Federal Migratory Bird Treaty Act; initiated federal involvement in wildlife management, including internationally with Canada (extended to Mexico in 1936)
1934	Duck Stamp Act; raised monies for wetland habitats
1937	Pittman-Robertson Act (Federal Aid in Wildlife and Sportfish Restoration Act); initiated sales tax on sporting guns and ammunition to fund wildlife management projects
1940	Bald Eagle Act; protected bald eagle
1940	Fish and Wildlife Service formed; consolidated efforts in wildlife conservation
1950	Federal Aid in Fish Restoration Act; tax added to fishing tackle to fund research
1964	The Land and Water Conservation Act; created a fund to buy land and water having scenic and recreational value and to protect endangered species
1964	The Wilderness Act; set up a wilderness preservation system to keep some areas untarnished
1966	Endangered Species Act; set up effort to protect endangered species
1971	Wild Free-roaming Horse and Burro Act; protected burros and horses on publicly owned land
1972	Marine Mammal Protection Act; limited killing dolphins to 112,000 a year
1973	Endangered Species Act; provided a comprehensive plan to protect endangered and threatened species
1985	Conservation Reserve Program established; provided for areas of wildlife habitat on farms near crops
1997	President Clinton initiated a plan to protect wildlife and the environment at Lake Tahoe and other areas in the United States

STATE ACTIONS

The states began taking action to conserve wildlife in the mid-1800s. As early as 1852, Maine had a person in each county to enforce deer and moose hunting regulations. In 1895, North Dakota was the first state to have a law requiring hunters to buy licenses. By 1900, many states had agencies to manage areas related to wildlife, especially game animals.

3-10. Waterfalls are popular attractions in the Chattahoochee National Forest in Georgia.

3-11. States often operate fish hatcheries to replenish wild stocks in streams. (This Washington hatchery raises and releases salmon into streams to enhance fish populations.)

Many states have taken actions to protect and enhance wildlife. Parks and preserves have been set up. Hatcheries have been used to enhance fish populations in streams. Laws have been enacted to restrict hunting to seasons of the year, bag limits, and harvest methods. Law officers specially trained in wildlife protect and enforce the laws.

Colleges and universities in the states carry out important roles that impact wildlife. Some have extensive research programs to learn more about wildlife populations. Many have educational programs to help people with wildlife initiatives.

LOCAL ACTIONS

Local governments support wildlife conservation in several ways. They often work with federal or state agencies or private organizations in carrying out wildlife conservation practices.

Cities and towns often have parks that protect wildlife and provide recreation for people. Some have parks where exotic wildlife is maintained, such as a zoo. Non-native wildlife species may be kept in a zoo.

3-12. Many cities operate zoological parks to protect wildlife and allow people to see rare species.

3-13. Carefully planned trails in city parks allow people to exercise as well as observe wildlife.

Local governments may set up shelters to receive and protect wildlife. In some cases, these are a part of animal compounds where stray dogs and cats are kept.

Areas or entire cities may be designated as sanctuaries for wildlife. A common example is the designation of a city or neighborhood as a bird sanctuary.

LEADERS IN WILDLIFE CONSERVATION

Several individuals are well known for their leadership in protecting wildlife and natural resources.

AUDUBON

John James Audubon (1785-1851) studied the birds of North America. He is well known for paintings depicting birds in their natural surroundings. Born in Haiti, Audubon came to North America as the adopted son of a sea captain. He learned to draw birds while growing up in Pennsylvania. He later moved to Kentucky, where he opened a business that failed because of his tendency to wander through the countryside studying and painting pictures of birds.

In 1820, Audubon came up with the idea of publishing a book of bird paintings; however, a publisher was not to be found in North America. In 1826 in Scotland, he began publishing works with 435 life-sized birds. His work was so successful that he returned to the United

States in 1839 and began publishing here. The American Audubon Society was formed in 1905 and named for the famed naturalist John James Audubon.

3-14. The Muir Woods National Monument commemorates the work of John Muir. The northern California monument is a part of the National Park Service.

Muir

John Muir (1838-1914) is known as an explorer, naturalist, and writer. He was born in Scotland, but grew up on a farm in Wisconsin after his parents immigrated to this country. He spent years hiking the forests of the United States and other nations.

Muir is best known for his study of areas that are now in Yosemite and Sequoia National Parks in California. His encouragement of President Theodore Roosevelt resulted in the two parks being set up in 1890. He was also active in exploring glaciers in Alaska, where one was named for him. Muir founded the Sierra Club in 1892 to promote conservation. A redwood forest north of San Francisco was named Muir Woods in his honor in 1908. This forest continues as a popular spot for tourists to visit.

3-15. Theodore "Teddy" Roosevelt is considered the father of the conservation movement.

Roosevelt

Theodore Roosevelt (1858-1919) served as president of the United States from 1901 to 1909 and used his power to influence wildlife conservation. Under his leadership, the U.S. Forest Service expanded and five national parks were set up. In addition, 18 national monuments were established and 51 bird reservations were set up.

Roosevelt is well known for his love of nature and the outdoors. After being shown in a cartoon with a bear cub, toy makers began manufacturing stuffed animals that were named "teddy bears." He supported irrigation projects to open dry areas in the western United States for crop farming.

Today, Teddy Roosevelt is generally considered the father of the conservation movement in the United States.

PINCHOT

Gifford Pinchot (1865-1946) promoted the conservation of forest lands in the United States. From 1898 until 1910, he was head of the agency in the federal government that became the U.S. Forest Service. It was his leadership that promoted an expanded interest in natural forests by the federal government.

Following his service with the federal government, Pinchot became president of the National Conservation Committee. He wrote of his efforts in the book, *The Fight for Conservation*, which was published in 1910. Pinchot later served as governor of Pennsylvania.

LEOPOLD

Aldo Leopold (1886-1948) was a pioneer in applying ecology to wildlife management. He felt strongly that people should enjoy natural areas, but that their presence should not damage the areas. He worked for the U.S. Forest Service from 1909 to 1927 and used his work there to promote his ideas.

A native of Iowa, Leopold stressed the importance of education in wildlife management and biology. His early ideas on game management were tested in New Mexico as a young person responsible for enforcing game laws. He later went to the University of Wisconsin, where he organized and set up an educational department that evolved as "wildlife ecology." In 1933, Leopold became the first professor of wildlife management in the United States. He is well known as the author of the textbook, *Game Management*. The book introduced new conservation concepts based on science. It emphasized wildlife management theories.

Leopold demonstrated the need to clearly understand the role of hunting and its impact on wildlife populations. He stressed the need to understand and respond to predators and disease. He pointed out the value of understanding reproduction, mortality, food, water, and cover requirements for animal wildlife.

DARLING

Jay Norwood "Ding" Darling (1876-1962) was a writer and cartoonist who took great interest in the conservation of natural resources. He used cartoons to promote his interest in wildlife. His cartoons were sometimes critical of those who threatened wildlife. He won the Pulitzer Prize on two occasions for his cartoons. His cartoons are classics that depict shameful waste of wildlife and natural resources.

Darling designed the first migratory bird hunting stamp (duck stamp) under provisions of the law that went into effect in 1934. That

3-16. J. N. "Ding" Darling used cartoons to alert the nation to the need for conservation. (Courtesy, "Ding" Darling Foundation)

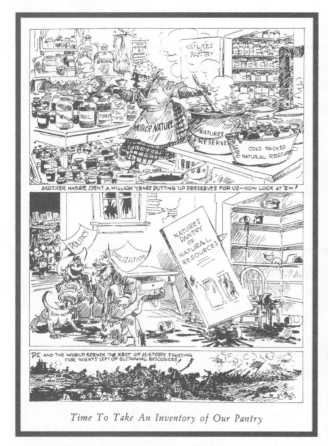

Time To Take An Inventory of Our Pantry

3-17. Darling cartoon showing how humans have treated natural resources. (Courtesy, "Ding" Darling Foundation)

Why not put *everything* we want to get rid of in the river ?

3-18. Darling cartoon showing how humans have treated rivers and one solution to the problem. The misspelling on the sign was characteristic of Darling's work, who once said, "Any man who can't spell a word at least two different ways doesn't show me much imagination." (Courtesy, "Ding" Darling Foundation)

same year, he was appointed chief of the Bureau of Biological Survey by President Franklin Roosevelt. He often disagreed with Roosevelt and used his leadership to organize conservation organizations in the nation. He later became president of the National Wildlife Federation.

EXAMPLES OF WILDLIFE MANAGEMENT

Wildlife conservation involves many approaches to management. A few examples of management activities are:

- Bird banding—**Banding** is placing a band around the leg of a bird to identify it for study. Flightless young or flying adults are captured in traps or with rocket-propelled nets. Bands are attached to their legs before they are released. Banded birds are eventually shot by hunters, found dead, or captured. Using the information on the band provides data on migration routes and the numbers of birds that survive each year. The information is also used to set annual hunting regulations and ensure bird populations are maintained.

3-19. Wildlife biologists preparing to band ducks captured in a swim-in trap.

- Trapping and transplanting—Trapping and transplanting is a process used to boost low wildlife populations or develop new populations. Animals are captured at locations where they are found in abundance. They are transported and released in suitable new areas. Here, the animals are expected to reproduce and increase in numbers.

- Land management—Land management is used to provide a secure habitat for species that require specially protected areas. It is most common in wildlife management areas or refuges. An example is Attwater's prairie chicken, which was once abundant

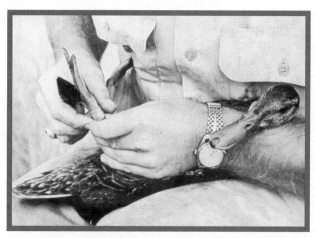

3-20. Placing a numbered metal leg band on a duck before releasing the bird as part of a migration study.

along the Texas and Louisiana Gulf Coast areas. The bird was forced into serious decline because land use changes destroyed its prairie habitat. A few birds now exist in refuges in Texas, where land is specifically managed to allow the birds to continue their existence.

- Wildlife population survey—A **wildlife population survey** is counting the number of wildlife in an area. This gives information about the relative abundance of a particular species. Making counts allows biologists to set up proper management programs. Waterfowl, and many other kinds of birds, are counted from low- and slow-flying airplanes. Alligators are counted at night. Lights are shined across the water to reflect their eyes. Deer are counted from helicopters and airplanes and by walking slowly in the late evening as they become active.

- Vegetation survey—A ***vegetation survey*** is determining the kinds and amounts of vegetation present in important wildlife areas. It is used to make certain that the plants needed by wildlife animals are in good supply with no danger of being depleted.

- Wildlife extension work—Wildlife extension work focuses on educational programs for the public. Different government agencies may be involved in carrying out the work. Landowners, hunters, and others may request the services of government biologists or other individuals in the area of wildlife.

- Implementation of regulations—Regulations about wildlife are made by state and federal agencies based on information on wildlife numbers and conditions. These regulations cover a wide range of activities including duck hunting and protecting rare and endangered plants and animals. (It is important to distinguish between laws and regulations. Laws are usually made by the Congress of the United States or by state legislatures. Regulations are usually made by government agencies in the implementation of the laws.)

Wildlife Connection

FISH HATCHERIES

Fish hatcheries may be operated by state or federal agencies. These facilities keep adult brood stock for spawning. The eggs are usually hatched artificially using trays, jars, or other methods. Following hatching, the fry are carefully tended as they grow into fingerlings and adult-size fish.

After the fish in a hatchery have grown to adequate size, they are released into streams and lakes. This enhances the population of fish and provides fish for taking by sport fishers. The kind of fish grown and released depends on the climate and quality of the water. For example, trout are released into flowing streams with cool fresh water.

WILDLIFE MANAGEMENT AND PRODUCTIVITY

Research and education have demonstrated that knowledge and training increase wildlife productivity. Wildlife management practices, when properly used, provide desired habitat and food sources for animal wildlife.

Proper wildlife management involves human attempts to influence and control wildlife populations in accordance with a balanced habitat. Threats to wildlife must be reduced. Several examples are:

- Threat One: Animal species may exist in shallow or limiting habitats, such as those limited to islands or confined bodies of water. An example is the Puerto Rican parrot.

- Threat Two: Animal species may be characterized as having high economic importance and often living in international territory. An example is the blue whale.

- Threat Three: Animal species that are large in size and often described as a predator are particularly threatened. An example is the grizzly bear.

- Threat Four: Animal species that have limited numbers of offspring, characterized by long gestation or incubation periods and often requiring extensive care, are especially threatened. An example is the California condor.

- Threat Five: Animal species that are highly specialized with physical or behavioral adaptations are often threatened. An example is the manatee.

Recognizing the factors that create threats helps in managing projects and procedures. Successful game management also requires a sequence of controls that are carefully studied and tracked. These include:

- hunting restrictions,

- predator control,

- game land reservations, such as forests and parks,

3-21. The Indian Elephant is an endangered species.

- replenishing wildlife species through artificial restocking and game farm methods, and
- environmental controls, such as food sources, habitat, disease, and other special factors.

Wildlife productivity is the rate at which mature wildlife organisms are produced. Game management uses strategies that consider animal populations and productivity impacted by natural causes, hunting, introduced predators, nonpredatory exotic species, and habitat modification.

Hunting that is not regulated can have devastating impacts on wildlife. Extinction of the passenger pigeon has often been attributed to over-hunting, though other factors were likely involved.

Exotic species may have difficulty adapting when introduced into new ecosystems. Native species may also have difficulty adjusting if moved to new environments.

REVIEWING

MAIN IDEAS

Wildlife conservation began in Europe in the Middle Ages. Pilgrims arriving in North America often ignored good wildlife conservation. Much wildlife was available. New areas could be opened and hunted. People pushed further westward from the Atlantic Ocean in pursuit of wildlife, fertile soil, abundant water, and other natural resources.

Local, state, and federal levels of government have laws and programs that conserve wildlife. Federal actions have had a big impact on wildlife conservation. Most important have been laws to set up national parks and forests, protect wildlife from illegal killing and sales, and carry out research and education programs dealing with wildlife. Early leaders in wildlife conservation include John James Audubon, John Muir, Theodore Roosevelt, Gifford Pinchot, Aldo Leopold, and Jay N. "Ding" Darling.

Proper wildlife management focuses on human efforts to influence wildlife populations within a balanced habitat. Good management assures wildlife productivity. Wildlife productivity is the rate at which wildlife organisms are produced annually.

QUESTIONS

Answer the following questions using correct spelling and complete sentences.

1. What wildlife did the Pilgrims find in North America?

2. What is wasteful exploitation of wildlife?

3. What is the name of the first national park? Why are national parks important in wildlife conservation?

4. What is the Lacey Act?

5. What is the Wildlife Refuge System?

6. What is the purpose of national forests?

7. What state actions conserve wildlife?

8. What local actions conserve wildlife?

9. Name six early leaders in wildlife conservation and indicate a major contribution of each.

10. What are several examples of wildlife conservation practices?

EVALUATING

Match the term with the correct definition.

a. Theodore Roosevelt
b. wildlife population survey
c. Aldo Leopold
d. vegetation survey
e. Lacey Act
f. John James Audubon
g. Gifford Pinchot
h. banding

_____1. Studied and painted birds of North America.

_____2. Promoted the conservation of forests in the United States.

_____3. Known as the father of wildlife conservation.

_____4. Placing a band around the leg of a bird to help identify its movement and life needs.

_____5. Authored a textbook entitled *Game Management*.

_____6. Regulates the shipment of wildlife.

_____7. Determining the kinds and amounts of plants in an area.

_____8. Counting the number of wildlife in an area.

EXPLORING

1. Take a field trip to a nearby wildlife refuge, national forest or park, or other place where wildlife conservation is practiced. Interview the manager of the facility to determine the kind of wildlife in the area, nature of the work in wildlife management, and threats to wildlife. Prepare a written report on your findings. Give an oral report in class.

2. Mark the locations of national parks, national forests, and wildlife refuges on a map of your state. Also, identify state parks and other places designed to conserve wildlife.

3. Use the World Wide Web to search for information on wildlife. Prepare a report on your findings. Select at least two sites and prepare a brief description of each.

CHAPTER 4

Endangered Species

OBJECTIVES

This chapter explains the meaning of endangered species, gives examples of endangered species, and offers suggestions on managing endangered species. The objectives of the chapter are:

1 Explain endangerment and extinction.

2 Describe the Endangered Species Act.

3 Explain how plants and animals become endangered.

4 List examples of endangered plants and animals.

5 Explain how endangered species are managed.

TERMS

endangered species
Endangered Species Act
endangerment

extinction
extinct wildlife
rare species

threatened species

4-1. Four endangered animal wildlife species: flightless cormorant (top left), greater panda (top right), great Indian one-horned rhino (bottom left), and Galapagos giant tortoise (bottom right).

LIVING things go about life in a changing world. They must adapt to the changes. If not, they will be unable to survive over a long time. Some wildlife populations are large and stable. Others are rare and number only a few individuals. Many species have permanently disappeared.

Wildlife populations with low numbers and living in places that are not fully favorable to them tend to decline and may possibly become extinct. Species that cannot tolerate gradual changes have population declines. In the United States, 59 species of identified birds and mammals have become extinct. These are gone forever!

Wildlife managers have always recognized the need for special care of species that had critically low population numbers and were in danger of being further reduced. In 1966, new laws were made to protect certain species with very low numbers.

ENDANGERMENT

Endangerment is threatening a species so its numbers become very low. Plants, animals, and other species may be endangered. Humans, as well as natural events on Earth, create endangerment.

Species are endangered when they are no longer able to reproduce. Food supply, loss of land or water areas, and other activities cause endangerment. Some species may lack the ability to adapt to new situations. When this occurs, their numbers decline and they may face extinction.

EXTINCTION

Extinction is the disappearance of a species from the earth. Species that fail to reproduce gradually die off. The species may be unable to adapt to changes in the environment where it lives. Once extinct, the species is gone forever.

Extinction is a natural process. Species that survive have the ability to adjust to changes through evolution. Some scientists feel that extinction is the fate of all species over longer periods. Humans sometimes create conditions that speed the process of extinction.

Over-hunting has endangered some wildlife species. Landscape alteration is the primary cause of extinction.

Today, the earth has nearly 10 million different surviving species. Many of these gradually evolved over millions of years into modern forms. Those that did not make the necessary adaptations became extinct, such as dinosaurs. Since the earth was formed, some 400 million species have become extinct, according to scientists.

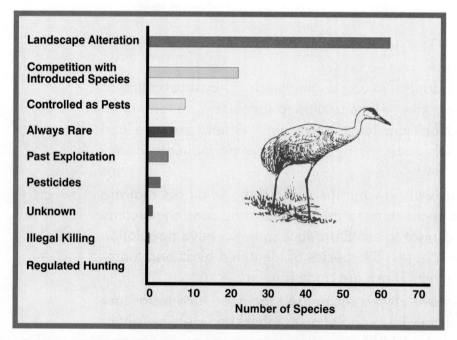

4-2. Primary causes of 114 wildlife species being placed on the threatened or endangered species list. (Note that none are on the list due to regulated hunting!)

Species that are no longer living on the earth are known as ***extinct wildlife***. Every member of those species has died. For example, all dinosaurs are now extinct. No living dinosaurs are on the earth.

Endangered Species

An ***endangered species*** is one that is in immediate danger of extinction. The rate of reproduction is not adequate to assure survival. In some cases, the only surviving members of the species may be in zoos or wildlife preserves. Worldwide, nearly 400 species are said to be endangered.

Wildlife species become endangered because of several reasons. Changes in the climate, condition of the land, flow of water, or other alterations can lead to a species being endangered. Human activities often lead to endangerment. Many government, industry, wildlife-interest, and other groups and individuals work to assure survival of endangered species. Table 4-1 lists examples of endangered species.

Threatened Species

A ***threatened species*** is one that is likely to become endangered in the future. The species is facing serious dangers. Populations of the species are low. More than 100 species are now listed as threatened in the United States.

Wildlife Connection

SPORT HUNTING

Many people enjoy sport hunting. Duck, deer, and rabbit are favorite species to hunt. People have not always hunted for sport. Early people had to hunt for their food, but things are different today. Hunting is sometimes controversial.

Sport hunters enjoy the outdoors. Most are careful to follow all laws and use safe practices. They do not take more game than is legal. Today's sport hunters are conservationists who care for wildlife by promoting good habitat. Some people oppose hunting. They cite the dangers of hunting, the number of people killed, and the taking of wildlife.

Before you go hunting, know the rules of safety and legal limits. Know where you are hunting. Never hunt on posted land without permission. Respect the property of others. Have a good time in the great outdoors!

Table 4-1. Examples of Endangered Wildlife Species in the United States

Common Name	Preferred Habitat	Possible Reason for Endangerment
Brown pelican	Coastal islands and bays	Pesticides and human disturbance
Southern bald eagle	Lakes, reservoirs, large rivers	Pesticides, shooting
Attwater's prairie chicken	Coastal prairies	Overgrazing, farming
Ivory-billed woodpecker	Mature hardwood forests	Lumbering
Red wolf	Coastal prairies and marshes	Predator control, interbreeding with coyotes, and loss of habitat
Black-footed ferret	Rocky Mountains and plains	Poisoning aimed at prairie dogs
Kemp's ridley turtle	Coastal waters and beaches	Overharvest of eggs and incidental capture in nets
Houston toad	Sand soils of post oak woodlands	Restricted distribution and planting exotic grasses
Star cactus	Brushlands	Restricted distribution and excessive collecting

Considerable effort is often made to improve habitat and get threatened species to reproduce. Research is carried out to identify threats and conditions needed for the species to thrive. Government policies protect threatened species from hunting and other activities that could further reduce their numbers.

4-3. Rare chimpanzees are often kept in zoos for the public to see.

RARE SPECIES

A *rare species* is one that exists in small numbers. For some reason, the species may appear to be declining. It could become threatened if the trend is not reversed. If not protected, a rare species first becomes threatened and may become endangered or extinct.

Rare species are often maintained in zoos, refuges, and other locations where they are protected. Efforts are often made to get the species to reproduce in captivity. This is sometimes difficult.

4-4. The value of the bark of the Pacific yew tree in producing taxol may threaten the existence of the trees. (Taxol is a drug used in fighting cancer.) This shows the bark being stripped from a cut tree. (Courtesy, U.S. Fish and Wildlife Service)

THE ENDANGERED SPECIES ACT

The United States Congress passed the **Endangered Species Act** in 1966. The regulations of this Act are carried out by the Office of Endangered Species of the U.S. Fish and Wildlife Service. The decision to list any species as endangered or threatened is based on information collected by wildlife biologists.

A list of endangered and threatened species is published and amended periodically. Some states also publish a list of plants and animals that are threatened or endangered on a local or statewide basis.

Each year, Congress provides money to be used to support the Endangered Species Act. Funding is used for biologists to update and maintain the lists of threatened and endangered species. Field biologists conduct surveys to determine if the various species are increasing or further declining. If populations are improving, they may be removed from the list. If a new species is found to be seriously declining, that name may be added to the list and given protection under the Endangered Species Act.

Money is also used to help threatened or endangered species. This may involve spending money on land management or buying land and setting it aside so a particular species may increase its numbers.

4-5. The California condor is nearly extinct—only about 50 survive! (The bird is the largest flying land bird in North America, with a wing span of 8 to 9 feet. A female condor lays just one egg every two years.) (Courtesy, Jeff Foott, U.S. Fish and Wildlife Service)

Section 6 of the Endangered Species Act allows federal money to be provided to state game and fish agencies for use in the management of endangered and threatened species. States can use this money to study wildlife populations, manage protected areas, or purchase land.

Section 9 of the Act includes wording that makes it illegal to "harm" endangered species. The term "harm" means the destruction of a habitat used for feeding, breeding, and sheltering. Under this section of the Endangered Species Act, "everybody" in the United States is restricted from destroying an endangered species habitat. This includes private citizens, farmers, ranchers, road builders, dam builders, government agencies, owners of forests, and all other groups and individuals that impact the land.

Section 9 of the Act is controversial and has been the center of many protests. An example is the protest over a tiny fish known as the snail darter. Work was stopped on the construction of a large dam because the dam would have destroyed the very limited habitat occupied by this endangered species. More recently, the northern spotted owl in the Pacific Coast forest region has been the center of controversy. Timber cutting has been halted to protect old growth trees in which the threatened spotted owl lives.

HOW WILDLIFE IS ENDANGERED

In modern times, changes in land use have been the primary reasons for animals becoming endangered or threatened. Some animals were reduced in number because they were

Career Profile

WILDLIFE RESEARCHER

Wildlife researchers seek to answer questions about wildlife. They study areas related to habitats, the requirements of a species, health and reproduction, and other areas. They often share their knowledge with others by writing or giving presentations.

Wildlife researchers need college degrees in wildlife biology or a related area. A baccalaureate degree plus masters or doctors degrees are usually needed. Practical experience working with wildlife and doing research is essential.

Most jobs are with government agencies, colleges or universities, or private businesses involved with wildlife or natural resources. The work typically involves being outside though office and indoor laboratory work are often included. This photo shows a researcher studying birds in a national wildlife refuge. (Courtesy, U.S. Fish and Wildlife Service)

controlled as pests. Others were reduced in number as a result of competition with introduced species. Some species were always rare, and illegal killing helped drive some numbers down. Sometimes, a wildlife animal's habitat may be so restricted that land use changes resulted in no place for the animal to live. They either dropped to lower levels or became extinct. It is important to note that no species under regulated hunting has become endangered.

Three examples of how wildlife species become endangered are included here. Each will indicate that endangerment resulted for different reasons, but was often related to human activities.

THE PASSENGER PIGEON

The most dramatic loss of a single species was the passenger pigeon. This medium-size bird once existed in great numbers in the east-central part of the United States. Early accounts described flocks that "darkened" the skies when the birds flew to feed and roost.

Today, not a single living passenger pigeon exists. Although the birds were hunted and trapped for food, large-scale destruction of hardwood forests for lumber and land clearing were identified as the causes for extinction of this species. When the passenger pigeon lost its feeding, breeding, and roosting habitat, populations could not sustain themselves and this species was lost forever.

4-6. A passenger pigeon. (Courtesy, U.S. Fish and Wildlife Service)

THE RED WOLF

The red wolf was an animal that lived in the southeastern United States. The wolf hunted and ate mostly small mammals and lived in both forests and open prairies. Large-scale land use changes occurred throughout the area used by red wolves.

4-7. A red wolf.

Like other wolf species, the red wolf was trapped and commonly shot on sight, but continued to exist in small numbers, especially in coastal Texas and Louisiana. A number of animals died each year from diseases, especially heart worms, which are carried by mosquitoes. As car traffic increased in rural areas, increasing numbers of red wolves were killed as they crossed roads.

As red wolf populations began to decline, a close relative, the coyote, began to occupy areas formerly used only by wolves. Interbreeding occurred and through time, red wolf populations became mixed with coyote genes. Because of continued interbreeding by coyotes, pure red wolf populations no longer exist and all animals living within the original red wolf range are now considered to be coyotes. Only a small number of purebred red wolves exist in captivity and at a few experimental release locations.

THE PRAIRIE CHICKEN

Today, another bird species, the Attwater's prairie chicken, is facing a very uncertain future. The birds once existed in an area of about 7 million acres along the Texas and Louisiana coastal region. The prairie chickens lived in tall prairie grasses. Populations were estimated at about 1 million birds.

Factory and home construction, intensive farming, and poorly managed livestock grazing at some locations severely reduced prairie grasses needed by Attwater's prairie chicken. The spring 1996 survey indicated only 42 prairie chickens living in the wild at several small locations in Texas. Although a prairie chicken refuge and a captive breeding program have been

4-8. The once abundant Attwater's prairie chicken faces an uncertain future. (Many experts believe that the species will become extinct even with the best management efforts.) (Courtesy, U.S. Fish and Wildlife Service)

established, some authorities fear the birds will become extinct in the wild in the near future because land use changes have been too overwhelming.

MANAGING ENDANGERED SPECIES

The endangered species story is not all gloom and doom. Numerous positive actions have occurred. Several species originally listed as endangered have been removed from the list. Others are nearing that point.

Some endangered species success stories are directly the result of preserving necessary habitats. Most others are the result of specific management actions that allowed low populations to increase.

THE WHOOPING CRANE

A good example of a species showing signs of improvement from habitat protection is the whooping crane. Although there was a small whooping crane nesting population in Louisiana that disappeared prior to 1950, the majority of whooping cranes nested in northern Canada and spent the winter along the Texas coast. The cranes were never abundant. In 1850, there were probably only about 1,500. By 1941, only 15 birds remained and it appeared the birds were headed for extinction.

The remaining 15 birds were wintering on a national wildlife refuge that was originally purchased for ducks and geese in 1937. Management actions have included planting food plots and constructing a marine impoundment. However, the most important management actions have involved providing a secure breeding and winter area and lowering population losses during spring and fall migration. Whooping cranes have slowly responded to management efforts and in 1996, a total of 158 birds were utilizing the Aransas National Wildlife Refuge and adjacent coastal area.

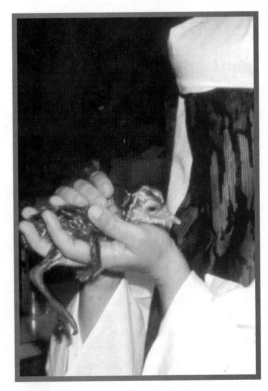

4-9. An artificially hatched whooping crane being held by a hatchery scientist. (Courtesy, David Ellis, U.S. Fish and Wildlife Service)

4-10. The brown pelican became endangered because of insecticide poisoning. (The bird is now increasing in numbers and will likely survive.) (Courtesy, U.S. Fish and Wildlife Service)

THE BROWN PELICAN

The brown pelican is the state bird of Louisiana and was originally a common bird along the Gulf Coast. By 1961, the brown pelican population had dropped to the point where birds were difficult to locate.

Investigations showed that few of the remaining birds were successfully nesting. It was discovered that large numbers of birds had died of insecticide poisoning. The pelicans had been eating fish contaminated with a pesticide. The pesticide was Endrin—a product widely used in cotton and grain fields upstream from coastal pelican habitats.

The state of Louisiana began to trap and transport live pelicans from Florida. The birds from Florida were released at locations where Louisiana pelicans had lived for years. At about the same time, restrictions were placed on the use of Endrin.

Pelican populations have increased to the point where the bird is now a candidate for removal from the endangered species list. The brown pelican population in Louisiana is healthy, expanding, and currently estimated to range from 30,000 to 40,000 birds.

4-11. Technicians are flushing spilled oil from a shoreline to restore habitat for waterfowl and other species. (Courtesy, Jill Parker, U.S. Fish and Wildlife Service)

REVIEWING

MAIN IDEAS

Throughout history, some wildlife populations have been very large and stable, while others have been rare and numbered only a few individuals. Within historic times, 59 species of animals alone have become extinct within the United States.

The need for special treatment for those species with critically low numbers was recognized. As a result, the U.S. Congress passed the Endangered Species Act. Under the Act, the Secretary of Interior has the authority to list wildlife species as either threatened or endangered. The list is based on abundance and the possibility of the species becoming extinct.

Most animals become endangered or extinct as a result of changes in land use. Not all endangered species stories are gloom and doom. The whooping crane and brown pelican are two species that have been restored to much higher numbers as a result of intensive management.

QUESTIONS

Answer the following questions using correct spelling and complete sentences.

1. List two endangered species and tell what caused them to be placed on the endangered species list.

2. List the various factors that caused wildlife populations to decline.

3. What is endangerment?

4. How many animal wildlife species have become extinct in the United States since records have been kept?

5. Under Section 9 of the Endangered Species Act, what does the term "harm" endangered species mean?

6. Explain how the red wolf became extinct in the wild.

7. Explain how the brown pelican population was increased from critically low numbers.

8. Indicate the number of wildlife species managed under regulated hunting that have become endangered.

EVALUATING

Match the term with the correct definition.

a. rare species   d. endangerment   g. Endangered Species Act
b. endangered species   e. extinction
c. threatened species   f. extinct wildlife

_____1. A federal law to protect wildlife.

_____2. A species that exists in small numbers, often kept in zoos, refuges, and other protected places.

_____3. A species that is in immediate danger of extinction.

_____4. Species of wildlife that no longer exists.

_____5. A species of wildlife likely to become endangered in the future.

_____6. The disappearance of wildlife from the earth.

_____7. Threatening a species of wildlife so its numbers are low or so the species goes out of existence.

EXPLORING

1. Scan through several magazines for pictures that show land use practices unfavorable to wildlife. Bring the magazines to class and discuss the problems and how they can be solved.

2. Divide the class into two groups. Have the first group offer justifications for building a large dam. Have the second group offer justifications for canceling dam construction based on the need to protect the habitat for an endangered species. Decide who offers the strongest argument about the dam for the welfare of people and wildlife.

3. Investigate the Endangered Species Act. Identify the major provisions of the Act and how the provisions are being implemented. Prepare a report on your findings.

Part Two

Science and Technology in Wildlife Management

CHAPTER 5

Wildlife Biology and Ecology

OBJECTIVES

This chapter covers the fundamentals of wildlife biology. It includes life processes as well as important biological and genetic information. The objectives of the chapter are:

1 Explain important life processes of living wildlife organisms.

2 Describe the life span stages of wildlife.

3 Explain the role of heredity and genetics with wildlife.

4 Describe how ecosystems are important in wildlife biology.

TERMS

abiotic factor
albinism
biophage
biotic factor
browse
carnivore
chromosome
circulation
community
digestion
elimination
food

food chain
food web
gene
genetics
growth
ingestion
herbivore
heredity
life processes
life span
locomotion
mutation

natural selection
niche
omnivore
owl pellet
photosynthesis
reproduction
respiration
saprophage
secretion
sensation

5-1. Moose have unique biological features that allow them to survive and raise young in their habitats.

ALL SPECIES of wildlife are living organisms! As such, they carry out processes that support life. Each organism must have the body structure for growing, living, reproducing, and going about life activities. If life processes stop, the organism can no longer live.

People have an important role in assuring adequate wildlife numbers. By understanding the basics of biology, people know how to provide for the needs of an organism. Knowing the unique environmental requirements of different species is also needed.

The life needs of most wildlife species are similar to domesticated species in the same family. Yet, each species in a family is different. This chapter covers important similarities and differences.

LIFE PROCESSES

5-2. Snakes, such as the broad-banded copperhead, must carry out essential life processes to live. (Courtesy, U.S. Fish and Wildlife Service)

All living things—no matter how diverse—have certain **life processes**. These are essential functions for maintaining the life of an organism. When they stop, the organism dies. Supporting these processes is part of managing wildlife populations.

Eight life processes are used in wildlife science. Seven of these are essential. One of the life processes—reproduction—is not essential for an individual wildlife organism to live, but is needed for the species to continue.

GROWTH AND REPAIR

Organisms must grow if they are to live. Growth occurs in several ways. **Growth** is

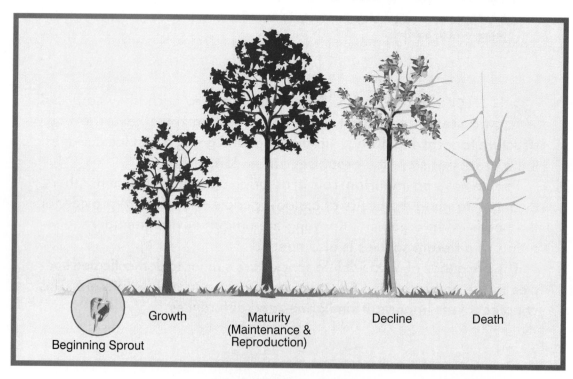

5-3. The life stages of a tree.

the process of an organism increasing in size by adding cells, by the cells getting larger, or by replacing cells. Cell replacement is known as repair.

With young organisms, growth is primarily adding cells to increase the size. For example, a newly hatched fish is tiny. It grows more cells to have a larger body. In some cases, the cells increase in size.

Growth is different with mature organisms. Replacement cells are needed. Age and activity result in cells dying or being damaged. Replacement is growing new cells to replace those that are lost. Some structures increase in size with mature organisms, such as the length of claws on adult bears or the antlers on male deer.

Growth requires food that provides essential nutrients. Without adequate nutrients, an organism fails to grow. It may become stunted or diseased and die from a lack of nutrients.

5-4. The terminal bud on this pine tree is evidence of rapid growth.

Food

All wildlife organisms need food. **Food** is any substance that nourishes an organism. Food provides energy and nutrients for growth. Growth, repair, and movement require food nutrients— even if the organism is in a resting stage, such as sleeping or hibernating.

Wildlife Connection

LEARNING FROM AN OWL PELLET

An owl pellet will provide considerable information about what an owl has consumed. A pellet is a mass of indigestible food material that is regurgitated. Owl pellets are collected by biological supply houses and dried. This removes odor and protects the pellet from decay.

Common probes and tweezers can be used to take an owl pellet apart. The items found are compared with sketches of skeletons of different animals an owl might have eaten. The major food items can be identified fairly easily. The photo shows bone structures being found in an owl pellet. This indicates that the owl had eaten a number of small animals (mostly rodents).

Follow appropriate safety procedures when dissecting an owl pellet. Be sure to properly clean up the work area when finished.

Organisms vary in how food is available. Animals consume their food materials. Plants make their food. The environment of an organism must provide the needed food. If not, it will fail to live and grow properly.

5-5. A fox squirrel is holding food—most likely an acorn or hickory nut. (Courtesy, U.S. Fish and Wildlife Service)

Animals

Animals get their food by ingestion. **Ingestion** is eating or taking in food. How animals ingest food varies. Deer and oysters are two contrasting examples. Deer move about in search of their food, known as browse. **Browse** is the leaves, stems, and shoots of trees, shrubs, and vines. Oysters remain still in the water and filter tiny particles of food materials from water that flows through their open shells.

Once ingested, animals digest the food materials. **Digestion** is the process that changes food into forms that can be absorbed by the animal. Various chemical processes occur in the animal's digestive system. This prepares the nutrients in the food for absorption by the body.

Once digested and the nutrients absorbed, the remaining food materials are expelled from the body by a process known as **elimination**. Both liquid and solid materials are eliminated. The solid materials, known as feces, can be studied to determine the food materials consumed by animals. Noting the presence of feces (also known as dung or droppings) helps identify the animal wildlife in an area. For example, rabbits leave distinct dung pellets and geese leave identifiable droppings.

Some animals have other methods of eliminating food materials that cannot be digested. The owl is an example. An owl will regurgitate materials it cannot digest. This material is known as an **owl pellet**. An owl pellet often contains the skeletons of tiny animals.

Plants

Plants make food by the process of **photosynthesis**. With this process, nutrients are converted to food—simple sugars. Nutrients are primarily absorbed by the roots of plants. A green material, known as chlorophyll, in the presence of light converts the nutrients to food.

Plants have different food needs. This means that the nutrients they require also vary. Understanding these nutrient differences helps in promoting wildlife plant growth. For example, some species of sedge prefer acidic soil. If other species are desired on the land, lime should be added to make the soil less acidic.

Circulation

Circulation is the movement of substances within an organism. Food nutrients, digested food, and other substances are involved. How it occurs varies with species. Big differences exist between plants and animals.

Animals have circulatory systems. The fluid in the circulatory system is blood. The heart and the blood vessels keep blood flowing throughout the body. The blood carries digested food, oxygen, and other substances to all parts of the body. The blood picks up wastes and carbon dioxide and carries the wastes for elimination.

Plants have vascular systems for circulation. Two major kinds of tissue are involved: xylem and phloem. Xylem carries water and raw food nutrients throughout a plant. Phloem moves the manufactured food from where photosynthesis occurs to where the food is needed.

Injuries to plants and animals cause loss of fluid. Animals bleed; plants lose sap. Preventing the loss of fluid helps maintain healthy plants and animals.

Respiration

Respiration is the process by which an organism provides its cells with food and oxygen. It is a continuous process in all living cells. Two primary substances are important in respiration: oxygen and carbon dioxide. All organisms need oxygen. In using food, the oxygen is changed to carbon dioxide. Carbon dioxide is given off by an organism.

Animals use structures, such as lungs and gills, in respiration. Oxygen is taken in through these structures and carbon dioxide is given off by them. Examples of animals with lungs include bear, elk, beaver, duck, and squirrel. Gills are on aquatic species, such as fish.

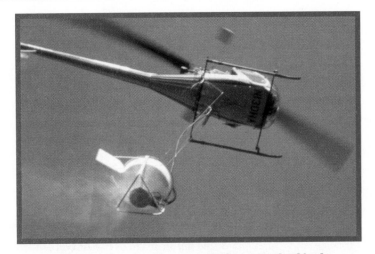

5-6. Fertilizer is often used to promote plant growth. This shows a helicopter applying fertilizer to a wildlife area. (Courtesy, U.S. Department of Agriculture)

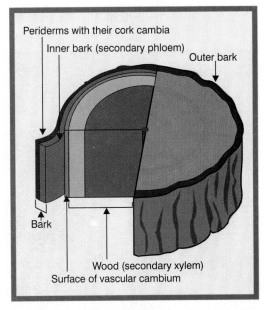

5-7. The cross-section of a tree stem shows the location of xylem and phloem.

Periderms with their cork cambia
Inner bark (secondary phloem)
Outer bark
Bark
Wood (secondary xylem)
Surface of vascular cambium

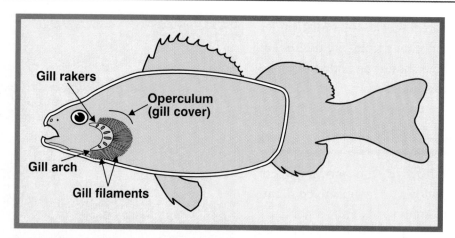

5-8. The gill structure of fish allows efficient respiration in an aquatic environment.

Plant respiration, likewise, involves the exchange of oxygen and carbon dioxide. One difference is plants also take in carbon dioxide as part of the process of photosynthesis. Tiny stoma in the leaves are the openings through which these gases are exchanged.

5-9. Fish secrete a substance externally on their skin or scales that promotes movement in water and makes them hard to grasp.

SECRETION

Secretion is the production within an organism of substances needed for life processes. These watery substances are known as secretions. The substances may be needed for a life process or excreted by the organism.

Specialized body structures, known as glands, are often responsible for secretion. An example with animals is the salivary glands. These glands produce a watery substance that makes it possible to swallow food or, with some animals, regurgitate food. Many other secretions are used by organisms in their life processes.

SENSATION

Sensation is the ability of an organism to feel or otherwise gather information and respond to its environment. Complex systems of nerves are involved.

Animal sensation is easier to understand than plants. Animals typically have touch, taste, smell, sight, and hearing. These receive information from an animal's environment. The animal responds to the sensations.

Plants respond to light, objects, and other items in their environment. The response of plants is known as a tropism. For example, the roots of plants often grow around rocks and other structures. This is known as thigmotropism. The response of plant leaves to light is another sensation known as phototropism.

Movement

All organisms move in some way. How they move varies. Many organisms move to acquire food or gain a better position in their environment. Movement may be obvious with some species and not evident with others.

Internal movements are needed for an organism to carry out life processes. An example is when an animal swallows food. Muscles of the mouth and throat move the food through the esophagus to the stomach.

Some organisms are anchored in place, such as plants anchored by their roots. Other organisms can move about, such as animals with legs, fins, or wings.

5-10. White-tailed deer are capable of rapid movement away from potential danger. (Courtesy, U.S. Fish and Wildlife Service)

Wildlife scientists often study the movement of animals. **Locomotion** is the movement of an animal from one place to another. A deer may quickly move through a forest to escape danger. Geese may fly long distances in migrating from one climate to another.

Reproduction

Reproduction is the process by which organisms give rise to new organisms of the same species. It is not a life process that is essential for living. It is, however, essential for a species to perpetuate itself.

The reproduction process varies widely among organisms, but has similarities in the creation of new life. It may involve sexual or asexual reproduction. Sexual reproduction involves the union of male and female sex cells. For example, the pollen (male sex cell) of

5-11. Killdeer nest in open areas on the ground. (This female is sitting on the eggs in the nest to keep them warm and promote embryo development.) (Courtesy, U.S. Fish and Wildlife Service)

plants joins with the ovule (plant female sex cell) to create a seed structure. The mature seed will grow into a new plant under the proper conditions.

Sexual reproduction in animals differs from plants. When animals reach a certain stage of maturity, they are capable of reproduction. By mating, the male sex cell, known as sperm, unites with the ovum or egg of the female. The egg develops into a new individual. In some cases, the development is in the reproductive tract of the female, such as a fox. In other cases, eggs are laid and incubated outside the body of the female, such as an eagle. The eggs are typically in a nest where either the female or the female and male alternately "sit" on the nest to incubate the eggs.

Asexual reproduction does not involve the union of cells. Only one parent is needed. Asexual reproduction is most common in plants and usually possible with animals only in experimental laboratory situations. Plant asexual reproduction is with sprouts, bulbs, or by other means. For example, a wild strawberry plant sends out a runner (stem structure) that produces another plant.

New methods with biotechnology are being used to reproduce organisms. An example is tissue culture. Small tissues or, in some cases, just a few cells can be used to create a new organism. This is commonly known as cloning.

LIFE SPAN

Life span is the period of life of an organism. The length of life spans varies. Within a species, the length of life span is similar. Fox squirrels may live 5 to 6 years; deer 7 to 8 years or more. Trees may live for a hundred years or more. Insects may live for only a few days.

All species have a fairly definite sequence of stages in their lives. Nutrition, disease, and other conditions may affect life span. Some species may never achieve maturity. If a food shortage is present, some are stunted and do not grow, whereas others may get disease and die prematurely. For example, an overpopulation of deer may result in some deer not having enough food. They will not grow well and will be unhealthy. Their life spans will be altered.

The five life span stages are:

1. Beginning—Life span begins in different ways. With animals, it begins with birth or hatching. With plants, life span begins with emergence of a new plant from the ground. Some babies are able to live independently; others must have support from parents. Most animal babies require at least some support from their mothers. Mammals are animal species whose young are nourished by milk from their mothers. Baby fish (known as fry) can usually live without care pro-vided food materials are in the water. Baby birds in a nest are brought worms, insects, and other foods by their mother.

2. Growth and development—New, immature organisms grow and develop to reach maturity. They typically grow rapidly if food is available and their envi-ronment is favorable. The rate of growth declines as they approach maturity.

3. Maturity—Mature organisms are fully developed. Some additional growth, or changes associated with maturity, may occur, but the organism does not con-tinue to increase in size. Most growth is associated with the repair and replace-ment of cells. Maturity includes the ability to reproduce.

4. Decline—After maturity, organisms begin to lose their ability to maintain them-selves. Aging sets in. Cells may no longer be repaired and replaced. Life pro-cesses may occur at a slower rate. The organism loses its strength and weakens. This leads to the next life span stage.

Career Profile

FORESTER

A forester studies plants, particularly trees. Wild-life animals are also included. The work may include assessing tree growth, identifying pests, establishing forests, and selectively harvesting trees. The work is often outdoors and in forest areas.

Foresters need college degrees in forestry, biol-ogy, wildlife biology, or related areas. A baccalaure-ate degree is sufficient for most entry-level forestry occupations. Masters and doctors degrees are required for advancement.

Jobs are with large timber and paper companies, wildlife preserves, national parks, national forests,

forestry agencies of state governments, and research departments of colleges. This photo shows a for-ester examining a core sample from a tree. Such a sample shows growth patterns and can be used to determine a tree's age. (Courtesy, U.S. Department of Agriculture)

WHAT DO TREES AND FISH HAVE IN COMMON?

Growth Rings. As a fish grows, its scales develop tiny annual rings like those found in wood. These rings mark the difference between the fish's rapid growth in summer and its slow winter growth.

5-12. Growth rings are found in many organisms. This shows the similarities of growth rings in a tree and the tiny annual rings in a fish scale.

5-13. A dead tree stands beside a mature tree in the Tahoe Basin of California.

5. Death—Death is the end of the life of an organism. The protoplasm in its cells ceases to be active. Disease and decline result in death. The nature of death varies. Upon death, an organism becomes nonliving material. It decays and the nutrients return to the earth to support future life.

GENETICS AND HEREDITY

Genetics is the study of how traits are transmitted from parents to offspring. All offspring are the products of their parents. Offspring always have characteristics of the species of their parents. Within these characteristics, their inheritance may vary considerably.

The basic principles of genetics are useful in wildlife management. Breeding programs may be developed to promote wildlife populations. Selection of members of a species that best represent species qualities helps assure that the desired traits are passed to future generations. In some cases, breeding individuals are selected because of their resistance to a particular problem, such as a tree that resists insect attack.

Heredity

Heredity is the acquisition of traits by offspring. Heredity is the reason offspring resemble their parents. For example, white tail deer always produce white tail deer offspring. Both parents contribute to the heredity of their offspring. This includes traits of health and strength as well as traits that result in an animal being weak, diseased, or different.

Albinism is an example of an inherited characteristic from both parents. It occurs in animals and plants as offspring with color that does not resemble that of parents. Albinism is the inability to produce pigment. Common animals with albinism are catfish and rabbits. Both are white. Their eye color is pink. Both the mother and father must have the genetic trait (not albinism) for the offspring to be albino. It is then only a one-in-four chance that the offspring will have the albinism condition.

Understanding genes and chromosomes helps in understanding heredity.

5-14. Genetics explains why the young wild turkeys resemble their parent. (Courtesy, Lynn Porter, Hinds County Soil and Water Conservation District, Mississippi)

Genes and Chromosomes

A **gene** is a unit of heredity. Genes are on chromosomes in each cell nucleus of an organism. Genes contain chemical instructions for the cells of an organism and direct the growth and functions of an organism. Inherited traits are passed on by genes.

A **chromosome** is a tiny, twisted, thread-like structure made of protein and DNA (deoxyribonucleic acid). In a cell, a

5-15. Short-eared owls have unique and distinguishing features that are hereditary.

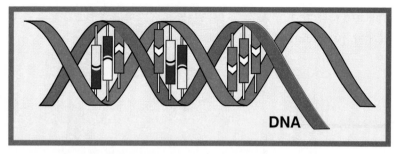

5-16. A DNA double helix is a twisted strand forming a spiral structure.

chromosome is about 1/50,000 of an inch long. If uncoiled and stretched out, a chromosome might be 2 inches long!

Cells of organisms of the same species have the same number of chromosomes. For example, field mice have 40 chromosomes and chimpanzees have 48 chromosomes. Chromosomes always occur in pairs, which means that a field mouse has 20 pairs of chromosomes.

Sex cells (eggs and sperms in animals) have half the number of chromosomes as body cells. These chromosomes are unpaired until the egg ovule is fertilized by a male sex cell. When they unite to form a new organism, the chromosomes join to form pairs. This gives each cell a full set of chromosomes for the organism. The genes on each chromosome determine the physical character of the new organism.

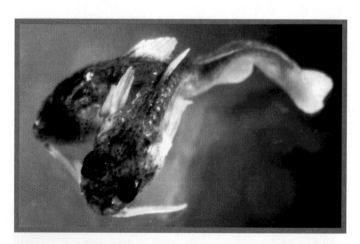

5-17. A two-headed fish could be the result of a mutation caused by water pollution. (Courtesy, U.S. Department of the Interior)

Mutations

Mutations sometimes occur. A **mutation** is a change in the DNA and resulting organism that is not inherited from parents. This results in an organism that departs from its parents in one or more inherited ways.

Mutations are not predictable. Some mutations are defects that weaken an organism. Other mutations result in superior organisms or those with desirable traits. For example, the colors of flowers on a plant may be different from its genetic inheritance. If so, the plant is a mutant.

Natural selection

Natural selection is the process of organisms with favorable traits being stronger and surviving longer than those without the traits. The weaker individuals of a species do not survive in nature. After several generations, the favorable trait becomes more common and contributes to survival of the species. Organisms which do not adapt may become weaker and disappear from the earth over a period of many years. It appears that this was the case with the dinosaurs.

Reproduction favors the stronger individuals, particularly the males. In some species, male animals fight among themselves to determine which animal mates with a female. The stronger male usually fights away other males. The genetic information of the stronger male is transmitted to future generations.

Humans can create conditions in the environment that are unfavorable to wildlife. These may result from pollution or change in a natural habitat. Pollution as acid rain has damaged trees in some areas of North America.

Construction activities change natural habitats so that organisms are unable to adapt. An example is blocking the flow of water in a stream. Trees that grow on land not regularly flooded will die if the land around them is flooded continuously. Beaver dams may back up water onto land where trees grow, killing the trees. Humans can partially block the flow of water by filling a stream and causing water to back up. This will result in the death of trees that cannot adapt.

WILDLIFE BIOLOGY AND ECOSYSTEMS

Living things are found in many different environments on the earth. This includes land, water, and air. Each living thing has a particular environment in which it survives. If the environment is changed, the organism may no longer survive. This environment is the ecosystem of an organism.

ECOSYSTEMS

An ecosystem is the community of living and nonliving things in a particular environment or area. Ecosystems may be large or small. An ocean forms an ecosystem as does a forest. The area under a log or rock also forms an ecosystem.

Ecosystems are always changing. Most never change so drastically that organisms cannot survive in them. If a drastic change does occur, the organism seeks a new place to live or dies. It dies because it cannot adjust to changes in its environment.

5-18. The physical area where a cottontail rabbit lives is its habitat. (Courtesy, James C. Loupold, U.S. Fish and Wildlife Service)

The physical area where an organism lives is its habitat. The elements needed for life must be present: food, water, shelter, and space. If these are no longer available, the organisms cannot survive. An example is clear-cutting a forest. The land area left will no longer support certain species of wildlife, such as squirrels, birds, tree frogs, and lichens. The habitat has changed. Other species may find the clear-cut area a good home. For example, new species of trees may grow where they could not have grown before the forest was cut.

BIOTIC AND ABIOTIC FACTORS

The two major factors in an ecosystem are biotic and abiotic.

A **biotic factor** is a living organism. Most ecosystems have several or many biotic factors. They depend on the abiotic factors for life-giving needs. If the appropriate abiotic factors are not present, living things must move to another location or cease to exist. Foxes and wolves, for example, often roam about to find adequate food, such as rabbits and mice. Fox and wolves may move to a location that better supports their needs if food supply gets short.

Abiotic factors are the nonliving things, such as water, soil, temperature, and sunlight. Without abiotic factors, organisms cannot live. Even living organisms become abiotic upon their death. Through decomposition, the nonliving organism returns to minerals and other materials.

5-19. A bison herd is feeding on plant materials on a hillside. What biotic and abiotic factors do the bison have in their ecosystem?

COMMUNITIES

All of the living things in an area form a **community**. The organisms live together in some sort of harmony. Those that cannot live in harmony must move on or they will cease to live in the community.

Communities may be on land, in water, or combinations of the two. Those on land are known as terrestrial communities, while those in water are known as aquatic communities. The two do not exist independently. What happens in a terrestrial community can have a big impact on an aquatic community and vice versa. For example, allowing land to erode so that tiny particles of soil enter a stream damages the community for oysters that live where the stream flows into an ocean. The oysters may not be able to feed and survive.

ORGANIZATION AND STRUCTURE

Communities have organization and structure. These provide varying habitats to which different species are adapted. Changes in one small part of a habitat may affect all living things. For example, lack of rain may result in plants and animals not growing. Seeds of plants cannot germinate without water. Animals may not get enough food and move to another location.

All organisms have a niche in their habitat. A **niche** is the special way an organism lives in a community. This includes its food, shelter, way of life, and relationships with the abiotic and biotic factors. Organisms make both contributions to and demands on their habitats.

Communities have vertical and horizontal structures. Vertical structure often depends on the height of trees and other features. Horizontal structure is the arrangements of the communities over the land area. More variety in plant species leads to greater variety in animal species.

5-20. A red fox has a niche in this community. (Courtesy, U.S. Fish and Wildlife Service)

ANIMAL WILDLIFE FOOD CHAINS

A **food chain** is the sequence in a community in which animal wildlife species get their food. All species have different food chains. These differences form unique, interconnected food webs.

A food chain begins with plants. Animals eat the plants. Some animals prey on the animals that eat plants. As animals and plants die, decay of the remains results in the return of fertility to the soil. This fertility supports the growth of plants.

A simple example occurs in a meadow. Grass and herb plants are food for grasshoppers. The grasshoppers may be eaten by sparrows. Sparrows are caught and eaten by foxes. The foxes die and decay to repeat the food chain.

5-21. Food web for terrestrial species.

A **food web** is formed by interconnected food chains. When plotted on paper, the graphic image depicts the interlinking of the food chains. The dependency of one species on another is easy to see with a food web.

Feeding Groups: Plant vs. Animal

In a food chain, species of animal wildlife vary in what they eat. Some eat only plant materials. Others eat combinations of plants and animals or only animals.

The three feeding groups based on food material are:

- Herbivore—A **_herbivore_** eats only plant foods. Herbivores may be aquatic or terrestrial animals. Plenty of suitable plant food materials must be in a habitat for herbivores to live and grow. An example is the field mouse.

- Carnivore—A **_carnivore_** eats only the flesh of other animals. Carnivores are typically larger animals that prey on smaller animals. The smaller animals are typically herbivores. An example of a carnivore is the hawk, which may eat field mice. All predators (animals that prey on others) are carnivores.

- Omnivore—An **_omnivore_** eats both plant and animal materials. Omnivores may be aquatic or terrestrial. An example of an aquatic organism that is an omnivore is a catfish. Catfish will eat aquatic vegetation as well as animals, including other catfish.

5-22. Bears primarily eat small terrestrial and aquatic animals though berries, acorns, nuts, and roots are also eaten.

Feeding Groups: Living vs. Nonliving

The feeding groups can also be classified by whether what they eat is living or dead. The two feeding groups based on living or nonliving food materials are:

- Biophage—A **_biophage_** is a wildlife animal that eats living plants or animals. Bison and deer prefer living plant materials though they will sometimes eat nonliving plants.

- Saprophage—A **_saprophage_** is a wildlife animal that eats dead animals or plants. These are sometimes known as scavengers. They serve a useful role in the environment by cleaning up dead animals. Vultures and crabs are examples of scavengers.

REVIEWING

MAIN IDEAS

All species of wildlife are living, biological organisms. They carry out life processes to remain in a living condition. These processes are growth and repair, food-getting, circulation, respiration, secretion, sensation, movement, and reproduction. The last—reproduction—is not essential for an organism to live. It is essential for a species to maintain itself.

Life span is the period of life of an organism. Life spans vary among species and range from a few hours or days to many years. A life span has five stages: beginning, growth and development, maturity, decline, and death. Food, disease, and other factors influence life span.

Genetics and heredity help explain the nature of wildlife species. Using heredity information helps maintain wildlife populations. Natural selection is a process of organisms with favorable traits surviving because they are stronger. Humans may pollute the environment and weaken the capacity of organisms to survive.

Wildlife species are important in ecosystems. They interact with other biotic factors and with the abiotic factors. In communities, species of wildlife form organization and structure. Part of this relates to food chains and feeding groups.

QUESTIONS

Answer the following questions using correct spelling and complete sentences.

1. What are life processes?
2. Name and describe each life process in one sentence.
3. How does food-getting vary between animals and plants?
4. What is life span?
5. What are the life span stages? Briefly explain each.
6. What is genetics?
7. What general characteristics do offspring always have?
8. What is a chromosome? How does the number of chromosomes vary?
9. What is natural selection?
10. What is an ecosystem?
11. What are the two major factors in ecosystems? Distinguish between the two.
12. What is a community?
13. What is a food chain? Give an example.
14. What are the feeding groups on the basis of plant vs. animal food and living vs. dead food?

EVALUATING

Match the term with the correct definition.

a. biophage
b. herbivore
c. saprophage
d. carnivore

e. growth
f. life span
g. food
h. digestion

i. browse
j. locomotion

_____1. Movement of an animal from one place to another.

_____2. An animal that eats only the flesh of other animals.

_____3. An organism that eats living plants or animals.

_____4. An organism that eats only plants.

_____5. Leaves, stems, and shoots eaten by deer.

_____6. Any substance that nourishes an organism.

_____7. Process that changes food so it can be absorbed by the body.

_____8. Period of life of an organism.

_____9. The process of adding new cells to increase in size.

_____10. An organism that eats dead plants and animals.

EXPLORING

1. Dissect an owl pellet. Follow instructions provided by the supplier of the pellet. Identify as many foods as possible that the owl had eaten.

2. Tour a wooded area or meadow where wildlife organisms are found. Study the ecosystem. Identify as many wildlife species as possible. Note signs such as dung and foot prints. Prepare a written report on your findings. In the report, assess the quality of the ecosystem in terms of food for various wildlife species.

3. Select a species of animal wildlife. Use reference materials, interviews with wildlife specialists, and other sources of information to determine the food chain in which the species is found. Draw a food web diagram that shows relationships within the food chain to the food chains of other organisms.

CHAPTER 6

Wildlife and the Earth

OBJECTIVES

This chapter covers important areas of earth science as related to wildlife. It emphasizes the importance of changes in the environment on wildlife. The objectives of the chapter are:

1 Describe important areas of earth science as related to wildlife.

2 Identify changes on the earth that impact wildlife.

3 Explain climate and weather as related to wildlife.

4 Explain soil as related to wildlife.

5 Describe how Earth's resources are used in succession.

TERMS

atmosphere	meteorology	soil degradation
climate	mulch	soil erosion
crust	nocturnal species	soil texture
diurnal species	oceanography	succession
earth science	rotation	troposphere
equinox	revolution	weather
geology	soil	weathering
global warming	soil aeration	
hydrology	soil conservation	

6-1. The prairie dog has a close relationship to the earth. (Courtesy, Claire Dobert, U.S. Fish and Wildlife Service)

THE environment is important to all organisms. Wildlife has an especially close relationship with the features of its environment. The relationship is ever changing. A wildlife species must adapt or it will cease to exist.

Changes in an organism's environment may be due to natural events or the result of human actions. Some changes are predictable; others are not. We know that the seasons of the year will follow each other and that night will follow day. Some things we do not know, such as the amount of rainfall or snow there will be in a year. Good information helps in managing wildlife species to assure their well being.

Earth has been forming, according to scientists, for about 700 million years. It is continuing to change. Human actions can help make Earth a better place for wildlife. Unfortunately, human actions often degrade Earth. People need to be smart and realize the importance of their activities to the well-being of wildlife!

EARTH SCIENCE AND WILDLIFE

Earth science is the study of the environment in which wildlife organisms live, grow, and die. It explains many of the natural events that take place on Earth. Areas of earth science have big influences on the habitat for wildlife as well as on the species themselves. Wildlife species are adapted to specific conditions created by areas in earth science.

AREAS OF EARTH SCIENCE

Several areas of earth science influence wildlife. The areas include:

- Meteorology—**Meteorology** is the study of the atmosphere. This includes climate and weather. Temperature, precipitation, humidity, and other climate and weather factors are a part of meteorology. (This area is covered in more detail later in the chapter.)

6-2. A secchi disk is used to measure turbidity in lake water. Turbidity is the amount of solid materials suspended in water.

- Geology—**Geology** is the study of solid parts of the earth's surface. This includes rocks, soil, and various formations that are found. Geology also includes movements in the earth's surface caused by earthquakes, volcanoes, and other shifts. (This area is covered in more detail later in the chapter.)

- Hydrology—**Hydrology** is the study of water found in the land areas of Earth. The water may be in streams or lakes on the earth's surface or as ground water aquifers. An aquifer is a stream or pool of water found in sand or gravel layers deep in the earth. Wells are often drilled into aquifers. In some cases, water naturally flows from aquifers as springs. Most ground water is cool—about the same temperature as the area of the earth from which it was obtained. Other ground water is warm, known as thermal water. Most ground water is freshwater or water with little or no salt. (A good source of additional information on hydrology is the book, *Environmental Science and Technology*, available from Prentice Hall/Interstate.)

- Oceanography—**Oceanography** is the study of water found in the oceans. It deals with content of the water as well as its movement as tides or currents. Oceanography is primarily about saltwater. Saltwater is water with a salt content of 16.5 ppt of salt or more. The term, ppt, refers to salt concentration or parts of salt per thousand parts of water. Ocean water is 33 to 37 ppt salt. Some wildlife species require saltwater, while others require freshwater. A few wildlife species live in a mixture of saltwater and freshwater, known as brackish water. Brackish water is found in areas where freshwater streams flow into saltwater areas. Aquatic wildlife species are usually adapted to either saltwater or freshwater. Some are dependent on brackish water.

EARTH CHANGES THAT IMPACT WILDLIFE

The earth changes in many ways. Some changes are in cycles and can be predicted. Other changes cannot be predicted. Species in an area and whether they survive are influenced by changes.

CYCLICAL CHANGES

Cyclical changes occur on a regular basis and follow a predictable pattern. These create day and night and the seasons of the year. Both are due to the movement of the planet Earth in its solar system.

Wildlife Connection

ATTRACTING WILDLIFE

If you want to see wildlife, take steps to make your home area attractive to wildlife. Nothing attracts wildlife better than food! You do not need a big area of land—a small lot in a city or just a balcony on an apartment will do for some kinds of wildlife.

Observe the various wildlife in your area. Note the weather—it has a big influence on wildlife. Sudden changes in the weather can have an adverse effect on animals. Birds and other animals need food when the weather turns bad. Use this to your advantage.

Put out some food for them. If you want birds, set up a bird feeder with sorghum and sunflower seed. If you want hummingbirds, set up a waterer with sweetened water. If you want squirrels, try corn in a convenient location. You can probably get a general feed mix at a local store. This photograph shows a feeder being assembled and made ready for hanging.

6-3. The raccoon is a nocturnal species which hunts for food at night and returns to its home during the day.

The two major movements are rotations and revolutions. These occur on a regular basis in Earth's solar system. The movement is predictable. Changes in rotations and revolutions are small.

Rotation

Rotation is the turning of Earth on an imaginary axis. One rotation requires 24 hours. A rotation includes a time of darkness and a time of light. Light results when an area of Earth's surface is toward the Sun. Darkness results when an area is turned away from the Sun.

The lives of many wildlife organisms are regulated by Earth's rotations. Some species are nocturnal. **Nocturnal species** are most active at night or twilight. They are active at night and rest during the day. Bats and owls are nocturnal birds. Several species of mammals are nocturnal, such as the raccoon and opossum.

Diurnal species are active during the day and typically rest at night. During the day, they seek food, shelter, and mates. Common diurnal species include squirrels, robins, and moose.

Wildlife plants respond to both light and dark. Light is needed for them to make food by the process of photosynthesis. In darkness, plants rest and stop photosynthesis.

Revolution

Revolutions of the planet Earth result in seasons. A **revolution** is the movement of Earth in space around the Sun. A revolution is one year in duration—365.24 days. A fairly definite orbit (path of travel) is followed. Seasons are based on the position of Earth in a revolution. How the earth is tilted toward or away from the Sun creates warm and cool seasons.

6-4. The bluebird is a diurnal species which hunts for food in the day and rests at night.

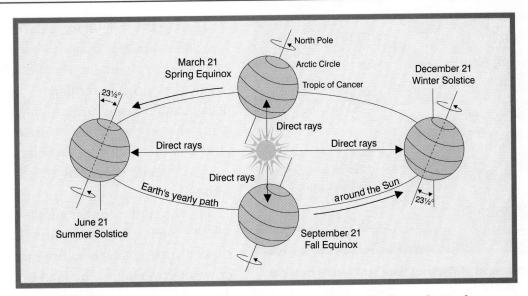

6-5. How Earth's revolution influences seasons. (Note: This diagram applies to the Northern Hemisphere.)

Each fall and spring the equinox occurs. The *equinox* is when the Sun is directly over the equator. Day and night are the same number of hours. Spring begins when the North Pole begins to slant toward the Sun. Fall begins when the South Pole begins to slant toward the Sun.

Wildlife organisms are strongly influenced by the seasons. Squirrels store nuts and seed in the fall for food in the winter. Bears hibernate (rest in the winter) based on season. Wild plants sprout leaves and grow in the spring. These plants shed leaves and stop growing in the fall when frost arrives. Animal reproduction is tied to seasons. Many animals give birth in the spring or early summer.

6-6. A winter ice storm has damaged the trees by breaking and bending them over. Most of these young trees will not recover from the injury.

MATERIALS CHANGES

The kind and amount of solid materials in the earth's crust influence wildlife. These materials often move or are pushed about. Mountains have been formed when pressure resulted in movements in the earth's crust.

6-7. The Teton Mountains of Wyoming show that Earth's crust can be rugged and beautiful.

The **crust** is the surface of the earth. It includes mountains and valleys, prairies and swamps, and rivers and lakes. Changes may occur over time, or earthquakes and volcanic action may suddenly change the surface of the earth. Heat and molten rock deep within the earth can cause shifts that change the surface.

The top of the crust is important to wildlife. Some crust has fertile soil that grows plants, while other crust has rock or water covering it. The kind of crust determines the plants that grow and the animals that can survive. Rock areas attract certain species, such as mountain cliffs that may attract some species of birds. Wet, swampy land may attract other species, such as snakes and alligators.

THE ATMOSPHERE: CLIMATE AND WEATHER

Everything on the earth is affected by climate and weather. The survival of wildlife depends on weather and climate extremes and the ability of the species to adapt.

THE ATMOSPHERE

The **atmosphere** is the air that surrounds Earth. It is made of five layers. Wildlife species exist only in the layer known as the troposphere. The **troposphere** is the layer of the atmosphere that is closest to the earth. It generally extends no more than 10 miles out from Earth.

The atmosphere is made of air, water vapor, and various kinds of tiny particles known as particulate. Air is a mixture of gases, with nitrogen and oxygen being most important. The air is 78 percent nitrogen and 21 percent oxygen. Pollution with smoke, chemical fumes, and other substances changes the composition of the air.

Conditions in the atmosphere create climate and weather. The troposphere layer is probably the most important layer. Other layers also have some influence on the earth. For example, ozone is found in the layer just above the troposphere, which is known as the stratosphere. The ozone protects the earth from ultraviolet rays of the Sun. Wildlife could not exist without this layer absorbing the rays. Some deterioration in the ozone layer is occurring. This will allow more rays to reach Earth.

Concentrations of methane, carbon dioxide, and nitrogen oxides in the atmosphere are creating a condition sometimes called the "greenhouse effect." This holds heat near the earth much as a greenhouse holds heat. This is creating an unproven condition known as **global warming**.

Global warming is the gradual increase in the temperature of Earth's surface. It may result in gradual melting of polar ice caps and plants growing in areas where they could not survive before warming. Global warming is a possible threat to species that live in cold climates. It changes where species requiring warm weather will be able to live.

6-8. Portable equipment is being used to measure and record weather conditions. (Courtesy, Agricultural Research Service, USDA)

Weather

Climate is determined by the weather. **Weather** is the current condition in the atmosphere. This includes temperature, moisture, wind, and atmospheric pressure. Large air masses move across areas of the earth as weather fronts. These may bring conditions that we know as rain, snow, changes in temperature, and damaging storms.

6-9. Musk oxen live in the Far North. (They have heavy coats of brown hair to protect against the cold. Their hooves are good for scratching through snow to find mosses and lichens for food.) (Courtesy, Jerry Hout, U.S. Fish and Wildlife Service)

All organisms are affected by the weather. Sudden changes in the weather may create conditions that are detrimental to wildlife. Extreme temperatures have a big influence on wildlife. Cold weather may injure or kill some wildlife. The same is true with hot weather. Wildlife management often involves providing some type of shelter, such as thickly growing trees, shrubs, or grass.

Climate

Climate is the weather that is generally present in a location. Average measurements of temperature, precipitation, and other traits of the weather are often used to describe climate.

Climates vary by temperature. Tropical climates are warm year round. Temperate climates are moderate, with seasons of warm weather and of cool or cold weather. Polar climates are cold year round but are colder in some seasons than others.

Climates vary by the presence of moisture and precipitation. Moist climates have much precipitation (rain, snow, etc.). Humidity is typically high. Climate affects wildlife. Wildlife species native to an area have adapted to the climate. Efforts to bring in nonnative species often fail because people do not consider the climate the wildlife need.

Wildlife enthusiasts often put out feed to help animals survive cold weather. People who live in town may have bird or squirrel feeders to provide food. These assure food for wildlife when the supply is short. It is difficult for animals to find food when the ground is covered with snow or ice! Feeders should provide a healthy diet for wildlife animals.

Career Profile

SOIL SCIENTIST

A soil scientist studies and recommends practices to conserve and improve the soil. The work may be outside walking over areas of land, preparing maps, and collecting soil samples. Inside work may involve studying materials to determine what should be done to improve the soil.

Soil scientists often have college degrees in agronomy or other areas of agriculture. Many have master's or doctor's degrees in soil science, geology, or a related area. Practical experience working with soil and land is helpful.

Most jobs for soil scientists are with government agencies. Many are with local offices of the U.S. Department of Agriculture or a local soil and water conservation district.

Some jobs are with parks, colleges, and private businesses. This shows a soil scientist collecting a soil sample for laboratory analysis. (Courtesy, Potash and Phosphate Institute)

SOIL

The crust of the earth is made of soil and materials that are being transformed into soil. *Soil* is the top few inches of the earth's crust that support the growth of plants. Wildflowers and other plants that grow in an area are influenced by the nature of the soil. In turn, the kinds of plants that grow influence the kinds of animal wildlife in an area.

Soil conservation is using the soil in a way to prevent loss or damage. The soil is used with proper care. Steep hillsides should be undisturbed. Areas that are plowed or excavated are covered to prevent loss. Water is managed to reduce the rate of runoff and increase soaking into the soil. Knowledge of what soil is made of and how it is degraded helps people be good conservationists.

SOIL MAKEUP

Soil is made of many ingredients. Some are living; most are nonliving. The nonliving materials support living organisms within and on the surface of the soil.

Living Organisms

A wide range of living organisms is found in soil. Some are large and easy to see. Others are small and can be seen only with a microscope. Many organisms make their homes in the soil. These range from bacteria to earthworms and moles. Other organisms use the soil for burrows in which to hide and escape danger. Still, others get nutrients for growth from the soil.

6-10. Earthworms improve soil.

6-11. Crawfish prefer soil—usually high in clay—where it is easy to build a chimney.

Living organisms have several important roles in the soil. One of the most important is the action of microscopic-size organisms in decaying dead wood, leaves, and other materials. Larger organisms help loosen and aerate the soil. **Soil aeration** is adding air to the soil. Tiny tunnels created by plant roots, earthworms, and ants allow air to enter.

The growth of soil organisms can be encouraged by protecting the soil from pollution and using fertilizer and other soil additives. In many cases, the action of tiny organisms in soil supports crop production, such as corn, wheat, and soybeans.

Non-Living Soil Components

Nonliving soil components are of two types: those that formerly lived and those that have never lived.

Formerly living materials are the remains of plants, animals, and other dead organisms. Decay processes convert the remains of organisms into soil. Leaves from trees fall to the ground and decay. Large animals die and decay. The decay process returns nutrients to the soil. This adds to soil fertility. Organic matter is the decaying parts of plants and animals. Humus is well-decayed organic matter. The most productive soils for plant wildlife are those with high organic matter. The mineral and organic matter are part of the chemical and physical nature of soil.

Texture and Formation

Soil texture is the proportion of sand, silt, and clay found in soil. These materials have a fine texture, with sand being larger and clay being the smaller of the materials. These materials are formed by the weathering of rock—the parent material of soil. **Weathering** is the process of gradual conversion of rock into soil. It occurs slowly over many years.

Soil texture determines the kinds of wildlife in an area. Sandy soil typically holds less moisture and dries out quickly. Soil high in clay holds more water and does not dry out quickly. Wildlife species that prefer moisture are more likely to be found in or living on soils that hold water. Crawfish, for example, prefer soil that is wet and holds water. They would be found in low areas near streams or swamps where the soil stays wet.

Soil Chemistry

Soil also has a chemical nature. This refers to the chemical elements present. These elements are used by plants and other organisms in growing and living. If these elements are in short supply, the organisms do not grow well. If present in the correct amount, wildlife will do well. Fertilizer is a chemical material that is often used to add elements to the soil. The chemical elements most likely added with fertilizer are nitrogen, phosphorus, and potassium.

Chemical elements also determine the pH of soil. This is how acidic or basic the soil may be. Many plants prefer soil within a specific pH range, usually 5 to 7. The scale of measurement for pH is from 0 to 14. Seven is neutral. Less than 7.0 is acidic, with acid increasing as the number lowers. A pH above 7.0 is basic, with basicity increasing as the number approaches 14. Lime is used to raise the pH (lower acidity) while ammonium sulfate is used to lower the pH (reduce basicity).

6-12. Collecting a soil sample for analysis.

Soil is chemically analyzed to determine the level of nutrients and pH. Small kits can be taken to a meadow or woods to test the soil. Most kits are fairly reliable. The most reliable tests are likely done in laboratories using samples of soil taken from the area being managed.

Soil Degradation

Soil can be lost or made non-productive. Wildlife managers are often concerned with maintaining good soil. The top few inches of soil are most valuable. If these are lost or destroyed, the productivity of the soil is lost or reduced.

Soil degradation is lowering the quality of land to grow crops and support wildlife. It results from using the soil improperly. Many years—often hundreds of years—are needed for nature to overcome soil degradation. During this time, the productivity of the soil has been reduced or, in severe cases, lost.

Construction and Contamination

Soil degradation results from how land is used. Most degradation is caused by humans. Since we cause it, we can also prevent it. Construction of highways, roads, malls, factories, and other structures causes loss. Mining has destroyed the surface of thousands of acres of land. Trees and grass are often destroyed in preparation for construction. The surface is moved by heavy construction equipment.

Soil can be contaminated. Soil contamination results when chemicals, oil, and other substances get onto or into the soil. Large areas can be degraded so they are not productive. They will not support wildlife or farming. People often degrade the land around their homes. A good example is emptying the oil from a small engine, such as a lawn mower, on the ground. Plants will not grow in the area covered by the oil. Water runoff will wash oil into streams and lakes creating water pollution. Always properly dispose of used engine oil. Used oil can be taken to a collection center for recycling.

Some soil degradation can result from farming. Plowing land or dumping refuse on it can degrade the soil. Today, most farmers are careful to use the appropriate methods of protecting the land. They often leave strips of land to support wildlife habitat.

6-13. A deep gully has formed at this abandoned sand mine.

Erosion

Soil erosion is the washing, blowing, or wearing away of the soil. Water from rain, melting snow, or other sources can wash soil away. Soil erosion is a big problem on hilly land that is plowed or excavated with earth-moving equipment. Grass, trees, shrubs, and other materials help prevent soil erosion.

Water that is muddy contains soil particles. In fact, soil erosion pollutes the water. Keeping a good vegetative cover on the land and using conservation practices helps prevent erosion. A heavy rain on freshly plowed land can result in a big loss of soil. The soil that is washed away goes into streams, lakes, and oceans. Many aquatic wildlife species cannot tolerate high levels of mud in their aquatic environment. Gills may get covered with mud. The growth of aquatic plants may stop.

Unprotected soil can be picked up by the wind. These tiny soil particles pollute the air. They may cause difficulty in breathing for humans and other animals. Buildings and other structures may be covered with dust as the particles settle from the air.

Soil erosion can be prevented by following conservation practices. Many of these support wildlife growth. Here are a few examples:

- Leaving land undisturbed— Plowing, excavating, and other work remove plants that cover the soil. Reducing these activities lowers exposure of the soil to water and wind. Loose soil is much more easily washed or blown away. Many agricultural producers now use cropping practices known as minimum-tillage or no-tillage. These practices avoid disturbing the surface of the land. Building houses, malls, and roads so the amount of excavation is kept to a minimum reduces soil erosion.

6-14. A silt fence is being installed to help prevent soil loss.

- Using silt fences—Silt fences are structures placed on and at the bottom of slopes to hold the soil particles back and allow the water to flow through. This keeps soil particles out of streams and keeps soil fertility on the land.

- Using plants—Planting grass, shrubs, vines, trees, and other plants on soil helps prevent erosion. Roots of plants hold soil particles in place. Leaves and stems help prevent water and wind contact with the soil.

- Mulching—**Mulch** is any material placed on land to prevent direct exposure of the soil to water or wind. Chopped wood and bark, straw, and leaves are often used as mulch. Mulch also reduces the rate of moisture loss from soil into the air.

6-15 A bale of straw will be taken apart and scattered as mulch to protect the soil from erosion.

- Using land contour—Hilly land is more likely to erode than level land. Building roads, plowing rows, and constructing buildings across a hill rather than up-and-down the slope reduces the threat of soil loss by erosion. Terraces are special structures that follow the contour of the land to slow the runoff of water and prevent erosion. Not only do these measures reduce erosion, they also slow water runoff. Water that runs off slowly is more likely to soak into the land and help restore groundwater levels.

- Leaving grassy strips—Cropland may be planted so that strips of grass are left in low places where water is likely to run. This provides a runoff area that is undisturbed by plowing. Washing away of the soil is reduced.

SUCCESSION

Areas of land that have had naturally growing plants removed undergo a sequence as the plant growth returns. An example is abandoned crop fields that return to native plants. The process is closely related to ecology and wildlife habitat. As the native plants return, other wildlife returns.

Succession is the natural and progressive change as one community replaces another. It occurs on land as well as in water. The land or water areas are not manipulated by humans. Nature takes it course. In effect, one ecological community gradually replaces another. With eroded land, the soil is often rebuilt in the process of succession.

In terrestrial succession, the sequence begins with land that is bare. It may be an abandoned field or an area burned over by a fire. Annual grasses and broad leaf plants are the first plants that grow. These attract insects and a few other small animals. The annuals are followed by perennials that may attract rodents and other small animals. Shrubs follow the perennials in a few years. After a few more years, young trees begin to grow and these become increasingly larger over the years. As the trees grow, the grasses, broadleaf plants, and shrubs disappear. The shade from the canopies of trees prevents sunlight from reaching smaller plants. Without sunlight, they cannot survive. Deer and other large wildlife animals return as plant succession continues.

In aquatic succession, a similar process occurs. Newly built ponds have no aquatic life and gradually develop many wildlife species. Algae begin to grow in the water. Fish and other aquatic animals grow. This begins to attract water birds and other animals. Surviving species age and die-off so younger species can live and repeat the cycle.

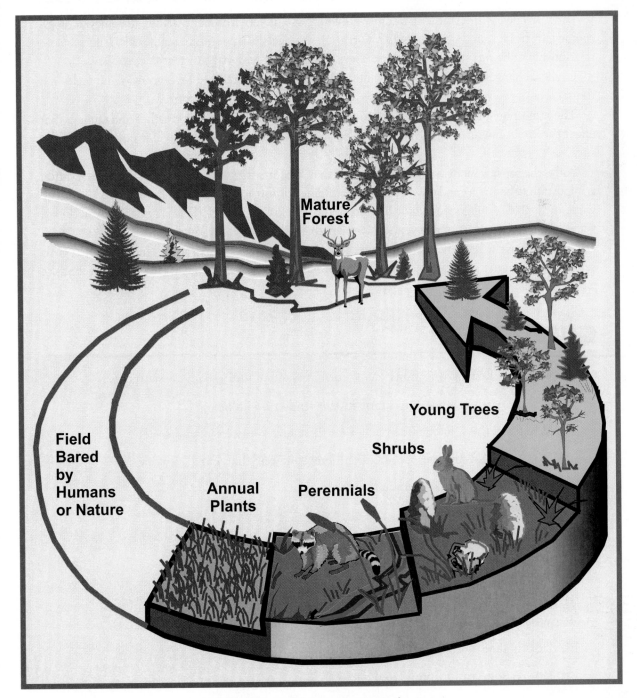

6-16 How terrestrial succession occurs in stages.

REVIEWING

MAIN IDEAS

Earth science is the study of where wildlife grows—its environment. It includes meteorology, geology, hydrology, and oceanography. Earth science deals with nonliving materials. It has a close relationship to living organisms because they use nonliving materials in their life processes.

Cyclical changes on Earth impact wildlife. As the planet rotates and revolves, day and night and the seasons of the year result. These have a big influence on living organisms.

The atmosphere is the air that surrounds the earth. It gives rise to the weather and climate that affect the environment. Organisms must adapt to the climate where they live. If not, they will not survive.

Soil is the top few inches of the earth's crust that supports the growth of plants. Soil conservation is important to assure a good environment for wildlife. Unfortunately, soil can be degraded. It can be made incapable of supporting plant life. Erosion is the loss of topsoil. This is typically by action of water or wind. Once lost, many years of care are needed for land to form new topsoil.

Succession is the sequence by which one community replaces another. Bare land will at first grow small plants that are gradually replaced by larger plants and trees. These attract particular kinds of animal wildlife.

QUESTIONS

Answer the following questions using correct spelling and complete sentences.

1. Why is earth science important in the study of wildlife?

2. What are the four major areas of earth science? Briefly explain each.

3. What cyclical changes occur in the environment that Earth provides?

4. What is a nocturnal species? Diurnal species?

5. What is the equinox?

6. What is the atmosphere?

7. What are the major constituents of air?

8. How do changes in the weather affect wildlife?

9. What is soil? What are the components of soil?

10. How is land use related to degradation?

11. How is soil erosion prevented?

12. What are the steps in succession?

EVALUATING

Match the term with the correct definition.

a. mulch
b. succession
c. hydrology
d. earth rotation

e. earth revolution
f. atmosphere
g. global warming
h. climate

i. weather
j. soil conservation
k. weathering

_____ 1. Natural change in an area of land as one community replaces another.

_____ 2. The process by which rock is changed into soil.

_____ 3. Properly using the soil to prevent loss or damage.

_____ 4. The weather that is generally present in an area.

_____ 5. The current conditions present in the atmosphere.

_____ 6. Any material placed on land to protect the soil.

_____ 7. Turning of the earth on an imaginary axis.

_____ 8. Gradual increase in the temperature of the earth's surface.

_____ 9. The study of water found in land areas of the earth.

_____ 10. The air that surrounds Earth.

_____ 11. The movement of the earth around the Sun.

EXPLORING

1. Invite a soil conservationist or scientist to serve as a resource person. Have the individual describe the soil conditions in the local area. Tour the school grounds or surrounding area to determine the nature of the soil. Identify any areas that have been degraded. Determine ways of overcoming the degradation. Also, investigate how the nature of the soil influences the kinds of wildlife found in the area. Prepare a written report on your findings.

2. Prepare a paper or poster that describes the climate in the area. This should include the seasons and general temperature and precipitation ranges. Get information from the local chamber of commerce, the local office of the Cooperative Extension Service, or a meteorologist. Explain how the climate impacts the kind of wildlife found in the area.

3. Locate areas in different stages of succession. The typical stages are bare land, annual plants, perennial plants, shrubs, young trees, and mature trees. Study the areas. Make photographs to document the stages of succession. Prepare a poster, bulletin board, or paper that summarizes your findings.

Habitat Establishment and Management

OBJECTIVES

This chapter introduces the importance of wildlife habitat and its management. The objectives of the chapter are:

1 Explain the four basic habitat requirements.

2 Describe how habitat growth is classified.

3 Explain the relationship of populations to habitat.

4 Describe habitat mix.

5 Identify the goals of habitat production and problems to be overcome.

TERMS

biotic pyramid
birth rate
climax stage
cover
death rate
dominance
edge

featured species
forb
habitat community
home range
interspersion
metabolism
population

predator
prey
space
species richness
territory
vertical stratification

7-1. Mountain goats use habitats at higher elevations with steep rocky cliffs.

HABITAT is where wildlife live and grow. It is the environment in which an organism lives. With animal wildlife, it is the natural food, physical and chemical conditions, and cover that support life. Without habitat that meets life requirements, wildlife species do not fare well. Their continued well-being would be threatened.

Promoting a wildlife species requires knowledge of their habitats. What kind of habitat do they need? Answering this question requires careful study of a species and where it is naturally found.

Habitat needs vary by species. Just think of the needs of a fish, deer, bird, wildflower, vine, or other species. A species that lives in an aquatic habitat obviously would not find habitat on land satisfactory. Neither would a terrestrial species find an aquatic habitat satisfactory.

HABITAT REQUIREMENTS

Wildlife species have life requirements that must be met by their habitat to insure well-being. If these are met, wildlife organisms live and grow properly. If not met, wildlife organisms generally decline.

Each wildlife species has its own set of specific habitat requirements. With animals, for example, a gray squirrel uses acorns for food and the woodpecker eats insects. Mallard ducks use thick grass for nesting, while thrashers nest in shrubs. Habitat requirements for many species change with the seasons of the year. Food eaten in winter may be quite different from that eaten in the summer. Cover needed for spring and summer nesting is different from that needed to survive winter weather.

Habitat must meet four basic requirements: food, water, cover, and space.

FOOD

All living organisms require food. Food provides the nutrients needed to live, grow, move about, and reproduce. How organisms get their food varies and is important in establishing and managing a habitat.

7-2. Habitat for waterfowl includes food, water, cover, and space.

A key component of food is energy. The source of energy for all living organisms is the Sun. Green plants use sunlight to make food energy and store part of the energy in their tissues. Herbivores obtain food energy by eating the plants. Carnivores obtain food energy by eating herbivores or omnivores. The series of transfers of food energy from one organism to another is called a **biotic pyramid**. The biotic pyramid is a graphical way of showing a food chain.

All food chains have a series of links. Some loss of energy occurs at each link because energy is used in the metabolism of organisms. **Metabolism** is the internal process by which an organism gets energy from food. It includes both physical and chemical processes and how the energy is used. The physical processes with animals include searching for food, the process of ingesting the food, movement of food within the organism, and elimination of food wastes. The chemical processes include the digestion activity within an organism to convert food nutrients into forms the organism can use.

Animals at the top of the biotic pyramid have unique physical characteristics. These animals are generally fewer in number and larger in size than those animals at lower levels on the pyramid.

Habitat needs to provide food year round. The kinds of food materials may

7-3. Habitat must support raising young if birds are to survive, such as the flycatcher with young shown here.

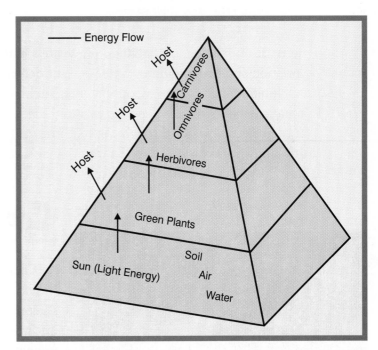

7-4. The biotic pyramid shows how energy is transferred in the food chain.

vary. The greater the variety of foods in an animal's diet, the better the chance of survival. Single-food animals are more susceptible to periodic die-offs. They may be threatened or face extinction when their food source vanishes or is no longer available.

7-5. Water needs vary for individual species, such as those of white-tailed deer are different from other species.

WATER

Water is a basic need of life. It is sometimes included as a food nutrient, though it does not supply energy. Water has a simple chemical structure: H_2O. Water quality varies from one location to another.

Water is an important part of a habitat. With terrestrial habitats, it determines the species of plants that will grow. In turn, the kinds of plants in an area determine the kinds of animals that will live there.

With aquatic habitats, a stream or lake is only as healthy as the water that enters the habitat. Siltation (entry of silt), sewage, and other pollutants are damaging to an aquatic habitat. Water level fluctuations are normal in most habitats. These are a natural part of existence. The nature of water variation and the amount of water present determine the size of an aquatic habitat.

Human-made water impoundments, such as ponds, often make it easier to manage aquatic habitats. Wildlife species vary in the need for water. Some species must obtain most of their needed water through the food they eat. Others need to have a watering area for drinking once or twice a day. If a watering hole or stream has good escape cover, a species is less susceptible to predation.

COVER

Cover is the vegetation or other material that provides safety in a habitat. It is also known as shelter. Cover is used by wildlife species in different ways. Most of the time "cover" refers to how animals use it.

Animals use cover for nesting, resting, escaping danger from predators, and for protecting themselves from adverse weather. For example, a rabbit going across a roadway quickly disappears into a cover of briars and broadleaf plants. Likewise, a deer can quickly disappear into a dense, brushy thicket.

7-6. A mule deer fawn is in cover that offers protection and makes it hard to see.

Cover needs vary depending on the season of the year. Cold, winter weather creates the need for a different kind of cover from hot, summer weather. Though cover needs vary, every species needs a "home."

Cover affects relationships between predators and prey. A **predator** is an animal species that hunts and uses other animals for food. The animal used for food is known as **prey**. A red fox is a predator when it consumes a bobwhite quail. Cover gives prey a place to hide from predators.

SPACE

Space is the area or territory around an organism. It is used by the organism for living. Space provides air, food sources, and cover. Space requirements vary by species, season of the year, and quality of the habitat.

Home range is the space an animal normally uses for living. It is where the animal gets food, water, and cover. Some animals do not travel very far nor very fast. Other animals go long distances and can move quickly.

Within a home range, an individual animal may establish a territory. **Territory** is an area smaller than the home range. It is well defined to other members of the same species. Some species are more territorial than others. Bats, for example, travel many miles from Carlsbad Caverns into the valleys of Mexico, Texas, and New Mexico each night in search of insects for food. Searching for food, squirrels may travel only a few yards each day from their den, the tree that is their home. Some species are quite protective of their territory. For example, a nesting robin will defend an area immediately around its nest. Researchers have found that robins maintain

7-7. The coyote often has a large home range covering several miles.

7-8. Abalone require saltwater habitats for their survival. (Abalone are marine snails found in the United States along the coast of California.)

a territory of about one-fourth acre during nesting season. Territorial traits help prevent overcrowding within a habitat. Competition among species for space will result in some individuals moving to new areas.

Within cover, species dominance and diversity appear. **Dominance** is when one or a few species control habitat conditions that influence other species. In a forest, for example, the dominant species may be one or more species of trees, such as oak or spruce. With aquatic environments, the dominant species may be mussels or oysters. Dominance has a big impact on the diversity of species in an area.

HABITAT GROWTH

Habitat growth follows a fairly definite sequence. This causes the development of changing wildlife communities. Humans can destroy or enhance a habitat and determine the kinds of communities that grow.

All of the species living in an area form a community. Some sort of harmony exists between species even though some are dominant. The living organisms must also adapt to their physical environment.

*H*ABITAT LAYERS

The physical nature of a community is often organized into layers or strata. This is known as **vertical stratification**. The layers are based on plant size and maturity and the physical features of rocky cliffs and deep gorges or caverns. The strata influence the physical environment and diversity of the wildlife species that are found.

Simple terrestrial communities, such as grasslands, have little vertical stratification. Grasslands usually have two layers: ground and herbaceous. Grasslands are limited by water and soil capability.

More complex terrestrial communities are found in forest areas. A forest may have up to six layers: ground, herbaceous, low shrub, low tree and high shrub, lower canopy, and upper canopy. Water and soil support the growth of native species to form these layers.

7-9. Bald eagles prefer habitats with considerable vertical stratification. (Courtesy, Ron Singer, U.S. Fish and Wildlife Service)

Vertical strata in an aquatic habitat are influenced by other physical conditions. These include depth, light, temperature, pressure, salinity, oxygen, and carbon dioxide.

Habitat Stages

The growth stages of a habitat are based on succession. A fairly definite sequence of growth occurs. Many years are often required for progression through the stages. For example, less than 50 years may be required for moving through the stages in a fast-growing pine forest in the southeastern United States. Several hundred years may be needed in the Sierra Nevada mountain areas of the western United States.

Plant succession on land occurs as stages with different vegetation types. These relate to the habitat that is provided. The stages are:

7-10. The cotton tail rabbit prefers habitats with forbs, grasses, and shrubs.

- Stage 1   Bare ground

- Stage 2   Annual forbs and/or grasses

- Stage 3   Perennial forbs and grasses

- Stage 4   Shrubs

- Stage 5   Young trees and woodland

- Stage 6   Mature trees—climax stage

Vertical stratification occurs as the stages progress. Annual forbs and grasses provide only a few inches or feet of vertical strata. A **forb** is a low-growing broadleaf plant. These grow on ground that was formerly bare.

The final stage in habitat growth is known as the **climax stage**. The vegetation tends to be stable and remain present for a long time. Based on the climate, the climax stage may occur in the earlier stages such as 3 or 4. If the climate allows all six stages, the last stage will have the development of mature trees that often shade the ground so smaller grasses and shrubs do not grow. Eventually, the mature trees will die and the climax stage will end. This is especially true if the area is harvested for logs. The stages start over and progressively move through each until the climax stage is reached.

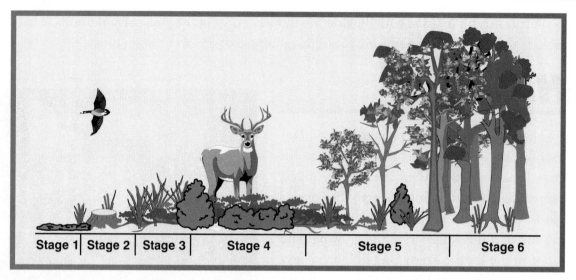

| Stage 1 | Stage 2 | Stage 3 | Stage 4 | Stage 5 | Stage 6 |

7-11. Six stages of plant succession in wildlife habitat growth.

7-12. Southern pine beetles may wipe out large areas of pine forests in a few years. The larva stage of the beetle bores underneath tree bark causing the trees to die. This allows succession to go to an earlier stage and begin the process of new development.

Soil and climate may restrict habitat to fewer stages. For example, in the Great Plains grassland region lack of precipitation often prevents succession from going beyond Stage 3. In this case, Stage 3 would be considered the climax stage.

One individual stage in habitat succession may require weeks, months, years, or centuries. This depends on a variety of natural and human-created factors. If the vegetation is destroyed, succession will revert to an earlier stage and start again. Disturbance can be caused by natural factors. Common natural factors include insect or disease outbreaks, hurricanes or tornadoes, volcano eruptions, avalanches in mountain areas, or naturally occurring fires.

Human activity is often associated with habitat destruction. Clearing land for highways, malls, factories, and homes destroys habitat on a long-term basis. Plowing, burning, cutting forests, grazing, and clearing areas of scrub trees result in succession beginning anew once the area is allowed to grow naturally. As long as crops are grown on a field, succession will not occur. Of course, grass or broadleaf weeds in a field of crops is evidence that nature is trying to move through the stages of succession. Crop producers use several methods to keep these plants out of their crops.

In the first years of recovery, bare earth becomes a grassland populated by species that can tolerate poor conditions. Soon, shrubs and other more competitive plants begin to grow. Dominant tree seedlings crop up as seed get scattered on the land by birds, wind, and other natural forces. After a few decades, a forest may cover land that was once overgrazed or barren soil. The initial forest may be replaced by species that are more competitive. For example, pine trees may be replaced by dominant hardwood trees, such as oak, gum, and hickory.

Nature never gives up! When abandoned, concrete parking lots are eventually taken over by plants. First, the plants grow in cracks in the concrete. As the concrete deteriorates, more plants grow and become larger. If left alone, a parking lot will eventually become wildlife habitat.

Habitat community

Habitat community is all the living things in an area. Plants, animals, and other organisms interact in the environment to provide certain qualities. Dynamic relationships develop among the species.

Attributes related to the presence of wildlife include:

- Pattern—Pattern is the distribution of biotic and abiotic factors in a habitat community. Soil, water, and exposure are used in planning a pattern. Exposure implies slope of the land as related to sunlight, wind, and other factors.

Wildlife Connection

UNDERGROUND HABITAT STUDY

Improving habitat requires careful study of living and nonliving features. Habitat improvements may involve both aquatic and terrestrial habitats. Most terrestrial habitats are above the ground though some are below the surface.

Wildlife that live below the surface are subterranean. This means that they live in the soil and rarely come out. Factors in subterranean habitat include moisture, air, organic matter, and soil composition.

This photograph shows a biologist studying the effects of various habitats on earthworms. Conditions found in soil are established in the small tubs. Comparisons are made to assess the effects of habitats on earthworm growth and reproduction. (Courtesy, Agricultural Research Service, USDA)

- Structure—Structure is the physical makeup of the area. It includes topography, vegetation, and fallen woody material, such as dead trees.

- Size—Size is measured in acres (hectares) and relates to the needs of species. For example, bear require much larger areas than rabbits.

- Layers—Layers refer to the heights of plants in a forest. Shrubs, young trees, and mature trees contribute to layers.

Consider these attributes in developing habitat communities. Know the habitats preferred by the species you wish to attract. Consider the topography, climate, and other features of the land.

POPULATION

7-13. A bobcat with a small kitten reflects population changes based on the birth of young.

Population is the term used to describe the number of organisms in an area. It may refer to the combined number of all species or to the number of one species. Animal and plant populations have important affects on each other. For example, a plant population may be unable to meet the food needs of a large animal population.

POPULATION DENSITY

Population density is a measure of how crowded or sparse organisms are in an area. Density is influenced by the number of new organisms added to the population and by the number that leave.

Birth rate and death rate are important factors in population density. **Birth rate** is the number of young produced per unit of population over a given time. Birth rate is often stated as the number of births per thousand population. **Death rate** is the number of deaths per thousand population each year.

Population is cyclical. The birth and death rates form a population curve. Population numbers are at the highest in late spring and early summer after the birth or hatching of

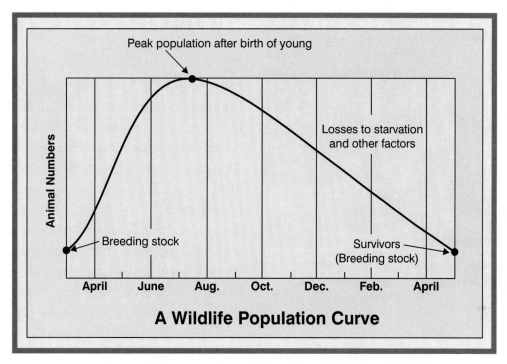

A Wildlife Population Curve

Peak population after birth of young

Losses to starvation and other factors

Animal Numbers

Breeding stock

Survivors (Breeding stock)

April   June   Aug.   Oct.   Dec.   Feb.   April

7-14. The population curve shows high and low populations of wildlife.

young. Afterward, the population declines due to disease, lack of food, hunting, and other conditions. By early spring, population has reached its lowest. The surviving animals are those that breed and start the cycle again.

In some cases, animals may migrate to other areas in search of food, water, or a mate. Regardless, when births exceed deaths and migration is combined, the population increases. A stable population is one where births and deaths are equal. The community has zero population growth.

7-15. Populations of snow geese can change rapidly due to migration.

POPULATION RESPONSE

Species respond differently in habitats. Some populations increase rapidly; others have slower rates of population growth.

7-16. Squirrels and rabbits may share some elements of habitat. Squirrels are primarily in tree tops and go to the ground to search for food. Rabbits are on the ground in grass, brush, and forbs.

In a favorable habitat, a small population may undergo large and rapid increases. Populations often have large growth in the early stages of habitat growth. This is because they can take over and drive out less dominant species. The increase will continue until the upper limits are reached. The upper limit is the point at which the available resources will not support a continued increase in the population. Some decline may occur due to starvation, disease, or competition from other species. In general, populations of plants and animals that experience cycles of large population growth are species that produce numerous young and provide little parental care.

Some species have population densities that reach the maximum carrying capacity of the habitat. This is the population level the habitat can support. Natural regulatory mechanisms appear to set up a balance or equilibrium. This is based on species' numbers and available resources. These species tend to produce fewer young and provide parental care, such as deer. These species tend to live longer and are slow to colonize (move into) disturbed habitats. As the population approaches the limit of the resources, birth rates decline and mortality of young and adults increases.

HABITAT MIX

Many animal species need access to more than one stage of succession in their habitat. These wildlife animals require successional stages that are relatively close to each other.

INTERSPERSION

In managing habitat, mixing lots of different stages within an area is known as **interspersion**. Interspersion supports a greater variety of wildlife.

One way of measuring the amount of interspersion is to use the interspersion index principle. Aerial photographs are used in identifying and counting the number of times a habitat changes. The count is made from east to west and north to south. The higher the number, the better the habitat for quail, rabbits, and other wildlife species that like areas of high interspersion.

Food, water, and cover must be spaced throughout the habitat for animals to thrive. Without dispersal, animals have limited access. This raises the concept of edge.

EDGE

Edge is the area where two habitats meet. It is comprised of a mix of vegetation from both habitats. The stages of succession may be in transition. Examples are where woods and grasslands meet and where woods and wetlands meet. Edge is closely related to interspersion. (Note: Edge is also known as ecotone.)

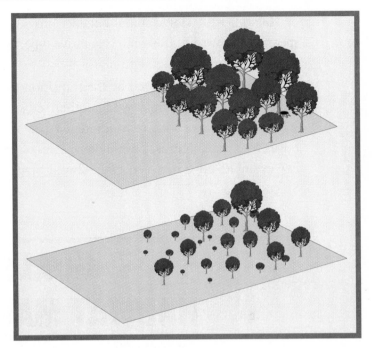

7-17. Contrast of abrupt edge with high contrast (top) and gradual edge with low contrast (bottom).

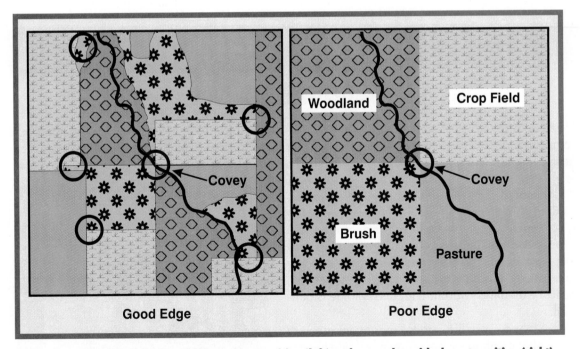

7-18. Comparison of good edge with irregular transition (left) and poor edge with sharp transition (right) for a covey of quail.

Habitats with a large amount of edge provide more food, water, and cover for a variety of species than areas of the same vegetative type. Better habitats involve irregular edges rather than edges formed in straight lines.

Edge quality is measured by the transition that occurs. A gradual transition of plants is more valuable to animal wildlife than edge with little transition. Edge produced by successional stages with very different types of vegetation are said to have high contrast. Edges with high contrast have more species of animal wildlife than those with low contrast. For example, edge between Stage 2 and Stage 6 has higher contrast than edge between Stages 2 and 3.

GOALS OF HABITAT MANAGEMENT

Wildlife habitat management has two basic goals. The first is to provide a habitat for a specific wildlife species. The second goal is to provide habitats for many different wildlife species. How the habitat is managed influences the kinds and diversity of species attracted to the area.

Career Profile

HABITAT MANAGER

Wildlife habitat managers carry out practices to improve wildlife habitat. The work is often outside studying features of an area as related to wildlife populations, habitat succession, and practices to improve habitat. This photograph shows a wildlife habitat manager examining the root system of a fallen tree.

Educational requirements usually include a college degree in an area of wildlife management, biology, or forestry. Many have master's degrees and a few have doctoral degrees. Assistant managers may have high school or associate degrees. Advancement usually requires higher levels of education. Practical experience with habitat and wildlife is beneficial.

Most jobs for wildlife habitat managers are with large timber companies, government wildlife or conservation agencies, and private wildlife areas. (Courtesy, U.S. Fish and Wildlife Service)

SPECIES SELECTION

Most habitat is managed for a featured species or for species richness. A **featured species** is one species that will be promoted through improved habitat. All considerations focus on the needs of that species. **Species richness** is the number of different species found in an area. Some habitats are managed to enhance species richness. Others are managed to promote several selected species.

Managing for Featured Species

When evaluating habitat for a featured species, the species to be featured must be selected. Habitat requirements must be studied. The requirements of the species must be matched to the capability of the environment to provide the requirements. If the area is unable to supply or only partially provide the necessary habitat, management practices must be used to improve the ability of the area to supply the needed requirements.

7-19. Some habitats are managed for a featured species, such as pheasant.

It is important to manage a habitat to provide for the needs that are in shortest supply. The short supply may be water, food, or cover. For example, with a species that requires trees for cover and a nearby water supply, assess what is needed most to improve the habitat. If plenty of trees are present, but no water, take steps to provide water.

In selecting habitat management practices, the effects of practices on species other than the featured species must be studied. Management practices that improve habitat for one species may be detrimental to another. It is impossible to manage for one species without affecting the other species in some way.

Managing for Species Richness

If a goal in wildlife management is to promote species richness (variety), see that the following are a part of the management plan:

• A mixture of successional stages is present.

7-20. Fires can destroy the habitat of wildlife. (Controlled fires are sometimes used as management tools.) (Courtesy, Karen Hollingsworth, U.S. Fish and Wildlife Service)

- A balance of edges with unbroken blocks of vegetation is found within successional stages.

- Unbroken block sizes are of 10 to 40 acres.

- The edges have high contrast.

- A wide variety of vegetation layers is present within each area containing only one successional stage.

Consider the above in managing an area. Use the management plan to identify the practices that could increase species richness. For example, an area that is in Stage 6 of plant succession can have several practices used on it. Depending on the size of the area and kind of vegetation, some of the trees could be harvested. One approach is to clear-cut one-half of the area, such as to clear-cut 40-acre blocks and leave 40-acre blocks unharvested. Strips of uncut trees could be left that connect the unharvested blocks to allow animal wildlife to travel from one block to another.

Corridors of unharvested habitat are sometimes used. These are strips of continuous habitat along roads, parking lots, and fields of crops. The corridors allow wildlife animals to move from one untouched area to another in search of habitat. In an urban area, unbroken corridors could be along streams or ravines so wildlife can move into parks or other suitable habitats. Corridors are important in wildlife management in suburban and urban areas.

When managing habitat for species richness, it is often not possible to provide the best habitat for a featured species. Instead of providing the best habitat possible for a few species, the goal is to provide some habitat for as many species as possible.

MANAGEMENT PROBLEMS

The major problems in terrestrial animal wildlife management deal with meeting habitat requirements. These include food, water, cover, territory, and home range. Human actions often destroy habitat. Here are some of the major problems in habitat management:

- Natural vegetation is destroyed, leading to loss of food and other habitat requirements.

- Wetlands are drained, destroying habitat.

- Natural waters are damaged by pollution, which causes the death of wildlife.

- Air pollution with sulfur dioxides, fluorides, and other acid gases endanger wildlife.

- Radioactive materials may create mutant and sterile animal wildlife.

- Animals are killed in the operation of power vehicles on roads, railways, landing strips, and in fields, pastures, and forests. Some predatory animals are killed to reduce loss of sheep and other domestic animals.

- Diseases from domestic animals are sometimes spread to animal wildlife creating epidemics that endanger large populations.

- Pesticide poisoning may kill some wildlife organisms and injure others. (Many users of pesticides are careful to use them only in approved ways to help protect animal wildlife.)

- The introduction of nonnative species can destroy wildlife habitat for native species.

7-21. Cover for the common loon (here on a nest) includes nesting cover and protective cover.

REVIEWING

MAIN IDEAS

Animal species need food, water, cover, and space. The requirements vary with the species. It is important to study the characteristics and needs of a species when managing habitat. Without this information, habitat cannot be managed properly.

Habitat follows successional stages in plant growth. Most habitat has vertical stratification. The amount of vertical stratification varies from grasslands to mature forests. Short annual grasses provide little vertical stratification. Tall trees have considerable vertical stratification. Mountains, rocky cliffs, and gorges deep in the earth's surface also create vertical stratification.

Habitat may grow in six stages. These range from bare ground to the mature, or climax, stage. Environmental factors may restrict habitat growth. Humans often disrupt habitat with highways, factories, home construction, and farms. More people are aware of the need for promoting habitat and are taking positive steps to assure the well-being of animal wildlife.

Population numbers are related to habitat quality. Population density is how crowded organisms are in a community. Death rate and birth rate influence density. Migration or natural movement of animal wildlife also influences population density. Unregulated sport hunting may also have major affects on wildlife populations.

Habitat management usually has a goal of meeting the needs of a featured species or a mix of species. The habitat requirements of the species must be known. The resources in an area must be assessed and practices followed to promote the desired species.

Problems in habitat management are often related to human uses of the land. Construction frequently degrades habitat. Practices can be followed to help assure habitat for wildlife.

QUESTIONS

Answer the following questions using correct spelling and complete sentences.

1. What are the four basic requirements of animal wildlife?
2. What is the biotic pyramid?
3. What is the distinction between predators and prey?
4. What is cover?
5. How are territory and home range related?
6. What is species dominance?
7. What is vertical stratification?
8. What are the habitat stages? How are they related to succession?
9. How does human activity affect habitat?
10. What is habitat population?
11. What is habitat mix? Edge?
12. What is the distinction between featured species and species richness in habitat management?

EVALUATING

Match the term with the correct definition.

a. cover	e. forb	i. featured species
b. space	f. climax stage	j. biotic pyramid
c. home range	g. interspersion	
d. dominance	h. edge	

_____1. A graphical representation of how food energy is transferred among organisms.

_____2. Space a wildlife animal normally uses for living.

_____3. The vegetation or other material that provides shelter for wildlife.

_____4. The area or territory around an organism.

_____5. Habitat control by one or a few species.

_____6. A small broadleaf plant; not grass.

_____7. Mixing different stages of succession within an area managed as an animal wildlife habitat.

_____8. The final stage in succession.

_____9. The area where two habitats meet.

_____10. The species that is to be promoted through improved habitat.

EXPLORING

1. Tour an area being managed as an animal wildlife habitat. Have the manager of the area explain how it is being managed to promote the desired species. Determine the featured species and species richness of the area. Assess the stages of habitat succession found in the area.

2. Use an aerial photograph to identify succession stages found in a local tract of land. Count the number of stages and arrange to make an individual assessment of the stages. Determine the management practices needed to improve the habitat for featured species.

3. Investigate a lawn, park, or school ground area for possible use as a habitat for small species of wildlife. First, identify the wildlife species that may be appropriate such as butterflies, squirrels, rabbits, and song birds. Second, identify the modifications that would be needed to attract the desired wildlife species to the area. Third, prepare a plan that includes sketches of the area and descriptions of the work to be done. Get the assistance of a wildlife specialist, biologist, or county agent. Sources of information on butterflies and butterfly gardens include:

"How to Make Butterfly Gardens"—
    www.uky.edu/agriculture/entomology/entfacts/misc/efoot.htm

"Attracting Butterflies to the Garden"—www.ext.colostate.edu/pubs/insect/o5504.html

"The Butterfly Farm"—www.butterflyfar.co.cr/

CHAPTER 8

Preventing Habitat Pollution and Destruction

OBJECTIVES

This chapter covers ways humans damage wildlife habitat and suggests approaches to reduce the damage. The chapter objectives are:

1 Describe pollution and types of pollutants.

2 Identify sources of pollutants that threaten wildlife.

3 Explain the effects of pollutants on wildlife.

4 List strategies for preventing pollution of wildlife habitat.

5 Discuss habitat destruction and how it can be prevented.

TERMS

air pollutant
biological magnification
degradable pollutant
engine emission
nondegradable pollutant

nonpoint source pollution
pesticide
point source pollution
pollutant
pollution

soil pollutant
thermal pollution
water pollutant

8-1. A trumpeter swan and cygnets need a good habitat for living and growing. (A cygnet is a young swan.)

WILDLIFE species need certain natural resources to live. Air, water, soil, and other resources are important to animal wildlife. If these are in short supply or damaged in some way, wildlife organisms may become sick, die, or otherwise suffer.

A good habitat is one that provides for the well-being of wildlife. Most polluted habitats do not provide for wildlife well-being. Certain kinds of pollution can be extremely damaging to wildlife. On the other hand, sewage lagoons provide a rich aquatic habitat. Fortunately, steps can be taken to identify and remove the pollutants that are most dangerous.

People produce pollution in their daily living. Finding ways to reduce the amount of pollution can make a healthier environment for humans and wildlife.

POLLUTION AND POLLUTANTS

Pollution is the presence of harmful substances in the environment. The substances damage the quality of the environment. An unclean, unsafe environment may result from pollution. As such, pollution impairs the ability of a habitat to provide for the well-being of wildlife. Severe pollution destroys wildlife habitats.

8-2. A dead deer is a sign of a problem which could be due to pollution. (In this case, the deer died from disease.)

8-3. Factories may release substances into the air that make the air unfit for wildlife and damage habitat.

TYPES OF POLLUTANTS

A **pollutant** is any substance that causes pollution. The substances may be released into the air, dumped into water, or thrown on the ground. The exhaust from the engine of your automobile is a pollutant. The wastewater from your bath and oil drained from an engine are pollutants.

The amount of damaging waste released into the environment can be reduced. Wastes can be treated to reduce damage to the environment. In some cases, wastes can be recycled and, thereby, reduce pollution. Proper disposal of wastes is essential.

A good example is the used oil drained from the engine of a lawn mower. Allowing used oil to run onto the ground damages the soil, which is the home of important wildlife organisms. Allowing used oil to get into streams damages the water and threatens aquatic wildlife. Further, many cities get their drinking water from streams. Do you want to drink used oil? No—and neither does wildlife! Proper disposal is essential. One good way of disposing of used oil is to take it to a disposal station where it is cleaned and reused.

Pollutants may be classified by the kind of resource that is damaged. Here are a few common examples:

- Air—An **air pollutant** is any material that gets into the air and degrades the quality of the air. The materials may be gases or very small particles of dust or other material. Smog and other substances may form in the air and damage habitat.

- Water—A **water pollutant** is any liquid or tiny solid material that gets into the water. The solid material is often called sediment. The solids may be suspended in the water causing it to be muddy. Water from a factory can damage an existing aquatic environment. If the wastewater is heated above or cooled below the natural temperature level in the environment, such as in a stream or lake, damage can result.

8-4. Testing a water sample for pollutants that could damage an aquatic habitat.

- Soil—A **soil pollutant** is any material that gets on or into the soil and degrades the quality of the soil. Wastes from homes, factories, offices, and other places can damage the soil.

Damage to the air, water, or soil has the potential of damaging wildlife. Much as humans, wildlife species depend on natural resources for healthy lives.

EASE OF DEGRADING

Pollutants can be classified by how easily they degrade when released into the environment. Two categories based on ease of degrading are: degradable and nondegradable.

A **degradable pollutant** is one that can be decomposed, removed, or consumed to acceptable levels through natural processes or by human-designed systems. Some materials are degraded by bacterial processes. Paper can degrade rather

8-5. Packaging material has been made easy to degrade by using corn starch in its manufacture. This shows that the "peanuts" made with corn starch dissolve in water almost instantly. Those without corn starch have not dissolved at all.

8-6. Water at a popular lake is being tested for phosphorous level. Note: Before eating wild fish, be sure that the water they have grown in is safe and will not transfer pollutants to the fish.

quickly in the presence of moisture and bacteria. The processes occur all of the time in the environment. The decay of leaves and stems on the floor of a forest is a good natural example. New kinds of plastics are being made to speed degrading. Adding corn starch to plastic helps make plastic products much more degradable.

A *nondegradable pollutant* is one that is not easily broken down through natural processes. Metals known as heavy metals are examples. These include mercury and lead. Even the cadmium in small batteries is a nondegradable material that can cause long-term damage. Properly dispose of used batteries to prevent unnecessary environmental pollution.

Nondegradable pollutants need to be kept out of the environment. In some cases, this is nearly impossible. Regardless, levels should be below those that cause damage.

Career Profile

WATER QUALITY TECHNICIAN

Water quality technicians test water and work to assure that only properly treated water is released into the environment. The work includes taking samples, testing the water, using procedures to clean up dirty water, and keeping water treatment systems in good repair. This photograph shows water samples being taken from a wastewater lagoon.

Educational requirements include specific training in water testing and management. A high school diploma is essential. Most have a college degree. Some water quality technicians have master's degrees in sanitary engineering or related areas. A good background in science is beneficial.

Water quality technicians work with manufacturing plants, government agencies, and wastewater treatment facilities. (Courtesy, Agricultural Research Service, USDA)

WIDE VARIETY

Most of the materials people use in daily living can, in some way, cause pollution. Unfortunately, some very dangerous materials have been used in the past. Today, regulations have tightened the use of many particularly hazardous materials. Government leaders have recognized the need to protect the environment and wildlife from the dangers.

Pesticides

A **pesticide** is a material used to control pests. Insects and weeds are pests in many ways and must be limited in the damage they do. People do not like to be bitten by insects. Who wants a picnic to be spoiled by biting mosquitoes? Many chemical products have been developed to control pests.

An example of a pesticide that was slow to degrade is DDT. The use of DDT was phased out in the late 1900s. Developed in 1940, DDT was a highly effective insecticide. It was at first used to kill mosquitoes that carried malaria—a human disease. DDT was later used to kill other insects, especially those that damaged crops. It was often used without regard to possible hazards.

DDT is said to be a persistent chemical because it does not readily degrade in the environment. Residues of the material could last for years in the soil, water, or on property. As a residue on products that are eaten, DDT becomes a part of the food chain. Some people contend that wildlife has been adversely affected by DDT in the food chain. One example involves the brown pelican. The population of brown pelicans was decreasing. Research indicated that the pelicans were eating fish that had traces of DDT. The DDT built up in the bodies of the pelicans. This supposedly resulted in the pelicans laying soft-shelled eggs that could not complete incubation without breaking. The number of young declined to the point where the brown pelican was headed for extinction. Other animals thought to be affected by DDT included the peregrine falcon, osprey, and the bald eagle. Fortunately, the use of DDT was stopped and the populations of these once-threatened fowl species are now increasing. But, not everyone thought DDT was the cause of problems!

8-7. Home gardeners should always read labels and use pesticides only as approved.

8-8. A silt fence has been used to reduce soil erosion. Soil particles pollute water in streams and damage aquatic habitats.

Many other products have had effects similar to DDT. Any pesticides on insects or weeds can result in problems. Crop producers must use these materials to meet the needs of humans for food. They now follow integrated pest management practices, which reduce the rate of pesticide use. New pesticides have been developed that are much safer to use.

Engine Emissions

Burning fossil fuels releases several materials into the air. The materials released into the air by an engine are known as **engine emissions**. Carbon monoxide is one of the materials released. It is poisonous to people and animal wildlife. Various nitrogen oxides and sulfur dioxides are also released by burning fuels. Once in the air, these materials rise in the atmosphere. They may create different conditions that affect wildlife. Some form acids that return to Earth as damaging acid rain. Others form destructive oxides in the atmosphere that are creating potential ozone and greenhouse-effect problems. All of these pose potential threats to wildlife.

Oil Spills

Oil spills usually gain considerable publicity in the radio, newspaper, and television media. These result when ships transporting oil suddenly leak the oil into oceans. Pipelines carrying oil may develop leaks. In some cases, oil wells drilled into the floor of an ocean may leak or have explosions releasing oil. Operating a boat on water releases some damaging oil. Oil can be washed from land into water.

Have you ever noticed the streaks on water running from a parking lot? The streaks are caused by oil. The running

8-9. Some people fear that boating on Lake Tahoe is damaging the crystal-clear water. Boats release oil into the water.

water is carrying the oil into a stream, lake, or ocean. Here it can cause damage! Fish gills may be damaged. Oysters and shellfish that ingest the polluted water may be damaged. Further, who wants to eat an oyster, shrimp, or fish from polluted water?

8-10. A duck destroyed by oil spilled on ocean water. (Courtesy, Brent Esmil, U.S. Fish and Wildlife Service)

Lead Shot

Pellets used in shotgun shells by sports hunters have traditionally been made of lead. Lead is toxic. The pellets are known to cause lead poisoning. Hunters now use shot made of other materials, such as steel.

Waterfowl have been particularly injured by lead. Waterfowl eat unused shot that falls to the ground. The fowl mistakenly think it is food or grit—a material needed in their digestive systems to grind food. Lead poisoning results from the absorption of lead salts broken down by the acidic nature of the gizzard. People who eat game killed with lead shot also risk ingesting small amounts of lead.

Thermal Pollution

Thermal pollution is a raised temperature in some component of the habitat of wildlife. Water released from factories may be warmed in the manufacturing process. Electric power plants use large amounts of water in generating electricity. The water is used to cool the equipment and is consequently warmed in the process.

8-11. These shotgun shells have shot made out of steel—not polluting lead.

If slightly warmed or cooled water is released into a stream, it can modify the habitat provided by the stream. This causes conditions in the stream which may or may not be favorable to the wildlife species. Suddenly releasing large amounts of heated water into a lake or stream can cause thermal shock among the aquatic wildlife. Migration patterns of fish can be altered by thermal pollution. Growth patterns of organisms in the water may change, such as an increase in certain kinds of algae.

8-12. A dead fish is a sign of a problem—most likely a poor aquatic habitat.

Most factories that produce wastewater that is warmer or cooler than the natural water in the area have ponds or basins in which the water is held for temperature adjustment.

Terrorism and Warfare

Terrorism and war release substances into the environment and damage wildlife habitat. The damage may occur many miles from the site of the release of the substances that are involved.

Smoke, dust, fumes, and other air-borne materials damage the air. Some of the same materials may get into water and become a part of streams and lakes. Disposal of wastes created by the destruction of buildings, highways, motor vehicles, and other losses is a huge challenge.

SOURCES OF POLLUTANTS

Pollution can come from many sources. Human activity creates wastes. Natural events on the earth's surface also create pollution.

COMMON SOURCES

Sources of pollutants are all about us. They include:

- Daily living—Daily living activities produce food scraps, wastewater, trash, and other materials that may pollute the environment.

- Storm water—Strom water runoff from streets, roof tops, and parking lots carries polluting materials into streams, lakes, and oceans.

- Manufacturing and processing—Manufacturing and food processing produce smoke, wastewater, and solid waste materials that may pollute the environment.

- Internal combustion engines—Engines in automobiles, airplanes, and other devices that use fossil fuel and produce hazardous exhaust that pollutes.

- Power generation—Electric power generation uses oil, coal, or other sources of fuel that release pollutants into the air.

- Construction—Construction work, such as on highways and malls, loosens the soil creating dust or particles of pollution in water runoff. (Construction also results in scraps of building materials that should be disposed of properly.)

- Home horticulture—Lawns, flower beds, and other landscaping around our homes often involves using pesticides, fertilizer, and other chemical substances that get into the environment.

- Production—Crop and lawn production where excessive fertilizer, pesticides, and other materials are used releases substances into the environment that can damage wildlife habitat.

- Animal production, such as cattle in feedlots, results in large amounts of liquid and solid wastes, which must be disposed of. Today, most animal producers have disposal systems that help keep the environment clean.

- Pets and companion animals kept in our homes in towns and cities also create wastes. If not properly disposed of, these wastes can harbor disease and create unsanitary conditions.

8-13. Homes use many different chemical products that contribute to air and water pollution. This shows just a sample of the products found in our homes. Always use only the smallest amounts possible and properly dispose of empty containers.

8-14. A wastewater treatment plant prepares water for release into a stream. Even with the best treatments, some hazardous substances may remain in the water.

Fortunately, many sources have control devices that reduce pollution. People are much more aware of the damage caused by pollution than just a few years ago. Responsible citizens try to reduce environmental pollution.

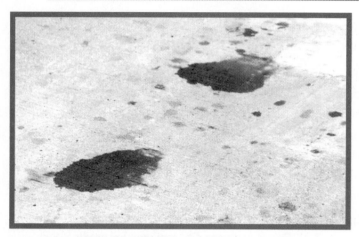

8-15. Oil that has dripped from automobile engines will wash away into streams and pollute the aquatic environment. (Keep engines in good condition to prevent dripping oil!)

SOURCE CLASSIFICATION

The sources of pollutants are classified as point or nonpoint sources.

Point source pollution is pollution that is discharged at places that are readily identifiable. A factory with a big stack expelling gases into the air is a point source. A food processing plant that is releasing wastewater directly into a stream is another example. Fortunately, government regulations are now in place to control point source pollution. Neither factories nor food processing plants can legally release untreated water into a stream. The water released must not alter the natural condition of the water found in the stream.

Nonpoint source pollution is pollution from sources that cannot be readily identified. There are many sources of nonpoint source pollution. They are scattered over wide areas and many individuals may be responsible. For example, the runoff water from a parking lot is polluted. Who is responsible? Everyone who parks a car in the lot is responsible! Paved parking lots are now required to have collection ponds to catch runoff and allow pollutants to settle out before the water is released into the environment.

Crop fields, animal barns, athletic fields, dog kennels, and fertilized lawns are nonpoint sources of pollution. Everyone has a role in reducing pollution and damage to wildlife habitat. All people can take steps to reduce habitat damage.

EFFECTS OF POLLUTION ON WILDLIFE

Pollution has wide-ranging effects on wildlife. Some species are more sensitive to pollutants than other species. When assessing pollution, it is common to base it on the number of different species impacted by the pollutant and the kinds of organisms that are present.

Pollutants are also measured through a process known as biological magnification. *Biological magnification* is the process in the food chain where pollutants increase to a concentrated level. A pollutant may enter a food chain at its bottom. The level gradually increases upward through the food chain to a point where it is most concentrated. This process involves biological magnification.

DIRECT OR INDIRECT EFFECTS

Pollution effects on wildlife may be direct or indirect. Direct effects are those that are initially present in the species. These include the following:

8-16. A turtle is being examined for growth and disease. It will be returned to its native habitat afterward.

- Disease—Wildlife organisms may become unhealthy and subject to disease because of pollution. In some cases, the disease may lead to death or stunted growth. Life spans may be shortened.

- Death—Wildlife organisms may die prematurely when the level of pollution becomes too great.

- Infertility—Wildlife organisms may fail to reproduce when certain pollutants are present in their environment. Shells of bird eggs are particularly damaged by some substances.

- Defects and mutations—Young wildlife organisms may hatch or be born with defects or changes from the normal condition. In many cases, the young will not survive.

- Physical impairments—Wildlife organisms may have physical abnormalities due to pollution.

8-17. A sample of duckweed from an Illinois lake appears healthy—a sign that the water is relatively free of pollution.

Indirect effects of pollution on wildlife include habitat that fails in its support of the species. The damaged habitat may yield inadequate food or cover. Wildlife species are unable to obtain the needed nutrients and other conditions needed for a normal life.

NATURAL EVENTS

Not all pollution that damages a habitat is created by humans. Some is from natural events on the earth's surface. Volcanoes may release large amounts of gas, ash, and other materials. Climate and weather patterns also have effects on habitat.

Dry weather may reduce wild fruit and nut production. This damages the quality of the habitat for some species. For example, acorns are a food of bears. From time to time, dry weather reduces acorn production in the Blue Ridge Mountains of northeastern Georgia. Bears have difficulty finding sufficient food during the fall and winter. They increase their territory and start approaching the homes of humans. They raid garbage cans and other places in search of food. Some are trapped and hauled to new places where the food supply is greater.

Storms sometimes injure and kill wildlife. In January, 1999, a sudden and violent storm in northeast Arkansas killed hundreds of snow geese. The geese were in flight when a large hail storm killed them with falling pieces of ice. Reports were that local residents filled pickup truck beds with the dead birds for hauling to a landfill.

8-18. Properly storing and sending used oil for recycling prevents pollution. Never pour used oil into a stream or storm sewer nor dump it on the ground!

PREVENTING POLLUTION

Preventing pollution is often not a simple matter. It is a complex problem with complex solutions. To prevent pollution, we must work to control it at its source. Substances that degrade the water, air, and land affect wildlife.

Sources of pollution must be identified before they can be controlled. Field studies, surveys, and monitoring help develop pollution prevention plans. Everyone can do their part by assessing their style of living and how it can be altered to reduce pollution. Doing this will benefit wildlife and the environment.

GAINING SUPPORT

Citizens must sometimes become advocates of pollution control. Support from those who can help alleviate pollution may be needed. Community groups may need to be involved.

The following process can be used to identify sources of pollution and attempt to gain support:

1. Identify pollutants and their sources.
2. Identify the pattern or movement of specific pollutants, paying close attention to biological magnification.

3. Identify interactions between pollutants and chemical and biological processes in the environment.

4. Determine the level of pollution tolerable to an organism within the ecosystem before harmful effects result.

5. Identify possible impacts of the pollutant within the studied ecosystem.

6. Estimate the cost of cleaning up or removing the pollutant source.

7. Develop short-term and long-term goals for cleaning up the pollution. (Keep economic considerations in mind.)

8-19. A sediment basin has been built near a highway to trap pollutants from the road surface. (Courtesy, U.S. Department of Agriculture)

8. When projects become large, network with others who can help in the work. This includes local conservationists who can identify political and economic processes to help gain results.

9. Communicate with public officials and media representatives to produce educational and awareness programs to gain support for cleaning up and controlling pollution.

TOMORROW'S WILDLIFE

Providing a good environment for wildlife today will help ensure wildlife tomorrow. Success stories have been tied to efforts in cleaning up the air, reducing pollution, and using science and technology.

Passage of the Clean Air Act passed by the U.S. Congress in 1970 was the first major step in controlling air pollution. Air quality regions were organized. Engine emissions from automobiles were reduced by using catalytic converters. New fuels, without dangerous heavy metals, were produced. Factories have installed scrubbers to remove harmful materials from the air they release.

Bans on using certain materials and efforts to clean up hazardous dumps have resulted in less pollution of some types going into the environment. Actions taken today affect wildlife in the future.

8-20. Clearing land for building a hotel and restaurant destroyed considerable wooded habitat and left the land exposed to erosion.

HABITAT DESTRUCTION

Habitat is destroyed by many human activities. Most every shopping center, factory, school, golf course, or home that is built destroys habitat. Limiting these activities helps prevent habitat destruction. Progress in our Nation does not have to stop to reduce habitat destruction. We can go about our work in ways that cause a minimum of damage.

CUTTING TIMBER

Habitat is destroyed when trees are cut. Fortunately, the tree farms in the United States plant more trees each year than are cut. Anyone who cuts trees should plant trees to replace those that are cut. New areas of forest can be created. This helps restore habitat though many years are required for trees to reach maturity.

CLEARING LAND

Using heavy equipment to clear land destroys habitat. Land must often be cleared for building houses, stores,

8-21. A young tree has been cut in preparing a construction site.

8-22. Earth moving equipment is destroying habitat in preparation for construction of a building.

schools, and other structures. The losses can be reduced by carefully planning where and how the structures are to be built.

STORING WASTE

Modern human life creates a lot of waste. Garbage, used computers, worn out cars, and many other products eventually become wastes. Some are recycled. Others are "stored" on land. Large land areas are used for junk automobiles, abandoned factories, closed businesses, and run-down houses that are no longer useful.

8-23. Junk yards are unsightly, destroy habitat, and often release pollutants into the air, soil, and water.

Properly disposing of wastes reduces habitat lost by storing on the land. Metals, plastics, paper, and glass can usually be recycled. Recycling not only saves storage but also conserves the need to mine new minerals.

Wildlife Connection

CLEANING THE GREAT LAKES

Aquatic wildlife species in the Great Lakes have been greatly affected by water pollution. These lakes are the largest body of freshwater in North America. The five interconnected bodies of water are Lakes Erie, Huron, Michigan, Ontario, and Superior. Problems that have been worked on include:

- Lake Superior being polluted with wastes from mining, which resulted in the death of many wildlife organisms.
- Lake Huron having such high dioxin that herring gulls developed dioxin levels.
- Lake Erie suffered eutrophication (low oxygen) because of the oil, grease, and other industrial wastes in the water.
- Lake Michigan fish had high levels of contamination with DDT and PCBs.
- Lake Ontario was polluted with mercury, pesticides, and other materials.

Fortunately, cooperative efforts involving Canada and the United States have resulted in major improvement in the lakes. Some wildlife species are increasing in population.

8-24. Mines take up a lot of land and destroy wildlife habitat.

8-25. Confined animal feeding operations produce many tons of animal wastes each year. (Courtesy, U.S. Department of Agriculture)

8-26. Forests are cleared and the land is plowed to make open fields where crops are planted. (Courtesy, U. S. Department of Agriculture)

MINING

Some areas have large mines to extract ores and other materials such as sand and gravel. Huge holes may be dug in the face of the earth to extract the minerals. The mines destroy habitat by digging as well as storing the materials that are wastes.

ANIMALS

Animals are important to many people. Some are kept in our homes as companions or pets. Others are kept for the services they provide such as guard dogs and guide dogs for the blind. These animals produce wastes that need proper disposal.

Large numbers of animals are kept for food and fiber production. Several examples are listed here. Dairy producers have many cows for milk production. Poultry producers may have thousands of chickens for growth or egg production. Pork producers may have hundreds of hogs. All of these various uses of animals produce wastes. Proper waste disposal is essential to prevent habitat damage.

CROP PRODUCTION

Large amounts of land are used for crop production in the United States. Wheat, corn, rice, and cotton are among the leading crops. These are often grown on land that is cleared of trees, plowed to create a good seedbed, and cultivated throughout the growing season. Plowing and other activities destroy wildlife habitat.

Many crop producers set aside land for wildlife habitat. In some cases, they take steps to improve habitat and make it better than what would naturally grow. Government programs help producers make good use of land and install conservation practices.

REVIEWING

MAIN IDEAS

Pollution results when harmful substances get into the environment. Some of these substances damage wildlife habitat resulting in harm to wildlife. Air, water, and soil are natural resources damaged by pollution, which may have major effects on wildlife. Pollution damages habitats resulting in wildlife disease, death, infertility, and physical abnormalities.

Some pollutants may be readily degraded; others are not. Those that are readily degraded are changed in form so they do not damage the environment on a long-term basis.

Common sources of pollution include our daily living activities, manufacturing and food processing, engine emissions, electric power generation, construction, home horticulture, and crop and animal production. Sources are classified as point and nonpoint pollution. Point source pollution is from sources that can be identified. Nonpoint source pollution is from many sources that cannot be readily identified.

Organizing to prevent pollution is often more than a one-person job, yet each person has a role in preventing pollution. Gaining support often requires getting community groups and officials involved. Minimizing the wastes we personally create can help prevent pollution.

Habitat destruction occurs in many ways. Meeting the needs of human life often involves clearing land for other uses. Building construction, roads, homes, animal and crop production, and other uses are important to human well-being but destroy habitat.

QUESTIONS

Answer the following questions using correct spelling and complete sentences.

1. What is pollution?
2. What important habitat resources are damaged by pollution?
3. What is the distinction between a degradable and a nondegradable pollutant?
4. What is an example of how pesticides have damaged wildlife?
5. How does thermal pollution affect aquatic wildlife?
6. What are the common sources of pollutants?
7. What is the distinction between point source and nonpoint source pollution?
8. What are some effects of pollution on wildlife?
9. What steps are sometimes needed to help solve a pollution problem?
10. What natural events can alter habitat?
11. What are the ways habitat is destroyed?
12. How can habitat destruction be reduced?

EVALUATING

Match the term with the correct definition.

a. pollution
b. degradable pollutant
c. nondegradable pollutant
d. thermal pollution

e. biological magnification
f. point source pollution
g. nonpoint source pollution
h. pollutant

i. engine emission
j. pesticide

_____ 1. A substance that causes pollution.

_____ 2. The act of releasing harmful substances into the environment.

_____ 3. An artificially created change in temperature in some part of the environment.

_____ 4. A readily identifiable source of pollution.

_____ 5. Point in the food chain where pollutants have increased to the most concentrated level.

_____ 6. A pollutant that will readily decompose.

_____ 7. A pollutant that is not easily broken down by natural processes.

_____ 8. Pollution from sources that cannot be readily identified.

_____ 9. A chemical used to control pests.

_____ 10. Substances released in the operation of engines.

EXPLORING

1. Identify a potential source of pollution that impacts wildlife in your community. Investigate the effect of the pollution on wildlife. Offer ways of alleviating the pollution. If possible, take action to do away with the pollution source.

2. Study sources of pollution on the school grounds that could damage habitat. Consider parking lot runoff, drainage ditches, use of chemicals in controlling pests, emissions from heating systems, and school transportation. What actions can be taken to reduce habitat damage?

3. Investigate the effects of terrorism and war on wildlife. Include the wildlife species themselves as well as their habitat in your investigation. Prepare a report on your findings.

Part Three

Animal Wildlife Management

CHAPTER 9

Animal Biological Systems and Needs

This chapter covers the basics of animal biology as related to wildlife. The classification, body structure, anatomy and physiology, body systems, and nutrient needs are included. The following objectives are included:

1 Describe scientific classification and the naming of animals.

2 Explain anatomy and physiology of animal species.

3 Discuss the reproductive processes of wildlife.

4 Describe important groups of animal wildlife.

5 Explain the major nutrient needs of animals.

TERMS

anatomy	excretory system	nutrient
arthropoda phylum	gestation	phylum
asexual reproduction	integumentary system	physiology
barbel	invertebrate	respiratory system
bird	kingdom	rodent
bivalve mollusk	mammal	ruminant
bony fish	metamorphosis	scientific name
cartilaginous fish	migration	sexual reproduction
chordata phylum	mollusca phylum	skeletal system
circulatory system	molting	univalve mollusk
cloning	monogastric	vertebrate
ectotherm	muscular system	waterfowl
endotherm	nervous system	

9-1. Wildlife biologists are working with polar bear cubs in the Arctic National Wildlife Refuge. (Courtesy, U.S. Fish and Wildlife Service)

ANIMALS are fun to study! They have many interesting traits. The species have different forms and live in different places. Size, body shape, color, food, habitat, and other characteristics vary. Among the one million animal species on Earth, all have differences and similarities. Understanding the differences and similarities helps us know the best ways of promoting the well-being of our favorite wildlife.

Most animals are complex organisms. Their bodies give each species unique characteristics. All must carry out essential life processes. These life processes are part of being a living organism that goes through stages of birth or hatching, growth, maturity, decline, and death.

Animal wildlife species are exciting to study. They have body structures that give beauty and serve the animals well in their habitats.

CLASSIFICATION AND NAMES

9-2. Spotted seals, here sunning on a rock, have unique features used in their classification.

Animal wildlife species are classified in several ways. Common bases for classification can use casual observations. For example, animal species can be classified by habitat, ability to fly, food choices, or foot shape. Many other characteristics could be used.

A system of scientific classification has been developed. Most wildlife species have been classified using the system.

SCIENTIFIC CLASSIFICATION

Scientific classification is based on carefully obtained information about the animals. A system of taxonomy is used consistently worldwide. Modern classification uses seven divisions or stages. These show relationships and differences between and among organisms. The seven-division classification system is as follows:

Kingdom
Phylum
Class
Order
Family
Genus
Species

Kingdom—The **kingdom** is the first and broadest classification. All living organisms are classified into five divisions: animalia, plantae, fungi, protista, and monera. In addition, viruses are sometimes classified separately. The Animalia Kingdom includes all animals—organisms that have many cells, can usually move about, and get food by ingestion (eating).

Phylum—The **phylum** is the second division in classification. The Animalia Kingdom has 14 phyla (phyla is the plural form of phylum). The three most important phyla in studying wildlife are:

1. Chordata—The **chordata phylum** includes most of the important wildlife animals. The vertebrate group is the largest group of the chordata. These are animals that have internal skeletons and backbones. Examples of chordates include deer, fish, snakes, and birds.

2. Arthropoda—The **arthropoda phylum** includes animals with external skeletons and bodies divided into segments. The legs are jointed. Examples of arthropods include ticks, insects, crawfish, shrimp, and lobster. This phylum has more different species than any other phylum of the Animalia Kingdom. This is due to the large number of insect species.

3. Mollusca—The **mollusca phylum** includes animals with hard outer shells. Their bodies are not divided into segments, as is the arthropoda phylum. Examples of mollusks include snails, octopus, squid, abalone, oysters, clams, and mussels.

9-3. A prairie dog can stand erect because of a vertebral column.

Class—The class is the third division in classification. Mammalia, Reptilia, and Aves are important classes in the chordata phylum of animals.

Order—The order consists of animals that are more alike than the class. Orders are based on feeding characteristics, such as foxes and wolves eat flesh and are known as

9-4. A crawfish is in the arthropoda phylum.

9-5. The mussel is a bivalve mollusk.

Carnivora. Those that eat insects are known as Insectivores, such as moles. Those that mainly eat plants are Herbivores, with deer and bison being examples. Those that eat both plants and animals are Omnivores, such as bear and opossum.

Family—The family is made up of animals that are more alike than the orders. Family is often based on anatomical features of animals. An example is the wolf (Carnivora order), which is the Canidae family because it has a long snout and bushy tail. Another example of family is the Felidae, which contains the tigers and bobcats.

Genus—The genus is made of very similar groups. The groups, however, do not naturally breed with each other. An example is the genus Canis containing coyotes and gray wolves. Coyotes and gray wolves do not breed with each other.

Species—The species contains very similar individuals within a genus. Members of a species breed with each other. Sometimes, distinctions are made within species to be subspecies or breeds.

SCIENTIFIC NAMES

People use the common names of animal wildlife, such as black bear. Scientists use names based on information about a species. For example, a black bear is an *Ursus americanus* to a scientist studying wildlife.

Wildlife Connection

TICKS AND DISEASE

Ticks are arachnid wildlife organisms that are often found in meadows of tall grass and woodlands. Some carry diseases that are dangerous to humans and other animals. Walking through these areas may result in ticks getting on you. Ticks are particularly apt to get on your clothes when you are picking wild berries.

Ticks bury their heads into the skin seeking blood for their food. In the process of getting blood, natural secretions from the tick enter the wound. If the tick is a disease carrier, the secretions convey the disease to their host—you!

Be careful in removing a tick. Do not pull a tick off so its head stays attached to the skin. Do not pull the tick with a squeezing motion as this forces secretions out of the tick into the wound. Put rubbing alcohol or petroleum jelly on the tick and the area where it is attached. Once it begins to back away, pick up the tick with tweezers. Place it inside of a paper towel or other material and dispose of it. Seek medical attention if any signs of disease appear, such as fever or swelling around the area.

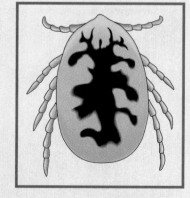

Table 9-1. Examples of Common and Scientific Names for Selected Species

Common Name	Scientific Name
Beaver	*Caston canadensis*
Gray squirrel	*Sciurus carolinensis*
White-tailed deer	*Odocoileus virginianus*
Killer whale	*Orcinus orca*
Brown pelican	*Pelecanus occidentalis*
Bald eagle	*Haliaeetus leucocephalus*
Great horned owl	*Bubo virginianus*
Harbor seal	*Phoca vitulina*
American alligator	*Alligator mississippiensis*
Bullfrog	*Rana catesbeiana*
Pacific seahorse	*Hippocampus ingens*
Rainbow trout	*Oncorhynchus mykiss*
Southern copperhead	*Agkistrodon contortrix*
Eastern diamondback rattlesnake	*Crotalus adamanteus*

9-6. As scientists gather information, names sometimes change. The scientific name of the rainbow trout was changed from *Salmo gairdneri* to *Oncorhynchus mykiss* a few years ago.

Each animal species has a **scientific name**. These names are used worldwide to help distinguish one species from the other. Common names often vary from one local area to another. Scientific names do not change unless information results in a new name for a species. For example, the scientific name of the rainbow trout has changed in the last few years due to new scientific information about the species.

The scientific name of an animal is a combination of its genus and species. The genus is the first word and is followed by the species name. The species name is usually one word but it can be two words. The name is written in italics with only the first letter of the genus being capitalized. For example, the scientific name of a gray wolf is *Canis lupus*. (It is in the *Canis* genus and *lupus* species.) All scientific names of animals, plants, and other species are written the same way.

ANATOMY AND PHYSIOLOGY

All animals have body systems that carry out life processes. These systems are essential for the health of the organism. If they fail, the organism becomes ill and may die. How organisms live and go about life processes is influenced by their anatomy and physiology.

9-7. The zebra-tailed lizard has a distinct anatomy as shown in its body form.

LIFE-SUSTAINING PROCESSES

Anatomy is the study of the form, shape, and appearance of animals. The differences are often obvious to our eyes. These differences make it possible for each species to live in its environment. For example, most all animals are capable of moving about, known as locomotion. Animal anatomy includes structures that make locomotion possible. Some animals have legs and others have fins and wings. Even with the differences, there are similarities in major anatomical structures since the essential life processes are the same.

Physiology is the study of the functions of parts of the anatomy. These functions are carried out in certain ways. How they are carried out is influenced by the form of the organ systems. It is impossible to separate the study of physiology from anatomy.

Skeletal System

A major difference in the anatomy of animals involves the skeletal system. The ***skeletal system*** is the bony framework that gives the body shape and protects the organs. Many animals have internal skeletal systems of bone or cartilage; others have external skeletal systems made of chitin.

9-8. The skeleton of a deer shows major features of a vertebrate mammal.

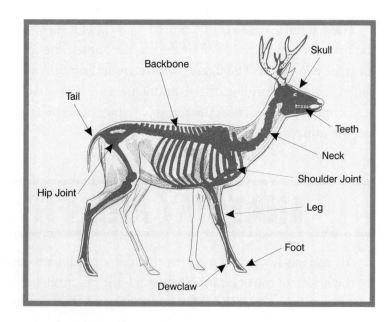

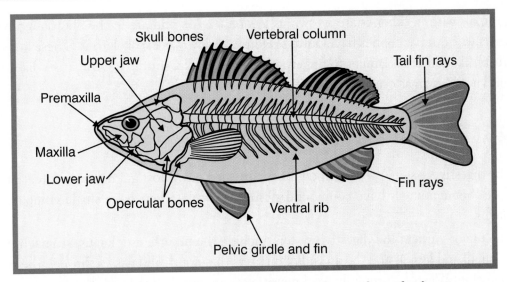

9-9. The skeleton of a bony fish shows important features of a vertebrate that is not a mammal.

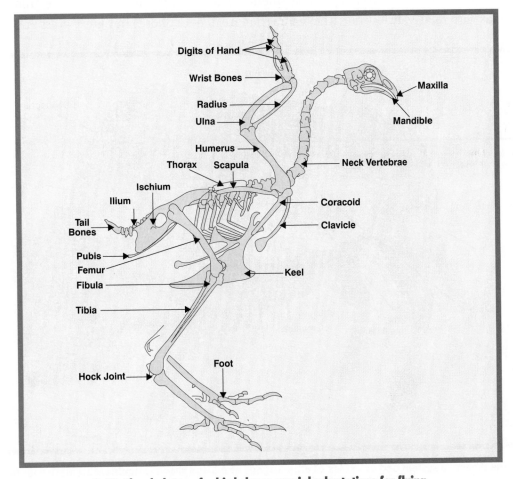

9-10. The skeleton of a bird shows special adaptations for flying.

Animals with backbones are known as **vertebrates** and are in the chordata phylum. Animals without backbones have outer skeletons, known as exoskeletons. These are shells or crusty-like materials similar to fingernails. For example, shrimp have a crusty-like skeleton and are known as crustaceans.

Digestive System

The digestive system prepares food for use by the body. Most animals ingest (eat or take in) food. Some animals have compound stomachs, while others have single-compartment stomachs.

The major parts of the digestive system include the mouth, esophagus, stomach, intestines (small and large), and the anus. Food enters the mouth and passes through the system for digestion. Wastes—primarily solid materials—are expelled through the anus.

Mammals are often classified as ruminants and nonruminants. A **ruminant** is an animal with a stomach divided into four compartments. These compartments allow the animals to eat foods with relatively low nutritive value that are high in fiber. They graze grass and other

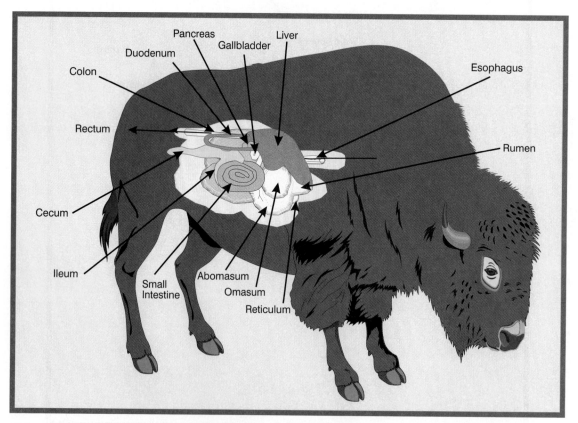

9-11. The digestive system and examples of other organs of a bison shows a ruminant stomach with four compartments: omasum, abomasum, rumen, and reticulum.

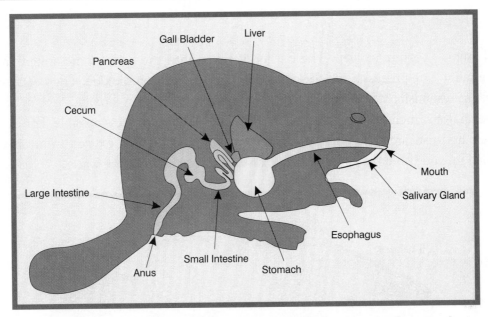

9-12. The digestive system of a beaver is an example of a monogastric mammal.

tender vegetation. Microorganisms in the stomachs act on the forage and help convert it into nutritious forms. Examples of ruminants include deer, bison, antelope, and mountain goats.

Nonruminants have **mono-gastric** digestive systems. These animals have a simple stomach with one compartment. Examples include rabbits, squirrels, raccoons, and wild hogs. Nonruminant animals must have foods that have higher concentrations of nutrients, such as squirrels eating hickory nuts. Their digestive systems are not designed to make efficient use of grasses.

Small gnawing and nibbling monogastric animals are known as rodents. A **rodent** is in the Rodentia order and has four large incisors. Rodents include mice, rats, beavers, squirrels, and chipmunks.

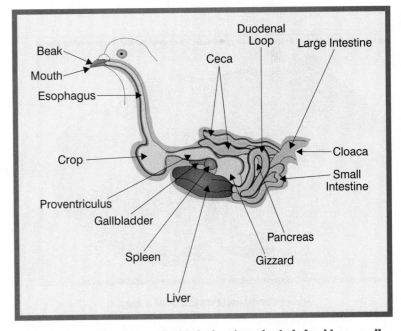

9-13. The digestive system of a bird. The gizzard grinds food into small pieces. It along with the proventriculus form the stomach of a bird.

Respiratory System

All animals require oxygen. The oxygen is taken into the body of the animal from its environment. Life processes use the oxygen and release carbon dioxide. The **respiratory system** is responsible for taking in oxygen and giving off carbon dioxide.

The anatomy includes structures to make the respiration process possible. For example, squirrels and fish are different. Squirrels have lungs to remove oxygen from air that is breathed in, and fish have gills to remove dissolved oxygen from the water.

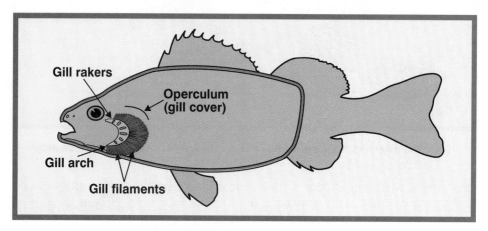

9-14. Gills remove dissolved oxygen from water and transfer it to blood in a fish. Water enters the mouth and passes over the gills out of the body.

9-15. General muscle system of a frog.

Muscular System

The **muscular system** creates bodily movement and support. This system consists of special tissues that form muscles. Muscles are attached to the skeletal system by ligaments. The contractions of the tissues in muscles cause body movement. Animals have a number of different muscles that serve specialized functions.

Circulatory System

The **circulatory system** is a network of vessels that move blood throughout the body of an organism.

The major organ in the circulatory system is the heart. The pumping action of the heart causes the blood to flow. One of the places the blood passes is the lungs or gills to pick up oxygen and release carbon dioxide.

Excretory System

The **excretory system** rids the body of wastes. The major wastes include carbon dioxide, water, nitrogen, and undigested solid food materials. Carbon dioxide and some water are given off by the lungs. Water is also released through the skin as perspiration by some species. Water, nitrogen, and other substances are removed from the blood by the kidneys and excreted as urine or with the solid material from the digestive system known as feces.

Nervous System

The **nervous system** conducts impulses from the brain to the muscles and from the muscles back to the brain. Animals with backbones have a spinal column containing a spinal cord. This is a major part of the nervous system. If the spinal cord is damaged, animals may suffer paralysis of parts of their bodies. This makes them unable to move and function normally.

Integumentary System

The **integumentary system** is the skin. Skin protects the internal organs and gives shape to the body. It provides a place for hair, scales, or fur to grow. It keeps body fluids from being lost and helps regulate body temperature.

Career Profile

WILDLIFE TECHNICAL SPECIALIST

Wildlife technical specialists (also known as wildlife technicians) provide a variety of services with wildlife. They may count wildlife populations, assess food production, establish habitat, and examine wildlife for health conditions.

Wildlife technical specialists need college degrees in wildlife management, wildlife biology, or closely related areas. They need work experience with wildlife and an appreciation for wildlife species and their habitats.

Most jobs for wildlife technical specialists are with government agencies, large timber companies, or associations involved with wildlife. This photograph shows the monitoring of Gray Bats at Logan Cave National Wildlife Refuge. (Courtesy, Karen Hollingsworth, U.S. Fish and Wildlife Service)

Other Systems

Many species have reproductive systems. Single-celled organisms typically reproduce by cell division. In animals, the reproductive systems are the only systems that vary by sex. In plants, reproductive structures may have male and female organs on the same plant or on separate plants.

Mammal females have mammary systems that provide milk as food for their babies. Male mammals have rudimentary mammary systems.

REPRODUCTIVE PROCESSES

Reproduction is the process by which a species produces new organisms. Young offspring grow and become mature adults. Reproduction is not essential for an individual organism to live. It is essential for a species to produce new individuals. Without reproduction, a species would become extinct over time.

SEXUAL REPRODUCTION

Sexual reproduction involves the union of a sperm with an egg. Sperm are produced by the testes in the male of a species. Sperm are the male sex cells. The ovaries of the female produce the eggs—female sex cells. Only one sperm is needed to fertilize an egg. Each fertilized egg develops into a new individual. Mating is the process of animals being together for breeding. Typically, mating involves two individuals of the same species but opposite sex joining together for the male to release sperm on or near the egg(s) of a female. The process varies with animal species.

Fertilization may occur internally or externally, depending on the species. Most large animals reproduce by internal mating. This involves sexual union of the male and female in a process known as copulation. The male of the species deposits semen, a liquid containing sperm, in the reproductive tract of the

9-16. Mating by quail includes the transfer of sperm from the male to the reproductive tract of the female.

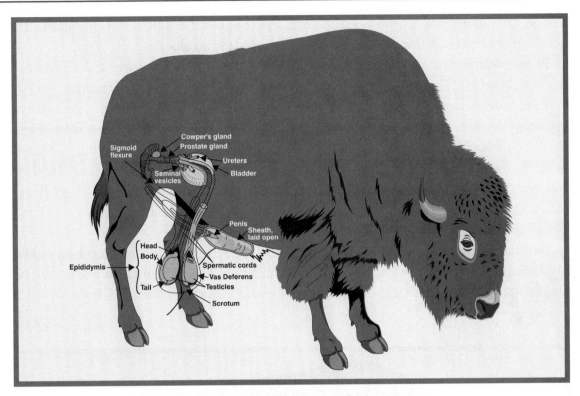

9-17. Parts of a male bison's reproductive system.

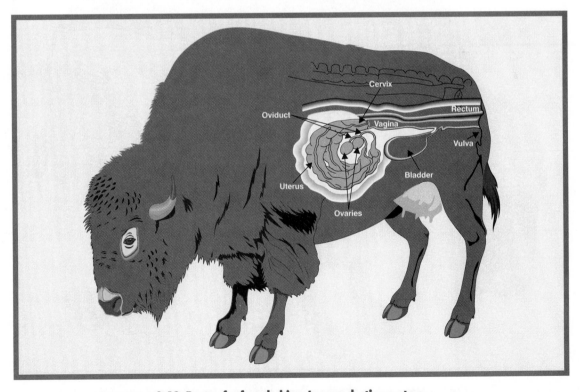

9-18. Parts of a female bison's reproductive system.

female. One sperm unites with a mature egg. The egg is either retained in the uterus for development or expelled by a process known as laying for incubation.

Female mammals carry the young in their uterus until a sufficient stage of development has been reached. The period of development is known as **gestation**. Gestation periods vary among different species. A female who is gestating is said to be pregnant. An embryo begins to develop and becomes a fetus once a sufficient stage of development has been reached. Birth (known as parturition) is when the fetus has developed sufficiently to be expelled by the uterus. The young animal is nourished by milk from its mother. The length of gestation varies from a few weeks to several months, depending on the species. A small animal, such as a rabbit, has a shorter gestation (a few weeks) than larger animals, such as bison (about nine months).

Birds lay eggs, which are incubated for a period. If fertile, an embryo develops during incubation. Hatching occurs when the young animal has reached sufficient maturity. The length of incubation varies with the species but is often about 21 days.

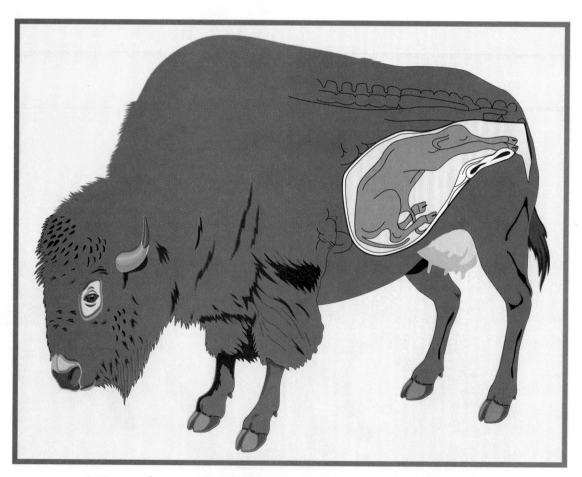

9-19. Normal presentation of unborn bison calf shows front feet and head first.

9-20. A sandhill crane hatching from an egg following artificial incubation. (Courtesy, U.S. Fish and Wildlife Service)

9-21. Catfish produce huge egg masses at spawning. (Courtesy, Progressive Farmer Magazine)

Fish, reptiles, and amphibians lay eggs that are externally fertilized. The female releases the eggs and the male releases sperm to fertilize them. After a period of incubation, the eggs develop sufficiently to hatch and become new organisms.

Only animals of the same species normally mate. This prevents species from naturally mixing. Researchers sometimes create artificial means so different species crosses are possible. One example is the hybrid striped bass, which is the result of breeding the striped bass and white bass.

ASEXUAL REPRODUCTION

Asexual reproduction is producing new organisms without the sexual union of male and female cells. It is common with plants, but not animals. The union of a sperm and egg is not needed with asexual reproduction.

The possibility of using biotechnology to produce animal organisms without sexual union is emerging. Known as **cloning**, cells are used to produce offspring identical to its parent. Sexual union of a male and female organism is not used. Another approach to cloning is embryo splitting. This involves cutting apart an embryo that is only a few days old to form two or more embryos that become normally developed individuals.

Opinions differ on cloning. When used wisely, cloning can offer important benefits. Some people fear the possibility of cloning. Others feel that cloning offers the possibility of preventing species from becoming extinct. Always get the facts before you decide what is best. Avoid decisions based on lack of information and emotion.

COMMON ANIMAL WILDLIFE

Animal wildlife species are often studied as vertebrates and invertebrates. This clusters the species into two groups based on skeletal structure. All of the common wildlife animals are in one of three phyla: chordata, arthropoda, and mollusca.

Black Bear *(Ursus americanus)*
(Courtesy, Lynn Rogers, U.S. Fish and Wildlife Service)

Long-tailed Weasel *(Mustela frenata)*
(Courtesy, Max Schroeder, U.S. Fish and Wildlife Service)

Bobcat *(Lynx rufus)*

Badger *(Taxidea taxus)*

Beaver *(Castor canadensis)*
(Courtesy, Tom Smylie, U.S. Fish and Wildlife Service)

White-tail Deer *(Odocoileus virginianus)*
(Courtesy, Fred Youngblood, U.S. Fish and Wildlife Service)

9-22. Examples of mammal wildlife.

VERTEBRATES

Vertebrates are animals with backbones. The backbone contains a spinal cord that is important in operation of the nervous system. The major groups of vertebrate animal wildlife are included here.

White-tail Jackrabbit *(Lepus townsendi)*
(Courtesy, Dean Briggins, U.S. Fish and Wildlife Service)

Fox Squirrel *(Sciurus niger)*
(Courtesy, W.H. Julian, U.S. Fish and Wildlife Service)

Gray Wolf *(Canis lupus)*
(Courtesy, U.S. Fish and Wildlife Service)

Porcupine *(Erethizon dorsatum)*
(Courtesy, U.S. Fish and Wildlife Service)

Mountain Sheep *(Ovis canadensis)*
(Courtesy, U.S. Fish and Wildlife Service)

Mountain Goat *(Oreamnos americanus)*
(Courtesy, David Erikson, U.S. Fish and Wildlife Service)

9-22 (Continued)

Mammals

Mammals are common forms of animal wildlife in the chordata phylum. Deer, bats, bear, dolphins, and monkeys are common mammals. A ***mammal*** is an animal species with a backbone. The females produce milk to feed their young.

The females of most mammal species have reproductive systems in which young develop following mating. After sufficient development as an embryo and fetus, the young go through a birth process. Milk is secreted by the mammary glands as food for babies. Baby young nurse nipples that release the milk from the mammary glands.

9-23. The red fox is a predatory mammal. (Courtesy, U.S. Fish and Wildlife Service)

Some 4,000 species of mammals have been identified. Many of these are popular animal wildlife. Scientists classify mammals into the class of vertebrates known as Mammalia.

Most mammals are terrestrial—live on land. Two scientific classes of mammals are aquatic—Cetacea, containing the dolphins, and Sirenia, containing the manatees. Only one class of mammal is capable of true flight and that is the Chiroptera, or bat.

Mammals are endothermic animals. An ***endotherm*** has the capacity to maintain a constant body temperature. This trait is also sometimes referred to as warm-blooded. Energy from food is used by the animal to provide body heat in cold weather. In warm weather, endothermic animals either sweat, pant, or have other adaptations for cooling. Disease can be detected by determining the temperature of an animal and comparing the reading with the normal temperature for the species. A temperature above normal indicates disease.

A listing and description of common species of mammal wildlife is presented in Appendix A.

Birds

A ***bird*** is an egg-laying vertebrate that has feathers, a pair of wings, and a pair of legs. Birds are the only animals with feathers. The feathers often give distinct and appealing colors. Most birds have the ability to fly. Birds are endothermic—warm-blooded. All birds hatch from eggs. Scientists have identified some 9,700 bird species worldwide. The smallest is the hummingbird and the largest is the ostrich.

Birds are in the Aves scientific class. This has led to calling the place where birds are kept an aviary. Only domesticated birds and wild birds that are being rehabilitated or otherwise studied are kept in an aviary.

Bird species are found in a wide range of environments. Some prefer to live around water and are known as **waterfowl**. Pelicans, ducks, loons, egrets, geese, and cranes are examples. Other species may prefer trees, grasslands, or tall cliffs. Some birds are predators—they feed on live animals. Many eat insects, berries, and seed.

9-24. Examples of songbirds in the United States.

Wild Turkey *(Meleagris gallopavo)*
(Courtesy, U.S. Fish and Wildlife Service)

Greater Prairie Chicken *(Tymphanuchus cupido)*
(Courtesy, U.S. Fish and Wildlife Service)

Mourning Dove *(Zenaida macroura)*
(Courtesy, U.S. Fish and Wildlife Service)

Sage Grouse *(Centrocercus urophasianus)*
(Courtesy, U.S. Fish and Wildlife Service)

Blue Grouse *(Dendragapus obscurus)*

Chukar *(Alectoris chukar)*

9-25. Examples of game birds in the United States.

Canada Goose *(Branta canadensis)*

Mallard Duck *(Anas platyrhynchos)*

Snowy Egret *(Egretta thula)*
(Courtesy, U.S. Fish and Wildlife Service)

Sandhill Crane *(Grus canadensis)*
(Courtesy, Glen Smart, U.S. Fish and Wildlife Service)

Double-crested Cormorant *(Phalacrocorax auritus)*
(Courtesy, Tim McCabe, U.S. Fish and Wildlife Service)

Pintail Duck *(Anas acuta)*

9-26. Examples of waterfowl in the United States.

BENEFITS AND PROBLEMS. Birds have valuable roles in nature. They help pollinate flowers and disperse seed in their droppings. Some species eat large numbers of insects, with robins and sparrows frequently seen eating worms and beetles from crop plants. Other species, such as hawks, feed on mice and rats, and this helps to control their populations. A few species eat dead animal flesh, such as the vulture, and this helps clean up after the death of an animal. Some bird species are popular with hunters—pheasants, ducks, and quail are examples. Of course, many people enjoy watching birds.

Birds are not always beneficial. Some are pests. Birds are pests when they cause particular problems. Pigeons and starlings are pests in some cities and rural areas. Cormorants are costly pests on fish farms because they consume several small fish each day. Over a growing season, the pesky double-crested cormorant can cost a fish producer hundreds of dollars in lost fish.

MIGRATION. Most species of birds in North America migrate. **Migration** is moving from one climate region to another for a particular purpose. The ability to fly allows birds to migrate long distances. Some birds migrate between North and South America, with distances reaching 2,000 miles or more. Others migrate from the northern part of North America to southern areas.

Most migration is to find an environment that has a particular advantage. Ducks and geese migrate from Canada to the southern United States in the winter seeking a warmer climate. They return to Canada in the summer to nest and raise their young. Most migration is in north-south directions.

Appendix B lists and describes examples of species of birds found in North America.

9-27. Snow geese migrate in large numbers and travel great distances.

Reptiles

Reptiles share common traits with other animals, such as having a backbone. They differ in several ways. Reptiles are ectothermic animals. An **ectotherm** does not maintain a constant body temperature. An ectotherm tends to have the same body temperature as its surroundings. Examples include lizards, snakes, and most fish. By virtue of being ectotherms, they are often found in areas with a warmer climate. Many are in tropical and subtropical regions. Only about 300 animal species have been classified as reptiles in North America.

Reptiles differ from another closely related class of animals—the amphibians—primarily by the nature of their body exterior. The outer covering of reptiles has scales or plates. These coverings protect against water loss by the body and offer protection from physical attack.

Reptiles reproduce by laying eggs. The eggs have a covering that is either hard or leathery in texture. The covering protects the egg from drying out on land.

Common reptiles include alligators and crocodiles, turtles, lizards, and snakes. Alligators are found in the southeastern United States, especially Florida, Texas, and Louisiana. Crocodiles are rare but a few have been spotted in the southern areas of Florida.

About 50 species of turtles are found in North America. Turtles prefer to live in or near water. They are often seen sunning on logs or stumps in water. Turtles are the only reptiles that do not have teeth (some can bite if handled). The bony shell of turtles is covered with shields, known as scutes. The top part of a shell is the carapace and the lower part is the plastron.

9-28. Two reptiles shown here are the banded sand snake (top) and the desert-horned lizard (bottom).

Lizards are fairly diverse. Only 115 species are found in North America. Most have four legs, though a few are legless. Lizards are active during the day and like sunshine. Their favorite habitats are brush piles, heaps of dead leaves, rocky canyons, and places around buildings. Most all species of lizards can bite, though only the Gila monster is venomous.

Snakes are reptiles with long, slender, legless bodies. Snakes give the appearance of staring because their eyes do not have lids. Some snakes are poisonous. Of the 115 species in North America, only six to eight are poisonous. Some snakes live in or near water; others live in dry areas long distances from water. Snakes are found under logs and in brush piles, in areas near streams or lakes, and in rocky areas.

Appendix C lists examples and descriptions of reptiles found in North America.

Amphibians

Closely related to the reptiles, amphibians have bodies covered with a thin skin. Amphibians typically live in water in the early stages of their lives and move to land as they mature. Common amphibians include frogs, toads, and salamanders.

9-29. A Houston toad with an inflated vocal sac for making mating calls. (Courtesy, Robert Thomas, U.S. Fish and Wildlife Service)

9-30. Two examples of amphibians are the rough-skin newt (top) and the Pacific tree frog (bottom).

Frogs and toads typically begin as eggs on or in water. After hatching, the young go through a series of changes, known as **metamorphosis**. The young are known as tadpoles and live in water. Tadpoles have gills and fins and eat plant materials. As adults, frogs and toads typically live on the land or near water. They have lungs, legs, and eat animal foods, such as insects. Most are nocturnal—they are active at night and rest during the day. The largest frog in North America is the bullfrog. In cooler climates, several years are required to move through metamorphosis of egg, tadpole, and adult. Other species pass through metamorphosis in a few days or weeks. Toads are distinguished from frogs by having dry, warty skin. Frogs tend to have smooth, moist skin. Both frogs and toads are in the Anura order, with most frogs in the family Ranidae.

Salamanders appear similar to lizards, but have thin, moist skin. Salamanders have four toes on their front feet (lizards have five toes). Most salamanders live close to water, especially flowing streams with rocks and logs. As adults, salamanders typically live on land, but return to streams to lay eggs under small rocks and similar crevices. As with tadpoles, salamanders begin as eggs and hatch into larvae with external gills. A few species keep gills and never leave the water. Most salamanders pass through metamorphosis in a few weeks to a few years.

Appendix D list examples of amphibians found in North America.

Fish

Fish are aquatic animals. More fish are found in North America than any other vertebrate, with some 2,000 species of fish found in

Northern Pike *(Esox lucius)*
(Courtesy, U.S. Fish and Wildlife Service)

Brook Trout *(Salvelinus fontinalis)*
(Courtesy, U.S. Fish and Wildlife Service)

Largemouth Bass *(Micropterus salmoides)*
(Courtesy, U.S. Fish and Wildlife Service)

Rainbow Trout *(Oncorhyenhus mykiss)*

Bluegill *(Lepomis macrochirus)*
(Courtesy, American Fisheries Society)

Channel Catfish *(Ictalurus punctatus)*

Striped Bass *(Morone saxatilis)*

Tilapia *(Tilapia* spp.)

9-31. Examples of freshwater fish.

Southern Stingray *(Dasyatis americana)*

Chinook Salmon *(Oncorhynchus tshawytscha)*
(Courtesy, U.S. Fish and Wildlife Service)

Blue Crab *(Callinectes sapidus)*

Red Snapper *(Lutjanus campechanus)*
(Courtesy, American Fisheries Society)

American Oyster *(Crassostrea virginica)*

Short Spine Starfish *(Pisaster ochraceus)*

Hermit Crab *(Paqurus samuelis)*

Sockeye Salmon (male) *(Oncorhynchus nerka)*
(Courtesy, Richard R. Whitney, Washington)

9-32. Examples of saltwater fish and shellfish.

the waters of the continent. Some species prefer saltwater; others prefer freshwater or brackish water. Some prefer cool water, while others prefer warm water.

A distinction in fish is the material that makes up the skeleton. Most are **bony fish**, meaning that their internal skeletons are made of bone. Bony fish are in the class Osteichthyes. They have swim bladders and nasal openings on each side. A swim bladder is a large organ that holds air inside the body to regulate the depth of the fish in the water. Common bony fish include bass, catfish, trout, and crappie.

Only about 10 percent of the fish have cartilage instead of bone. Cartilaginous fish include sharks and rays. **Cartilaginous fish** do not have swim bladders and must keep moving to stay positioned in the water.

Fish are identified on the basis of body shape, fin shape and location, head features, scales, and color and other markings. Body shape influences the location of the natural habitat of a fish. Long, streamline fish are in rapidly flowing streams. Flat fish are found on the bottoms of streams and lakes. Narrow fish live around rocks and coral and can easily pass through small crevices.

Some fish have barbels. A **barbel** is a slender, fleshy structure that extends from the mouth area. Barbels are sense organs that help fish navigate and maintain proper distances from objects. Catfish are the best-known fish with barbels.

The bodies of many species are covered with scales over a thin layer of skin. Examples are bass, perch, trout, tilapia, and goldfish. Some species do not have scales and have relatively thick, leathery skin. An example of a fish without scales is the catfish. One species group—the sturgeon—is covered with lateral plates.

9-33. A bluegill with an identification tag for studying its movement and growth. (Courtesy, U.S. Fish and Wildlife Service)

Fish have often been sought by commercial fishers for their value as food. Others are prized by sport fishers for their game value. Increasingly, fish are being cultured as a farm crop. This helps reduce dependence upon streams and oceans for wild fish. Catfish, trout, and tilapia are the most widely cultured fish.

Appendix E lists examples of fish found in North America.

INVERTEBRATES

An ***invertebrate*** is an animal without an internal skeleton. It has an exoskeleton or body covering made of hard materials that provide body structure and protect the internal organs. Common invertebrates include mollusks, crustaceans, insects, arachnids, and a few others, such as centipedes, millipedes, sea stars (starfish), and jellyfish.

Mollusks

Mollusks are in the mollusca phylum, which includes soft-bodied animals often inside of hard shells. Most mollusks are aquatic or prefer to live close to water. Some prefer freshwater; others, saltwater.

Some mollusks have shells divided into sections that are hinged and can be opened by the organism. These are known as ***bivalve mollusks***. Examples of bivalve mollusks include oysters, mussels, scallops, and clams—all popular seafoods.

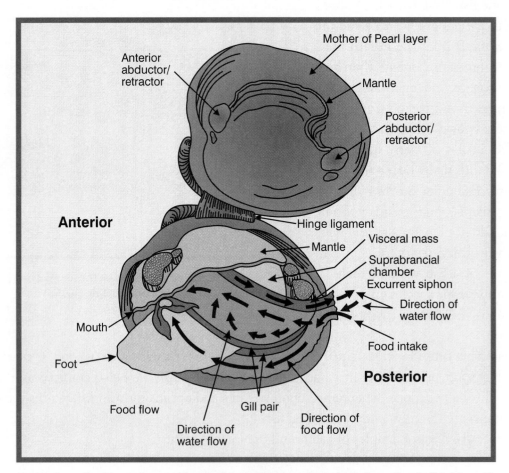

9-34. The major internal parts of a bivalve mollusk—a clam. (Note how the shell is hinged.)

A ***univalve mollusk*** has a single, coiled shell. These animals are also known as gastropods. Snails, conchs, dogwinkles, whelks, and limpets are univalves—not bivalves—because their shells do not open. Some snails are food delicacies, known in French as escargot. Another food delicacy is the red abalone, a large gastropod, that is farmed at a few locations in California.

Decapod Crustaceans

The decapod crustaceans are in the same order as insects. They are sometimes known as decapods. Decapod species include lobsters, shrimp, crawfish, and crabs.

The shells of decapods are of thin, cartilage-type material made of chitin and protein. Most decapods prefer water environments. Decapods grow by ***molting***. It occurs when the outer shell comes off and a new outer shell is forming. During molting, the animal has little protection and is often referred to as a soft-shell decapod, such as a soft-shell crab or crawfish.

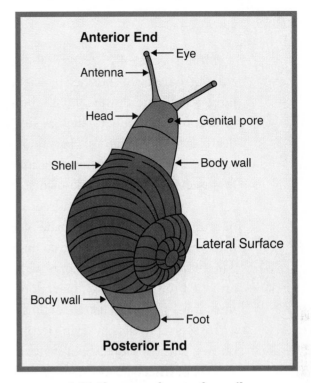

9-35. The external parts of a snail.

The bodies of decapods are in three sections: head, carapace, and abdomen. The head has antenna, eyes, and maxilliped. The carapace is the mid-section of the body and has walking legs and chelipeds (claw-like appendages). The abdomen has attached swimmerets. The tip of the abdomen is the tail, which has structures to aid movement.

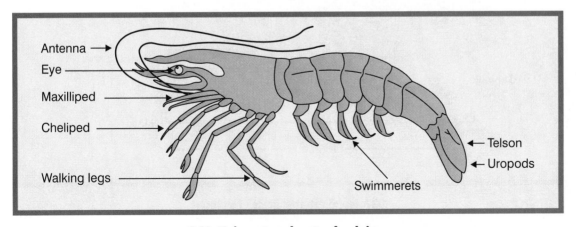

9-36. Major external parts of a shrimp.

Insects

More species of insects are found on the earth than of any other animal! More than 800,000 have been classified by scientists. Insects are both beneficial and harmful. Beneficial insects pollinate flowers, attack harmful insects, serve as food for other animals, such as birds, provide products, such as silk and honey, and clean the environment by feeding on dead plants and animals. Harmful insects (less than 1 percent of all insects) damage crops, homes, and clothing; some carry disease; and others sting humans and other animals. Harmful insects are sometimes known as pests.

The outside of a mature insect is its skeleton. The skeleton is known as an exoskeleton because it is outside and is made of a chitin material. The bodies of insects are divided into three main parts: head, thorax, and abdomen. The head has antennae, eyes, and mouth. The thorax has three segments with a pair of legs attached to each section. Wings are also attached to the thorax. The abdomen contains important organs for the insect: stomach, intestines, and reproductive organs.

Insects reproduce by laying fertile eggs. In developing, most insects go through metamorphosis. This is a sequence of stages from egg to adult. The stages vary somewhat among the species of insects. Most damage by certain harmful insects occurs during the developing stages in caterpillar forms.

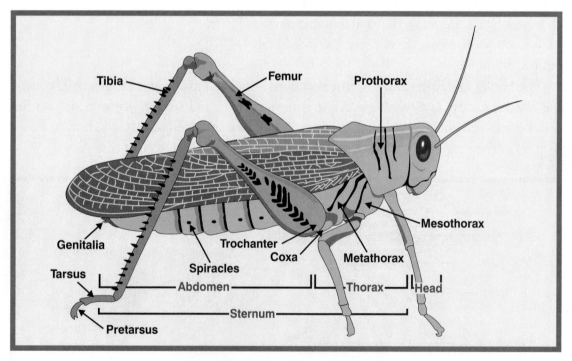

9-37. Major external parts of an insect.

Some 25 orders are used in classifying insects. Distinctions are often based on structure of mouthparts, presence and structure of wings, nature of metamorphosis, and preferred habitat.

9-38. Examples of insects.

9-39. Scorpions sometimes get into homes and can inflict stings if touched. (This scorpion is about 3 inches long.) (Courtesy, Jim Williams, U.S. Fish and Wildlife Service)

Arachnids

Arachnids are similar to insects, but have other distinctive characteristics. The easiest way to distinguish arachnids from insects is by the number of legs—most arachnids have four pairs and insects have three pairs.

Arachnids include spiders, mites, ticks, and scorpions. Appearance and body structure vary. Spiders build webs, with some webs being architectural wonders. Mites and ticks are external parasites on humans and other animals that sometimes carry disease. Spiders are the most diverse and widely found arachnids. Nearly every place we go has spiders!

Scorpions, like spiders, have four pairs of walking legs. They also have one pair of large pincers that seizes and crushes prey and one pair of small pincers at the very front. The tail of most scorpions has a stinger that can inflict a painful sting, but rarely causes death to humans. The whip scorpion (*Mastigoproctus giganteus*) has a long tail, but no stinger. Scorpions are sometimes pests in homes.

NUTRITION AND FOOD

Animals need food to live and grow. Without adequate food, animals are not healthy, become stunted, and live a shortened life span.

Food provides nutrients. A **nutrient** is a chemical substance in food that supports life. Several different kinds of nutrients are needed. The food material eaten must provide the essential nutrients in adequate amounts. If not, the animal will have inadequate nutrition.

Most animal wildlife species obtain food from their environment. Deer eat twigs and branches. Squirrels eat acorns and seeds. Birds eat seed and fruit. Fish eat aquatic plants, insects, and other fish. Toads eat insects. Foxes eat mice and rabbits.

*E*SSENTIAL NUTRIENTS

The essential nutrients are those that are needed to provide properly for an organism depending on its stage in life. Young animals need foods that promote growth. Adult animals need foods that provide for activity, maintenance, and reproduction. Lactating females need nutrients for milk production and secretion.

Young mammals get milk from their mothers, such as a nursing elk calf. The digestive systems of baby mammals are not sufficiently developed to eat solid foods. Other young must have food that provides nutrients for their growth. Baby birds are fed worms and other foods by their mothers. Birds, fish, and some other animals have digestive systems that can handle some kinds of solid foods on the day of hatching or within a few days. Fry, newly-hatched fish, have yolk sacs attached that provide nutrients for a few days while the digestive system continues to develop.

Energy Nutrients

The energy nutrients are carbohydrates and fats. Starches, sugars, plant oils, and other substances provide energy nutrients. Energy is needed for an animal to be active and carry out life processes.

The ability of an animal to use nutrients must be considered. Ruminants can use grasses and leaves as foods because of their digestive processes. Monogastric animals do not make good use of grasses and leaves and must eat more concentrated sources of energy nutrients, such as berries and nuts.

Protein

Protein is needed for growth, maintenance, and reproduction. It is used to build new tissue and replace old tissue. Young animals need more protein than adult animals to promote

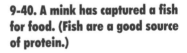

9-40. A mink has captured a fish for food. (Fish are a good source of protein.)

9-41. The white pelican has a beak that is good for scooping up food. (Courtesy, U.S. Fish and Wildlife Service)

growth. Pregnant and lactating animals need more protein. Females need protein to produce eggs. All animals need some protein.

Sources of protein vary with the species of animal. Some animals are carnivorous and get their protein from eating meat. A hawk, for example, gets protein from its prey. Other animals are herbivorous and get their protein from plants, including seeds. Tender, young plant leaves and shoots have higher protein content than older leaves and shoots. Omnivorous animals get protein from both animal and plant sources.

Minerals

Minerals are needed for a wide range of animal life processes, including growth and reproduction. They are used to build bones, shells, hooves, horns, teeth, and other body parts. The kind and amount of minerals needed varies with the species of animal. Calcium, phosphorus, salt, magnesium, sulfur, and potassium are minerals needed by most animals in greater quantities. The minerals are removed by digestive system processes from food and water. Most animals get adequate minerals from their foods.

Vitamins

Vitamins are substances present in many foods and are needed to regulate body functions. The good health of animals depends on adequate vitamins being in the foods they eat. Vitamins A, D, E, K, and the B complex are needed. Most animals obtain adequate vitamins from their foods.

Water

Water is an important nutrient. Most animals require considerable amounts of water, since their bodies contain 40 percent or more of water. Water needs vary with the species and conditions in which it is living. A few animals need less water, such as those especially adapted to desert climates. Water should be available and of adequate quality for the animal. Excessive salt can make water unfit for animal use. Pollution can result in water that is injurious to animals.

Sources of Foods

Animal wildlife species typically live where they have food. Over the years, animals migrate to areas where food is plentiful. Food shortages can sometimes occur. This is most common in times of drought or other weather changes.

Weather conditions can result in trees not producing berries or nuts that some animals eat. If this happens, animals will migrate or starve. Starvation results in death and the creation of a kind of balance between available foods and demand for the foods. The lack of food for herbivores also creates problems for the carnivores. If prey migrates, predators lose their food supply.

In some situations, humans can promote wildlife foods. Leaving strips of untilled land around fields results in plants growing that are needed by some species. Planting food-producing trees or other plants can promote food supplies for wildlife. In forestry, leaving selected food-producing trees, such as oak trees, at the time of harvest can provide food for wildlife. Feed for domesticated animals can be used to supplement food supplies, such as corn for wild turkeys. The use of manufactured feed should not be so great that wildlife animals become dependent upon it.

With aquatic animals, fertilizers can be added to water to promote the growth of food organisms in fish ponds. Always follow the recommendations from local authorities in using fertilizer. Commercial feeds are also available.

REVIEWING

MAIN IDEAS

Many forms of animal wildlife are found in North America. These have been classified and named by scientists. Using scientific names prevents confusion that may result with common names, which tend to vary from one local area to another. In the Animalia Kingdom, the major animal wildlife species are in three phyla: chordata, arthropoda, and mollusca.

Anatomy and physiology deal with body parts and their functions. Several systems are present in animals to make it possible for life processes to occur. The systems are: skeletal, digestive, respiratory, muscular, circulatory, excretory, nervous, and integumentary. In addition, the reproductive system makes it possible for members of a species to produce offspring.

To have good health and to grow, reproduce, and maintain themselves, animals must have nutrients. The nutrients are obtained from the foods that they eat. Animals are usually able to obtain needed foods from the environment in which they live. If not, they migrate to new areas with the food or become unhealthy and die.

Wildlife animals have been grouped for ease of study. The major groups are the vertebrates (mammals, birds, reptiles, amphibians, and fish) and the invertebrates (mollusks, decapod crustaceans, insects, and arachnids).

QUESTIONS

Answer the following questions using correct spelling and complete sentences.

1. What is a scientific classification system?

2. What divisions or stages are used in the modern scientific classification system?

3. What are the three most important phyla of wildlife in the Animalia Kingdom? Distinguish between the three phyla.

4. What is a scientific name?

5. What is the importance of using the scientific name for a species?

6. Why are anatomy and physiology important in studying animal wildlife?

7. What are the major life-sustaining systems of animals? What is the purpose of each system?

8. What is the purpose of the reproductive system?

9. What is sexual reproduction? How does sexual reproduction differ among mammals, birds, and fish?

10. What is an endothermic animal? Ectothermic animal?

11. List examples of two species included in each of the following groups of animals: mammals, arachnids, reptiles, amphibians, birds, and fish.

12. What are the major nutrient needs of animals? What are the sources of these nutrients?

EVALUATING

Match the term with the correct definition. Write the letter by the term in the space provided.

a. protein
b. rodent
c. cloning
d. ruminant

e. waterfowl
f. migration
g. bony fish
h. metamorphosis

i. barbel
j. bivalve mollusk

_____ 1. Slender fleshy structure that extends from the mouths of some species.

_____ 2. Small animal with four large front teeth.

_____ 3. Bird that lives in and around water.

_____ 4. Series of changes between young and adult.

_____ 5. Fish in which the skeleton is primarily made of bone.

_____ 6. Organism with a hinged shell.

_____ 7. An essential food nutrient needed for growth.

_____ 8. Moving from one area to another for a purpose.

_____ 9. A method of asexually reproducing organisms.

_____ 10. A mammal whose stomach has more than one compartment.

EXPLORING

1. Set up a feeder to attract desirable native birds. Gather information on the species in the area, what they eat, sources of the feed, and best arrangement of the feeder. Regularly observe the feeder and determine the species of birds that eat. Be sure to keep the feeder well-stocked with food.

2. Prepare a written report on the major animal wildlife in your area. Obtain reports from a local wildlife conservation officer or the Cooperative Extension Service at the land-grant university in your state. Make photographs of the species or prepare a video that includes narration to accompany your report.

3. Make a survey of the animal wildlife foods in your area. Identify the food species and assess the quantity and quality of what you observe. Prepare a written report on your findings.

CHAPTER 10

Animal Habitat

OBJECTIVES

The habitat needs of common terrestrial animal wildlife are covered in this chapter. This includes species of wildlife, methods of habitat management, and kinds of habitat. The objectives of the chapter are:

1 List and describe global habitat classification.

2 Explain selected practices used in managing animal wildlife habitat.

3 Explain how to develop a habitat management plan.

4 Describe selected management practices for small areas of habitat.

5 List habitat requirements for selected species of animal wildlife.

TERMS

alpine tundra
biome
desert
estuary
girdling
habitat management plan

marsh
mast
savanna
shelterbelt
snag
swamp

taiga
tundra
understory
vegetation management
woodland
woodlot

10-1. A wolf has adapted to the cold, snowy weather of an Alaskan forest.

YOU want a good home—one that meets your needs. An animal also wants a good home—one that meets its needs. Food, water, cover, and space are important needs of people as well as animal wildlife.

Knowledge of animal wildlife habitat is essential in providing for its needs. Species vary in their habitat requirements. What kind of habitat does your favorite species need? The needs of a rabbit are different from those of a duck or moose.

Habitat management is the major way people control wildlife. We can encourage or discourage wildlife by the way we manage habitat. Most of the practices also involve good environmental stewardship. And, all of us want to have a good environment!

HABITAT CLASSIFICATION: BIOMES

10-2. A black vulture is perching on a saguaro cactus searching for food in an Arizona desert.

Habitat for animal wildlife can be classified based on ecosystem. The earth's ecosystems are in areas known as biomes. A **biome** is a large area with a distinct combination of plants and animals. Biomes are influenced by climate, precipitation, soil, and other factors. Biomes can be aquatic or terrestrial. Knowing the general nature of biomes helps in providing habitat. However, conditions within the biomes cover a wide range. Local habitat planning is needed.

TERRESTRIAL BIOMES

Five kinds of terrestrial biomes are included here. All are found to some extent in the United States.

Tropical

Tropical areas are near and on either side of the equator. Some have high rainfall; others can be quite dry. Warm temperature is a commonality among the tropical biomes. Two major tropical areas are those in forest and grassland.

Forested tropical areas often have high rainfall—90 inches or more a year. Many kinds of animals are found in the lush plant growth. In some places, large trees with big canopies shade the ground so smaller plants do not grow. Birds, frogs, insects, and many other kinds of animal wildlife live in the tops of trees. The tropical forest areas do not have the four seasons, but tend to have two seasons: wet and dry. Most rain occurs in the wet season. In the dry season, little or no rain may fall for a few weeks. Once thought to be quite vast, the tropical rain forests are now threatened. Timber harvesting has left areas of land bare. Animal wildlife has been threatened with declining habitat.

Tropical grassland areas have low rainfall. They share the warm temperature of the forested areas, but provide habitats of small grasses and forbs. Some brush and shrubs may grow. This may provide good habitats for grazing animals, small rodents, snakes, lizards, and some birds. Any damage to the grass results in the loss of habitat for the animal wildlife.

Few areas of the United States have tropical biomes. Hawaii and Pacific Island possessions have areas with tropical forests and grasslands.

Temperate

Temperate forest habitats cover much of the earth. This includes much of the southern United States, especially the area east of the Mississippi River Delta. Precipitation varies from moderate to heavy. Large trees with considerable value for wood may grow. Pine trees (often referred to as conifers) cover much of the temperate land in the southern United States. Oak and other hardwoods are found in areas outside the areas adjacent to the Gulf of Mexico. In some areas, hardwood trees gradually replace the pines in natural succession.

10-3. An opossum climbs a small tree in a temperate forest.

Temperate forests are home to many kinds of wildlife. Squirrel, deer, quail, rabbit, and others are common. Habitat management typically focuses on providing for the well-being of these species. Acorns, cones, berries, and fruit are frequently produced by the trees and smaller plants in the temperate areas.

Grasslands and Savannas

The predominant vegetation in the grasslands and savannas is grass. Precipitation is too low to support the growth of trees. The plains of the western United States and Canada have large areas of grassland.

The fertile soil in these areas supports the growth of grass and forbs. The plants serve as food for grazing and browsing animals, such as deer, elk, and bison. Small rodents, birds, and reptiles are found in these areas. Some predatory animals, such as fox and hawks, are found here. Much of this land has been converted to vast fields of grain crops, such as wheat and grain sorghum.

A **savanna** is an area similar to grassland where the soil fertility is too low to support the growth of much grass. No savannas are found in North America. They are primarily in areas of Africa, India, Australia, and Brazil.

Tundra and Taiga

Tundra and taiga are both found in North America. **Tundra** is either in the Arctic area or at high elevations. Tundra at high elevations is known as **alpine tundra**. All tundra is characterized by low temperatures and permafrost. Permafrost is permanently frozen ground. Tundra has a very short growing season. Lichens, mosses, a few shrubs, and some grasses grow in tundra.

10-4. Fragile plants grow in the alpine tundra of Colorado's Rocky Mountains. (Courtesy, Greg N. Freeman)

10-5. Aquatic animals, such as the garibaldi fish, get life-sustaining needs from water.

Taiga areas are in cold climates where large conifer forests grow. They are found in North America. The trees that grow can withstand heavy loads of snow and low temperatures. This area is known as the boreal forest.

Desert

A **desert** is an area that forms a very dry habitat. It has little or no rain. Temperatures range from very hot to cold. Some deserts have high winds that rearrange the sand and other materials on the surface of the land. Moist areas in deserts may grow shrubs and scrub trees. Some desert areas are found in the western United States, especially Nevada, Arizona, and California.

Aquatic Biomes

Aquatic biomes are areas of water. These biomes may involve freshwater, saltwater, or brackish water habitats. Four aquatic biomes are given here.

Lakes and Ponds

Lakes and ponds are natural or artificial reservoirs of earth that hold water. Most have freshwater. Water temperature varies with the surrounding climate and the source of the water. Algae, insects, and other small creatures are sources of food for fish, shellfish, and other aquatic wildlife. Treetops, limbs, and other debris are sometimes placed in water to improve habitat. Fertilizer may be used to promote aquatic plant growth, which is used as food by the aquatic animals.

Swamps often have natural areas with year-round water on the land. These are managed much as ponds for aquatic wildlife.

Streams

A **stream** is flowing water that moves from higher to lower elevations. The water is from ground runoff, springs, or released by users. Stream size varies. Creeks are small streams; rivers are large streams. The water is typically classified as freshwater. Unfortunately, many streams have been polluted and need improvements to be good wildlife habitats.

Streams in North America range from the mighty Mississippi River to those that are much smaller. Some flow with muddy water containing silt and pollution from land along the river bottom. Small streams are more likely to have clear, unpolluted water. An example is the Soque River in Northeast Georgia. It begins in a wilderness area of the Blue Ridge Mountains from springs that flow from the earth. The cool, clear, rapidly flowing water is noted for trout fishing. The Soque flows into the Chattahoochee while it is also clear. As it flows south toward the Gulf of Mexico, it picks up muddy water, industrial effluent, storm runoff from highways and parking lots, and other pollutants.

Oceans and Seas

Oceans and seas typically have saltwater. The water where freshwater streams flow into them has lower salt content and is brackish water. Some wildlife species prefer the mix of fresh and saltwater as habitats. Keeping pollution out of oceans and seas has become a major challenge. Fish caught in polluted water are sometimes unsafe for human consumption.

Wildlife Connection

WILDLIFE FOOD

Making an inventory of the plants in an area that will provide food for animals is part of developing a habitat management plan. Identify the plants and determine the animals that feed on them. Animals may eat leaves, stems, bark, fruit, or seed and other plant parts.

Careful observation of the plant may be needed. Look at the leaves, bark, and flowers or fruit. Use references to help identify the kind of plant. Specialists in nature or wildlife can help. Of course, plant materials vary from one area to another.

This photograph shows a plant being identified based on its leaf shape and fruit. The plant is a swamp dogwood (*Cornus amomum*), which grows in moist areas near streams in the southeastern United States. Swamp dogwoods primarily grow as large shrubs, though some reach tree size.

Wetlands and Estuaries

Water has a big effect on land areas near lakes, streams, and oceans. In many cases, the land may be covered with water some of the time. Regardless, these areas serve as important habitats for some species of animal wildlife. Both terrestrial and aquatic wildlife species are found in these areas. Swamps and marshes are wetland areas along inland streams. They typically have freshwater. A **swamp** is a land area where water stands on the surface during wet times of the year. Swamps typically have dense vegetation, including cypress trees and various hardwoods. A **marsh** is a low-lying land area that is wet and sometimes covered with water. Marshes are typically covered with grasses. Many kinds of wildlife, especially waterfowl, use these areas. Laws now protect swamps and marshes from being drained.

An **estuary** is the area where a stream flows into an ocean. The wildlife species that live in an estuary tolerate both saltwater and freshwater. Preventing pollution from coastal areas is a major goal in maintaining a habitat.

10-6. Some waterfowl thrive in swampy environments. (Note the cypress tree "knees" in the background. A "knee" is a root structure that extends above the water level to get oxygen for the root system.)

HABITAT MANAGEMENT PRACTICES

Several practices are widely used in managing habitats. These practices vary with the local area. Select only practices approved where you are managing habitat. Never use a practice that poses a danger to surrounding areas. The major practices include: vegetation management, seeding, water sources, fire, fertilizer, and site preservation.

VEGETATION MANAGEMENT

Vegetation management is using practices that promote the growth of desired plant species. It can involve cutting selected trees and other plants. The practice used depends on the featured species and the kind and amount of vegetation. Timber with market value can sometimes be harvested in making habitat improvements. A few examples of vegetation management are included.

10-7. These wild turkeys are in an opening near a wooded area.

Remove Understory

Understory is vegetation that grows beneath trees in a woodland. Scrub trees, shrubs, and forbs can be removed to promote large animals. The trees that provide a canopy are not cut. Edge habitat should be provided nearby so the animals have access to grasses and forbs.

Create Clearings

Small areas can be clear-cut within thickly wooded areas to attract deer and elk. (Clear-cut means that all trees are cut—none are left.) These cut areas grow browse preferred by some species. Making the cut areas too large may result in a reduced population of deer and elk.

Thinning

Thinning is selectively removing some of the trees in a wooded area. Thinning creates holes in the tree canopy. This allows the remaining trees more room to grow. The practice may also result in income from marketable timber products. Herbaceous plants will grow in areas thinned where sunlight can reach the ground.

10-8. A small clearing in these woods is growing browse for deer.

Combinations

Vegetation management may involve a combination of practices, such as thinning and fertilizing or burning and seeding.

SEEDING

Wildlife are attracted to food. Establishing food plots promotes wildlife populations. Using species preferred by the target population helps attract the desired species.

Seeding is used to increase the plant population in wildlife habitat. Grasses, forbs, trees, and other species may be seeded. In some cases, trees are planted as seedlings—small trees only a few inches tall. Seeding should be used only in areas where it can produce good results. It is used on sites where the plants will grow. Too much shade, inadequate moisture, and lack of soil fertility will result in poor results from seeding.

WATER SOURCES

Animals need water to live. Water is an essential part of all habitats. Small ponds or other impoundments can be used to improve water supply for terrestrial wildlife. Larger ponds or lakes can be created to attract waterfowl. Careful study of the nearby land features may be needed to assure that adequate water can be collected. Building ponds without considering

Career Profile

CONSERVATION EDUCATOR

A conservation educator plans and conducts educational programs about natural resources, including wildlife habitat. The work involves relating nature to people. Programs may be as walking tours through wooded areas, lectures in auditoriums, or in other ways. This photograph shows a guided tour through a wooded area.

Conservation educators need a college degree in wildlife, agriculture, biology, or closely related areas. Skills in effective speaking, writing, and preparing presentations are needed. Some have master's degrees; a few have less than a college degree. Experience with wildlife, the climate, and other aspects of the local area is important.

Most conservation educators are with government agencies. Some work with industries, associations, or wildlife refuges. (Courtesy, U.S. Fish and Wildlife Service)

water runoff results in ponds that may not collect any water. In some cases, ponds can be shared by wildlife and domestic animals, such as cattle.

FIRE

Carefully planned fires can aid habitat growth. Fire is most commonly used in the southeastern United States. Fires should never be used in dry areas where wildfires can develop. Using fires involves creating firebreaks to assure the fire is controlled.

Fire removes leaves, twigs, and other dead vegetation on the ground. If big accumulations of these materials have developed, fires may burn too big and damage the tops of trees or kill the trees. Always avoid fires at dry times of the year when they are more difficult to control.

Properly using fire helps to renew the understory and allows browse to grow. Areas burned at one time should be confined to small acreage. Large areas may destroy needed food supplies. Wildlife biologists have found that fires increase species diversity in an area. In some cases, seeding and applying fertilizer follow burning.

10-9. A small natural pond in this area of Denali National Park in Alaska provides water for many different species. (Courtesy, Environmental Protection Agency)

10-10. A controlled burn is being used in habitat management. (Note that the fire is being carefully watched to keep it under control.) (Courtesy, U.S. Fish and Wildlife Service)

FERTILIZER

Fertilizer is used to assure nutrients for plant growth. Good plant growth attracts animals. In using fertilizer, soil testing may be needed to determine the kind to use. Plant species also have different nutrient requirements. It is often a waste of money to use fertilizer without knowing what the soil needs. The fertilizer needs to be applied evenly over the land. Fertilizer produces best results on grasses, forbs, and small trees.

SITE PRESERVATION

In some cases, the best management is to leave an area undisturbed. Study the area and get the advice of wildlife specialists. Some practices used in an attempt to improve habitat may disturb existing wildlife animals and cause them to leave. Fire may destroy food supply for some species. Harvesting timber disrupts habitat and destroys food supplies and cover for other species.

Of course, clearing areas for construction destroys a habitat so wildlife species leave. Keeping strips of habitat help keep wildlife in an area.

DEVELOPING A MANAGEMENT PLAN

Planning is an essential part of managing animal wildlife habitat. Habitat management plans are products of the planning process.

10-11. Determining the wildlife existing in an area often involves looking for signs, such as evidence of feeding, digging, footprints, and feces. (These gnawed pine cone remains are evidence that squirrels are in the area.)

THE PLAN

A *habitat management plan* is a written document describing the needs of an area to improve a habitat for a featured species and specifies how and when the work will be done. Plans are a part of overall use of land areas for habitat, aesthetics of the area, income from harvested crops, and sport hunting. Since plans often require several years to implement, be sure to gather good information and make the best possible decisions.

Without a good plan, efforts to improve habitat lack direction. Money may be wasted on projects that do not give good results. The best plans focus on what now exists and what is needed to meet the wildlife goals.

STEPS IN PLANNING

A habitat management plan involves the following steps:

- Step 1: Animal Inventory—Make a list of the animal wildlife in the area. Be sure to include all species, including mammals, birds, reptiles, amphibians, and fish. In some cases, plans list interesting insects such as butterflies and arachnids such as spiders. The inventory may also include a short description of the species, such as where they were seen, or evidence, such as footprints or feces. Also, note the size of the population as best possible. Many people are surprised at the large number they find in a small area of land!

- Step 2: Plant Inventory—Make a list of the plant species and assess the number found. Since animals depend on plants for food, plant types have much to do with the animals that will be found. Make a note where the plant materials are typically found.

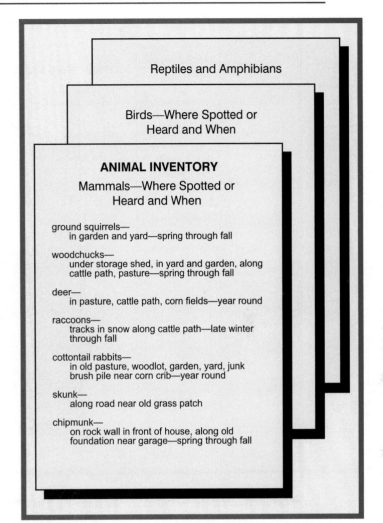

10-12. This shows an easy-to-use method of inventorying animals.

- Step 3: Make an Analysis—Examine the animal and plant inventories. Compare what you found with the climate and other conditions that species need to flourish. Set priorities for the area—these are based on your preferred wildlife species. Consider what you now have and what you can reasonably expect to attract to the area. Estimate costs and benefits of projected improvements to help make an informed decision. Request the assistance of a wildlife specialist and continue to use the person's knowledge as the planning process is continued. Assess what can be done quickly and at a low cost and what will take longer and be more expensive.

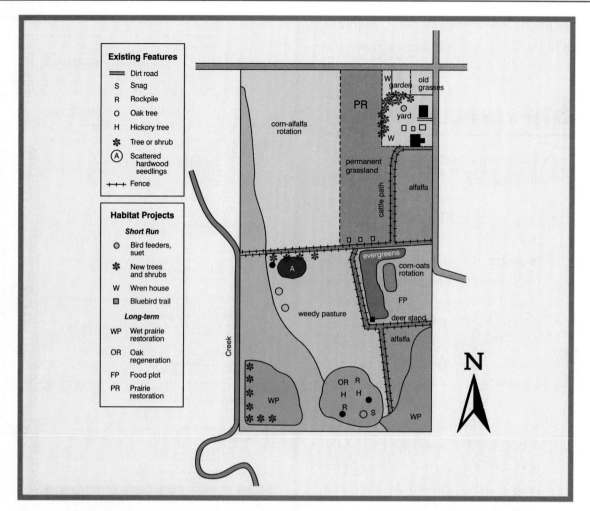

10-13. Sample map showing the location of features and projects to improve the habitat.

- Step 4: Prepare a Map—Sketch the area selected for improvement. (In some cases, an up-to-date aerial photograph of the area may be available from the local U.S. Department of Agriculture office.) Show major land features, including streams, trees, and elevation changes. As the written plan is developed, indicate the locations where habitat improvement projects are to be done. Consider uses made of nearby areas, such as land for livestock, crops, forests, roads, factories, and homes. Study what others have done in the community to improve habitat and the results from their efforts.

- Step 5: The Plan—Write a plan that lists the goals to be achieved and how they will be done. Indicate those that are short-term and long-term. List the projects needed to achieve the goals. Describe how and when the projects will be carried out. Match the projects to the improvements identified on the map. Be sure each wildlife goal has adequate site description and steps needed to achieve the goal.

Habitat Management Goals and Projects

Overall Goal:
Manage for wildlife viewing and hunting purposes, while still allowing income from contract farming.

Short-run Goals:
Manage for deer, grassland birds, small mammals, songbirds, and amphibians.

Projects Planned:
✓ Backyard wildlife landscaping project:
  Songbird food and shelter, shelterbelt
  and miniwoodland
✓ Bluebird trail
✓ Prairie patch and butterfly garden

Long-run Goals:
Manage for squirrels, turkeys, waterfowl, sandhill cranes, and upland game.

Projects Planned:
✓ Wet prairie, tamarack community restoration
✓ Oak regeneration
✓ Food plot and pine planting

10-14. Sample goals for a habitat improvement plan.

The Plan

Project 1: Backyard Wildlife Landscaping

Wildlife Goal: To attract a variety of wildlife year-round

Description of Site: House sits near peak of a glacial hill, or drumlin. Yard is gently sloping to moderately sloping. Soil is well drained to moderately well drained. Much clay in soil. Soil is good for tree and shrub planting. Total area of yard, including the house is 5 acres. The yard contains a variety of common trees and shrubs typical of old farmsteads. There are also fruit trees and grapes—a bonus for wildlife.

Part 1: *Songbird food and shelter*

Wildlife Goal: To immediately attract local and winter resident songbirds.

Time frame: Weekend projects throughout the year begin immediately, complete by year end.

1. Install small bird feeder near east kitchen window.
2. Hang one tubular thistle seed bird feeder, sunflower seed bird feeder, and one suet cage from pear tree on north side of house.
3. Hang one house wren nest box in lilac near old outhouse.
4. Install one large hopper-style bird feeder on west side of house, outside of living room windows. Put nuts, bread and corn on old box elder stump. Hang one tubular sunflower seed bird feeder and one suet "bell" from red cedar on northwest side of house.
5. Purchase bird bath and bird bath heater for winter water source.
6. Remove old purple martin house. Build and erect new one. Keep sparrows and starlings from moving in.
7. Purchase a house sparrow trap and remove these pests.

10-15. Part of a sample plan for a backyard habitat to attract songbirds. (Courtesy, Wisconsin Department of Natural Resources)

- Step 6: Assessment—Regularly assess the progress and the results of the habitat improvement. Determine how well the plan is working. Make needed changes in the plan. Have experts assist with the process.

SMALL AREA MANAGEMENT

Within biomes, small areas can be managed to promote habitat. These are found on farms or in forests, parks, residential areas, and many other places.

WOODLAND

Woodland is land that has some covering of trees. It is often in various stages of maturity and mixed species. Some shrubs and forbs may be present in open areas. Trees in a cultured forest hardly have the same woodland characteristics. These forests, known as tree farms, typically have uniform species at the same stage of growth. Farm woodland lacks uniformity of species and maturity. A woodland area on a farm may be referred to as a **woodlot**.

Woodland is habitat for many wildlife animals. Herbivores (plant-eating species) will feed on mast, browse, and forage. **Mast** is nuts, seeds, and fruit from trees and shrubs. Trees producing the most mast are the oaks, hickory, beech, walnut, butternut, cherry, ash, and conifers. Browse is the current growth of woody plants, including buds and flowers. Forage is vegetation, such as grasses and grass-like plants.

Clear-cutting small areas within the woodland may be needed to promote the growth of grasses, forbs, and young trees that require sunlight. Selective cutting may be used within a wooded area to increase space for young trees. Selective cutting also allows the removal of undesirable species and promotes the desired species. For example, if the desired animal wildlife feeds on acorns, leave oak trees and cut other species. Some dead trees are needed for certain kinds of wildlife. Trees that have perches or places for nests should be left.

10-16. A snag attracts several kinds of wildlife, such as woodpeckers and owls.

DEAD WOOD

Dead wood is used for food, nesting, and as a perch. As a food source, the wood itself may not be eaten, but the worms and insects in the decaying wood are used as food. Nesting is important to assure reproduction of species. A perch is a place for birds to rest and search for prey and other food.

Some species prefer dead wood, including snags. (A **snag** is a standing dead tree.) Older trees that are partially dead are often left for this purpose. Snag cavities (holes) are used by woodpeckers, nuthatches, insects, owls, and squirrels. Downed trees make logs on the ground. These are used by mice, snakes, salamanders, chipmunks, and bears (if large enough). Hollow logs and snags may be used by raccoon and other species.

The amount of dead wood in an area can be increased by leaving old trees to fall naturally or by causing the death of live trees. Girdling can be used to kill a tree. **Girdling** is cutting a small trench around the circumference of a tree trunk. An axe is used for girdling. The cut must be through the bark and into the wood and wide enough to prevent tree growth.

10-17. A fallen tree attracts wildlife, such as mice and chipmunks.

Table 10-1. Examples of Wildlife Species that Use Dead Wood (snags or fallen)

Species	Use
Wood duck	nesting and perching
Turkey vulture	nesting and perching
Red-headed woodpecker	feeding, nesting, and perching
Screech owl	nesting and perching
Winter wren	nesting
Opossum	nesting
Big brown bat	nesting
Black bear	feeding and nesting
Gray fox	nesting
Gray squirrel	nesting and perching
Porcupine	nesting
Tree frog	nesting
Eastern chipmunk	perching
Deer mouse	feeding, food storage, and perching

10-18. A brush pile will attract rabbits, red fox, and chipmunks.

Brush piles

Brush piles are made of limbs, twigs, logs, stones, and other materials. They may be created by harvesting timber or artificially to serve as habitats. Brush piles attract rabbits, red fox, skunks, chipmunks, cardinals, garter snakes, and many other species, including insects.

In building a brush pile, begin with larger pieces of wood, stone, or other material on the bottom. Allow spaces between the materials so wildlife animals will have areas where they can hide and nest. Cover the top with smaller limbs and twigs. Most brush piles are within or near woodland.

10-19. A Canada goose is nesting in a marsh off the coast of Virginia.

Shelterbelts and food plots

A **shelterbelt** is a row or several parallel rows of trees and shrubs planted to reduce wind currents and drifting snow in northern climates. Shelterbelts are also known as windbreaks. With care, they can be designed to attract squirrels, rabbits, mice, chip-

10-20. A sample habitat arrangement of shelterbelt, food plots, edges, and water.

munks, and other species that need ground cover. Ground nesting birds are also attracted to these areas.

Most shelterbelts are designed with five rows, though some have seven. The middle three rows are large trees, with the middle row being a deciduous tree and the other tree rows being planted in evergreens. Small trees and shrubs are planted next to the trees. Grass is outside the shrubs.

Food plots are areas planted to domestic crops or wild plants that produce food. Corn, wheat, and similar farm crops may be used. Sunflowers, nut trees (hickories and oaks), and other plants that produce edible seed may be used. In some cases, farmers leave a few rows of grain crop in the field to help feed wildlife through the winter. Carefully study the location of a food plot so wildlife will use it. Also, choose the plant species carefully. For example, planting oak trees for acorns is a long-term commitment.

GRASSLANDS

Grassland is the habitat for many species of animals. Wolves, prairie chickens, badgers, field sparrows, meadowlarks, and grouse are examples of animals that need grassland habitat. This type of habitat is particularly important in prairie and dry areas where trees and other plants do not grow well naturally. Grasses, of course, require more moisture than desert land. Grassland is often used for livestock production. Some control of scrub trees and other undesirable plants may be needed. Cutting once a year with a pasture clipper usually provides adequate control.

Select grass species that are adapted to the area. Some common grasses and legumes to include in habitats are switch grass, red clover, alfalfa, smooth brome grass, orchard grass, big bluestem, and wild oats. Use care in planting these. Some species are considered weeds by crop producers. Be sure to use good seed and properly fertilize areas where the seed are planted. Most of these seed are planted by broadcasting. Broadcasting is evenly disbursing the seed over an area. Larger areas are planted with drills and air seeders. Small areas may be planted by hand.

SPECIES HABITAT REQUIREMENTS

Animal wildlife species have varying habitat requirements. Some species are found nearly everywhere—in all kinds of habitats. Knowing the habitat requirements helps in making habitat improvements.

10-21. A squirrel nest has been built in the darkened area of this pine treetop.

Table 10-2. Habitat Requirements of Selected Species

Species (common and scientific names)	Preferred Habitat
Armadillo (Dasypus novemcinctus)	brushy or rocky areas
Badger (Taxidea taxus)	arid grasslands and sagebrush
Bison (Bison bison)	prairie grasslands
Black bear (Ursus americanus)	forested areas with swamps and streams and thick vegetation with berries and nuts; winter dens are under fallen trees lined with leaves, moss, and bark
Bighorn sheep (Ovis canadensis)	mountain areas with rugged features
Bobcat (Lynx rufus)	heavily forested areas; alder thickets and coniferous swamps
California sea lion (Zalophus californianus)	rocky coastal water areas
Canada goose (Branta canadensis)	winter (southern migration): farm fields, refuges, bays, estuaries, saltwater marshes; summer (northern migration): lakes, rivers, grain fields, large marshes, and grassy areas
Caribou (Rangifer tarandus)	northern forests, bogs, and tundra
Elk (Cervus elaphus)	adaptable to open land grasses and forest browse
Gray squirrel (Sciurus carolinensis)	hardwood forests (will thrive in parks)
Manatee (Trichechus manatus)	warm coastal waters
Mountain goat (Oreamnos americanus)	steep slopes above the timberline
Moose (Alces alces)	northern forests
Mule deer (Odcoileus hemionus)	mountain forests
Raccoon (Procyon lotor)	forested edges near streams and lakes
Porcupine (Erethizon dorsatum)	temperate forested areas
Ring-necked pheasant (Phasianus colchicus)	gently rolling open country with roosting on ground near wetlands, hayfields, and small grain areas
Striped skunk (Mephitis mephitis)	woodlands and farming areas
Timber wolf (Canid lupus lycaon)	open forests
Opossum (Virginia) (Didelphis virginiana)	woodland areas with streams and swamps
White-tailed deer (Odocoileus virginianus)	forested and swampy areas with browse
Woodchuck (Marmota monax)	dense forest

REVIEWING

MAIN IDEAS

Wildlife management involves providing habitats. Without habitats, wildlife organisms are not attracted to an area. They must have food, water, cover, and space. The earth's surface has large areas that share similar general ecosystem characteristics. These form biomes. The biomes may be classed as terrestrial or aquatic. Most kinds of biomes are found in North America. The major terrestrial biomes are tropical forests and grassland, temperate forests, grasslands and savannas, tundra and taiga, and desert. The major aquatic biomes are lakes and ponds, streams, oceans and seas, and wetlands and estuaries.

Habitat management includes several practices. Most efforts focus on growing plants that provide food for the featured animal species. Vegetation management is often used. Seeding, providing water, fertilizing, using controlled burns (fire), and site preservation are also used.

Most habitat improvement should begin with a management plan. The plan should be written. Good planning is based on the wildlife species that are currently in an area as well as goals for reasonable improvements.

Managing small areas may involve woodland improvements, using dead wood and brush piles, and constructing shelterbelts and food plots. Grasslands cover much of the central part of the United States. These are managed to attract and sustain the desired wildlife.

QUESTIONS

Answer the following questions using correct spelling and complete sentences.

1. What is a biome?

2. What are the major biomes that affect animal wildlife habitat?

3. What biome is your home located in? How does this affect your approach to wildlife habitat?

4. What are the major habitat management practices? Briefly explain each.

5. What is a habitat management plan?

6. What are the steps in preparing a habitat management plan?

7. How are small woodland areas managed for wildlife habitat?

8. How is dead wood important as habitat?

9. How are brush piles used as habitat?

10. What is the general habitat requirement of any three animal wildlife species found in your area?

EVALUATING

Match the term with the correct definition.

a. snag   e. swamp   i. alpine tundra
b. mast   f. understory   j. marsh
c. tundra   g. woodland
d. desert   h. biome

_____ 1. Area where water stands on the surface of the land during wet times of the year.

_____ 2. A low-lying area that is wet year-round and sometimes covered with water.

_____ 3. Vegetation that grows beneath tree canopies in a wooded area.

_____ 4. Nuts, seeds, and fruit from trees and shrubs.

_____ 5. A standing dead tree.

_____ 6. A large area of the earth with distinct plant and animal wildlife.

_____ 7. Plant growth in cold climate areas.

_____ 8. Plant growth in areas of high altitude.

_____ 9. Area of very dry habitat.

_____ 10. Land that has some covering of trees.

EXPLORING

1. Prepare a habitat management plan for an area in your community or a part of the school grounds. Get the assistance of an individual qualified in habitat management, such as a staff member of the local soil and water conservation district. Follow the steps as listed in the chapter for preparing such a plan.

2. Install a selected habitat management practice. Consider the needs of the habitat and featured animal wildlife species. Work with the land owner and only implement practices approved by the owner and a specialist in wildlife management.

3. Create a miniature habitat display using paper maché. Use your creativity to design habitat components (trees, grass, ponds, animal wildlife, etc.) Share your display to encourage others to care for and practice wise conservation of natural resources while preserving wildlife habitat.

11

Protecting Animal Wildlife

OBJECTIVES

This chapter covers important areas affecting animal populations, including natural and human roles. The objectives of the chapter are:

1 Explain the concept of population status.

2 Explain habitat factors that affect wildlife populations.

3 Describe the role of disease and predation on animal wildlife.

4 Explain how human activities threaten wildlife.

5 List examples of how proper wildlife management has enhanced wildlife.

TERMS

carrying capacity
controlled hunting
declining population
disease
game species
habitat degradation

habitat destruction
health
healthy population
land use
limiting factor
malnutrition

nongame species
parasite
parasite burden
population status
predation
reproductive potential

ANIMAL populations are dynamic and constantly changing in numeric size. This is true of all wild populations. Human activity sometimes disrupts wildlife. These disruptions interfere with the natural cycles and systems of wildlife. Some combinations of human and natural factors often place wildlife populations in jeopardy.

The science of wildlife management makes it possible to apply proper management techniques. These techniques protect and preserve wildlife populations for the future. This assures continued enjoyment and other benefits provided by animal wildlife.

11-1. The grizzly bear mother will raise healthy cubs in good habitat. (A mother bear is known as a she-bear or sow.)

POPULATION STATUS

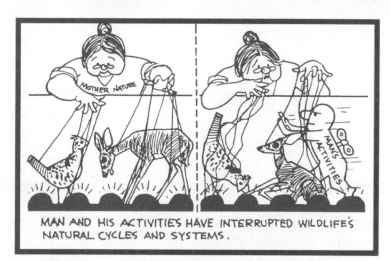

11-2. This cartoon by Oscar Warbach illustrates how human activities disrupt the natural cycles of nature. (Courtesy, Wildlife Management Institute)

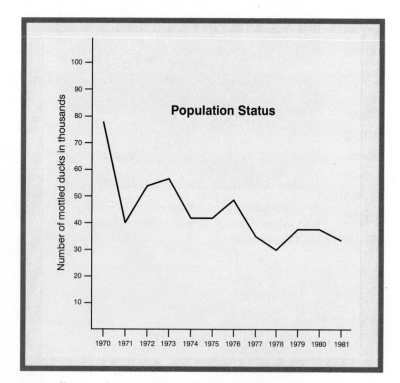

11-3. A line graph shows the trend in mottled duck population for one decade. Overall, what has been the population trend?

The overall health condition and numerical count of wildlife populations comprises **population status**. Knowing population status is important in managing and protecting animal wildlife. Health is a major concern in management.

Healthy populations are those that have the capability of increasing or maintaining stable numbers from year to year. These populations are made up of animals that are relatively disease-free. Adequate food is available to assure continued good health. *Declining populations* are those that receive no gains, but lose numbers from year to year and show declining trends over the long term.

The number of animals in any population is the number of births minus the number of deaths. This is the law of all populations whether human or wild. Populations swell each year and reach their highest point when young of the year are added to the adult population that has survived the year. After populations reach their peak, they begin to decline as individual animals begin to die of various causes.

On a yearly-cycle basis of gains and losses, populations are the lowest just before the breeding season begins. Populations are directly related to reproduction. *Reproduc-*

tive potential is the ability of a population to increase. Populations with a large number of diseased or older animals have lower reproductive potential. A shortage of food also lowers reproductive potential. Providing good habitat helps assure that a population will reproduce.

In nearly every habitat, some factor limits the potential of animals. A *limiting factor* is any one action working alone, or in combination, to decrease the population. Knowing the limiting factors helps in management. It is usually not effective to try to improve populations without first identifying and correcting the limiting factors.

MAJOR LIMITING FACTORS AFFECTING WILDLIFE POPULATIONS

Several limiting factors affect wildlife populations. The most common are presented.

HABITAT LOSS

Wildlife habitat is the area that wildlife needs to perform daily, seasonal, and yearly activities. Habitat includes food, water, space, and cover. Habitat varies for different species. For gray squirrels, habitat is a dense forest with large trees that produce acorns or other nuts. Ducks need grasslands to nest in and wetlands to feed and rest in. Antelope need vast open prairies and mountain lions need broad expanses of rocky or brushy land.

11-4. Cultivation of crops is an important area of land use. (Intensive farming often destroys habitat and can be detrimental to wildlife.)

11-5. How land is used can cause wildlife populations to increase or decrease. (Courtesy, Oscar Warbach, Wildlife Management Institute)

11-6. Two contrasting situations—the top photo shows wetlands in a natural condition and the bottom shows wetlands that have been used for housing development. (The construction of homes resulted in habitat loss for wildlife.)

Land use is how humans use or treat land. Various land uses include factories, ball parks, crop production, livestock grazing, timber production, roads, homes, schools, power lines, dams, and digging canals and channels.

All land use affects wildlife in some manner. Some land use activities can result in total loss of wildlife habitat through *habitat destruction*. This often results in the elimination of those animals dependent on what naturally grew on the land for their existence. An example is the construction of a large reservoir in an area that originally supported a dense forest. Because of deep-water flooding by the new dam and eventual loss of all trees and shrubs, all dry-land wildlife species, such as deer, turkey, squirrels, and song birds, would lose their habitat. The end result of this complete habitat loss would be a population depletion.

Habitat loss is the single most important threat (limiting factor) to wildlife in the United States as well as the other areas of the earth.

HABITAT DEGRADATION

Following closely after habitat loss, the second most important factor impacting wildlife is habitat degradation. *Habitat degradation* is reducing quality of the habitat. It generally results in reduced wildlife populations, but if degradation is severe, total loss of populations can occur.

An example of habitat degradation is the removal of large trees in a forest. The loss of large, old den trees (cavities in trees used by small mammals and birds) along with reduced food production (acorns, nuts, fruits) causes wildlife populations to decline due to reduced nutrition, and quality and quantity of habitat (living space).

Moderate habitat degradation (loss of only a few large trees) generally results in moderate population reductions. However, there is a direct relationship between severity of degradation and animal abundance.

Habitat requirements are often quite different for individual species, even though they may live in the same area. As an example, woodpeckers live in forested areas, but depend on old or dead and dying trees that provide insects as a food source as well as nesting sites. Small mammals, such as shrews, moles, and mice, live on the forest floor and in small grassy openings. These small mammals may live their entire life in the area of an acre or less (roughly the size of a football playing field). The raccoon, living in the same forest area, requires shallow water in which to forage for crawfish, fish, insects, and other aquatic food items.

If the basics of habitat are present in sufficient quantity and quality, wildlife populations generally thrive. Removing even one of the basic elements can cause reduction or elimination of a population. As an example, woodpeckers would be placed under severe stress if deprived of old, dead, or dying trees. Loss of old trees would result in elimination of food and nesting sites. The resulting lack of food, shelter, and nesting cavities would cause the population to eventually disappear.

ACCIDENTS

Wildlife populations are susceptible to a wide range of accidents that remove a substantial number of animals from the population each year. Birds have a tendency to have flying

Wildlife Connection

PROPER WASTE DISPOSAL

Humans create much waste. Trash from our homes, factories, and farms can pollute wildlife habitat. Fortunately, ways of properly disposing of most wastes are readily available.

People sometimes wonder how materials can damage wildlife. A decoy is used here to show how the waste from the plastic packaging of six soft drink cans might slip over the bird's head. If the material were thrown down, there is the possibility that it might become entangled around the neck of a bird. The bird would be unable to lead a normal life. The photograph also shows that materials designed differently, but for the same purpose, do not pose the same hazard.

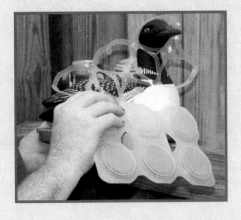

11-7. Thousands of wildlife animals are killed each year by automobiles and equipment. (This skunk lies dead in the middle of a highway.)

accidents. They sometimes crash into buildings, bridges, fences, and power lines, especially during cloudy or windy weather. There are many documented records of bird collisions with airplanes, and flocks of birds are sometimes hit by lightning.

Mammals crossing the road are susceptible to being killed by automobiles. Rabbits, deer, squirrels, skunks, opossums, porcupines, and coyotes are particularly vulnerable. Deer are commonly attracted by fresh vegetation to roadsides in late evening or at night. The deer, vulnerable to high speed road traffic, are temporarily blinded by headlights at night, which causes them to stop or run across the road.

Other accidents include getting caught in fences, drowning, falling from high places, and suffering injuries from fighting other animals of the same species.

OVERPOPULATION

All wildlife populations have a maximum numerical level at which they can comfortably live. That number is referred to as *carrying capacity*. More precisely, carrying capacity is the number of animals that a particular area can safely support. Big game animals, especially deer, provide an excellent example of carrying capacity.

As an example, a deer population of 100 animals living in a given area will have adequate food and cover to feed and maintain the entire population. If the population increases, there is less food and cover for each animal. If populations continue to increase and seriously deplete food and cover, carrying capacity has been exceeded. In

11-8. Overpopulation depletes habitat resources. (Too many water buffalo will result in hunger, disease, and other problems.)

most cases, the end result is reduced health due to malnutrition and eventual die-offs that may range from a few to many animals.

Overpopulation is a number that exceeds carrying capacity. This is a serious problem for wildlife managers. Once populations deplete food resources by over-utilization (consuming too much food), years may be required for food supplies to grow back to original abundance. Sometimes, vegetation is so severely damaged by overpopulation, it never recovers. As a result, wildlife populations disappear or never fully recover.

Controlled hunting is used to keep wildlife populations from exceeding carrying capacity. This involves using well-planned legal hunting to keep populations at proper numbers. Controlled hunting helps ensure healthy populations.

LACK OF WILDLIFE MANAGEMENT

Lack of wildlife management is a serious threat to all wildlife species. Management provides safeguards for wildlife populations and their habitat and offers solutions to problems. Proper management also prevents problems from arising. Management includes setting proper hunting seasons and bag limits for **game species** (species hunted for sport or food). Protection should be offered to **nongame species** (those that are not hunted).

Proper management provides for management of habitat and ensures adequate food, water, and cover for all species. Proper management actions are based on sound information and considers all limiting factors in decision making. Strict protectionism (setting land aside from all uses) often results in deteriorating habitat and reduction in wildlife populations if active wildlife management is not included.

11-9. Resource managers provide proper wildlife management by fitting all the pieces of the puzzle together. (Courtesy, Oscar Warbach, Wildlife Management Institute)

CAUSES OF POPULATION LOSSES

In each wildlife population, animals die each year from a wide assortment of ailments. These losses include old age, poor health and diseases, pollution, and predation.

11-10. Size and structure of antlers are factors in aging bull elk.

11-11. Observe the posture, alert eyes, fur quality, and behavior of a red fox in assessing health.

AGE

When animals reach advanced age, their body systems (heart, lungs, etc.) are less reliable. Animals become more susceptible to adverse weather, food shortages, diseases, and other conditions that seldom affect younger, more robust animals. Keeping a wildlife population continually at an adequate level requires the production of young animals. Animals of different ages are needed—some young, some mature, and some older. Those of reproductive ages assure a continuing population.

HEALTH

Health is the general body condition of an animal. Good health is characterized by efficient performance of life functions. Sometimes, these functions fail. Health becomes diseased.

Disease is any condition that disturbs normal body functions or structures. The nature of disease varies widely. In some cases, only one organ may be involved. At other times, the entire animal will show evidence of disease. Close observation of animals helps determine if disease is present.

This is often difficult with some animals because they want to keep a distance from people. It is important to know the normal behavior for a particular species.

Good health is indicated by an animal's behavior. Eating behavior is important—healthy animals eat! Shiny fur or coats, bright eyes, alert and content behavior, normal feces and urine, and normal reproduction are signs of good health. Animals that have dull coats, show a loss of weight, do not move about actively, and have sores on their bodies are not healthy. Closer examination may reveal a raised body temperature, difficulty breathing, lumps on their bodies, and rapid pulse rates.

11-12. This beechy ground squirrel appears to enjoy good health in its habitat of rock on the California coast.

Diseases may be contagious or noncontagious. Contagious diseases are spread from one animal to another. They may be caused by viruses, bacteria, fungi, or parasites. Noncontagious diseases may be due to poor nutrition, defects in tissues, or injuries caused by falls or scrapes against objects, attacks from other animals, or stray gun shots.

A **parasite** is an animal that lives in or on another animal. Parasites take their food from the blood or flesh of its host. Ticks, fleas, and mites are common external parasites. Internal parasites include grubs, tapeworms, heartworms, and roundworms.

Most animals (birds and mammals) carry a **parasite burden**. This means that individual animals have parasites. A small parasite burden means that the number of parasites and the damage caused is too low to affect an animal's health. A heavy parasite burden results in damage to an animal. Heavy parasite burdens result in weakened conditions and susceptibility to other diseases. Internal parasites are most common in the stomach, intestines, respiratory passages, and liver.

At low levels of infestation, most parasites are not life threatening. With some exceptions, **malnutrition** (lack of proper food) is most often the trigger that causes parasites to eventually further reduce the vigor of the animal resulting in death.

Like humans, all wildlife species suffer from various diseases. Some are diseases of the population and some are diseases of the environment. Diseases of the environment are generally found in the soil or water and are passed on to animals as they feed and drink. Botulism (food poisoning) is a deadly disease of the environment that can kill thousands of water birds, especially waterfowl, in the matter of only a few hours.

Avian cholera is a disease that affects birds—mostly ducks, geese, and other water-loving birds. Birds infected with the disease can spread the disease to other birds. Like botulism, avian cholera can kill thousands of birds in a very short time.

POLLUTION

Pollution is the presence of materials in an animal's environment that may cause harm. Most pollution results from human activity, though some is caused by natural events.

Food, water, cover (shelter), and space are the essential parts of a habitat for all animals. Animal populations prosper if the essential habitat components are present in sufficient quality and quantity. If elements of a habitat are polluted, animal health is threatened.

Many examples could be cited. Large fish kills result in streams when the water is polluted by toxic wastes from a factory or farm. Birds can fail to reproduce if certain pesticides are in their food chain.

PREDATION

Predation is the capture and consumption of one animal by another. The animals captured are prey. Those that do the capturing are predators. Predators are responsible for re-

Career Profile

WILDLIFE VETERINARIAN

Wildlife veterinarians care for the well-being of animal wildlife. They treat sick or injured wildlife and implement disease prevention programs to assure good health. The work is often outside, but can be in veterinary medical clinics. This photograph shows a veterinarian examining a sedated wolf in Canada before the wolf is moved to a new home in the United States.

Wildlife veterinarians need a degree in veterinary medicine. Most also have baccalaureate degrees in animal science, wildlife management, or biology. Veterinarians in research also usually have a doctorate degree in biology or a related area.

Most jobs are with government agencies that deal with wildlife. Some jobs are with research stations and universities. A few work with international agencies that transport wildlife. (Courtesy, U.S. Fish and Wildlife Service)

moving portions of prey populations (those that are killed and eaten) each year. The most notable predators are wolves, coyotes, and mountain lions. Other predators include crows, hawks, owls, eagles, foxes, and bobcats. Some cormorants (a species of bird) capture and consume hundreds of fish a year! Large populations of cormorants can destroy a fish population in a pond or lake.

Predators are important in the life cycles of all wildlife. Predators control populations to keep them in proper balance (proper numbers) and help keep them from exceeding carrying capacity. When prey animals are in great abundance, predators increase in numbers. Conversely, as prey species decline, predators also begin a decline as their food source is diminished.

11-13. A grizzly bear has captured a salmon as prey.

Hunting

Legal sport hunting is one of the most important management tools that wildlife managers (biologists) have available. Legal, controlled sport hunting, working in concert with the other limiting factors, can keep wildlife populations at proper numerical levels. Excessively high wildlife populations are a serious danger, just as excessively low populations are.

Illegal hunting is a potentially serious problem for numerically weak wildlife populations for which there are no legal hunting seasons. Although illegal hunting is frowned upon by society, it has little impact on numerically strong populations. Illegal hunting often has large fines and/or imprisonment.

MANAGEMENT ENHANCES POPULATIONS

Human activities have eliminated a number of wildlife species and greatly reduced others. Intensive farming eliminated habitat for many species, especially birds that nest on the ground in grassy cover. Intensive harvest of timber has reduced squirrel, deer, and turkey numbers. A few years ago, egrets and herons had been reduced as a result of killing large numbers of birds to provide feathers for the millinery trade (manufacture of hats with feathers).

The greatest threat to all forms of wildlife is habitat destruction. Human activities are encroaching into formerly remote lands where wildlife populations remained relatively secure. As towns and cities increase in size and the human population grows, wildlife is being pushed into smaller areas. Land is being used for purposes other than growing wildlife.

Around 1900, most authorities believed there was little hope for many wildlife species surviving beyond 1920. They gave many species only a 20 year survival span before extinction. This view failed to foresee the role of wildlife management.

A few examples of successful wildlife management programs are:

11-14. Populations of the pronghorn antelope have increased because of wildlife management programs.

- Pronghorn antelope—Around 1910, only about 13,000 antelope were living in Montana and Wyoming. After wildlife management actions, the current antelope population exceeds 750,000 in western states south to Texas.

- Bison—In 1895, fewer than 1,000 bison were surviving from numbers originally estimated in the millions. Currently, there is an estimated population in excess of 100,000 living on refuges, parks, and private ranches.

- Giant Canada geese—In 1954, biologists believed that the last of this race of geese had been lost. However, a few birds were discovered in a city park and on remote farms. Propagation programs (selective breeding) were set up. Young birds were released into the wild and special hunting seasons were initiated.

Currently, more than 100,000 of these birds exist and provide high levels of hunting recreation.

- White-tailed deer—In 1895, less than 500,000 deer existed in the United States and Canada. Deer had been eliminated by advancing civilization in most of their original range. Strict hunting regulations, coupled with live-trapping animals in areas of abundance and releasing them in areas of suitable habitat, have increased the population to over 15 million in the United States and Canada.

- Sea otter—In 1907, the sea otter was nearly extinct. Under scientific management, the current population is estimated at well over 100,000 animals along Pacific coastal waters of Alaska, British Columbia, Oregon, Washington, and California.

- Wood duck—In 1915, authorities considered the wood duck a candidate for extinction because of greatly reduced numbers. As a result of carefully regulated hunting

11-15. The Chincoteague National Wildlife Refuge provides a protected environment for wildlife to live and raise young, such as these Canada geese.

11-16. The bald eagle is an example of recovery of an endangered species.

and other management programs, the wood duck is abundant and provides important annual hunting opportunities.

- Bald eagle—Recovery of the bald eagle is one of the most recent success stories in regaining population. Populations of the bald eagle had declined so rapidly that the Bald Eagle Recovery Act was passed in 1940. The population continued to decline. This continued decline was felt to be due to several factors. The use of DDT and over-hunting have often been stated. Another factor was execution from power lines as their long wings bridged two wires. In the minds of some people, bald eagles were also killed by lead poisoning from hunter shots into game that eluded the hunter and later died. These were eaten by the eagles resulting in lead poisoning (three shot pellets can kill an eagle). In 1976, the bald eagle was listed as an endangered species. By 1999, the numbers had recovered and the bald eagle was no longer in danger of extinction.

Currently, wildlife management programs are aimed at preserving and maintaining all wildlife populations and all forms of habitat. Special emphasis is being placed on preserving wetlands and restoring and managing those that were drained for agriculture or because people originally thought they had no use or value.

Conservation agencies have set up programs to assist thousands of landowners with habitat improvement programs, often sharing the cost of these programs. Examples of these programs are growing food and cover or reflooding ponds or marshes that were drained earlier. At other locations, game species (especially deer and turkey) are live-trapped and transported to unoccupied habitat to start new populations.

At many locations, governmental agencies and citizens erect and maintain wood duck and blue bird nesting boxes that provide secure nesting sites for those species.

Public conservation education programs are routinely provided for school teachers and students. This is done to promote understanding of wildlife needs through literature and broadcast media.

Hunter education programs provide hands-on education, especially for young or inexperienced hunters. Most states currently have mandatory hunter education programs for young hunters. There are also expanding programs to protect both hunted and non-hunted species from illegal hunting.

Research has had a major role in wildlife recovery. It has been carried out to determine habitat needs, diseases, population trends, predator/prey relationships, reproduction, and wildlife-crop relationships. All information is used to formulate management programs aimed at providing sufficient protection to allow all wildlife populations to prosper. Under modern wildlife management, not a single legally hunted species has come under jeopardy and most have shown dramatic population gains.

REVIEWING

MAIN IDEAS

Animal wildlife populations are constantly changing. Population numbers are highest immediately after the breeding season when young have been added to the parent population. During the course of a year, numbers begin to drop and reach a low point just before the next breeding season. The number of animals in any population is the number of births minus the number of deaths. Birth adds numbers and death subtracts numbers.

Each year, some animals die from a number of causes, including old age, disease, parasites, accidents, pollution, predation, and hunting. The factors causing wildlife population to decline are called limiting factors.

Reproductive potential is the ability of individual wildlife populations to increase despite limiting factors that attempt to reduce population numbers.

When habitat is degraded, wildlife populations generally decline in numbers. Total loss of habitat results in total loss of those populations dependent on that particular habitat for survival. The single greatest threat to wildlife populations is habitat destruction caused by human activities.

Carrying capacity is the number of animals that can safely live in a given area. Each habitat has a limit to the number of animals the land can support. Overpopulation is a serious problem for wildlife populations.

There are many examples of how proper management has brought wildlife populations back from the brink of extinction. Today, those populations are numerically strong and have the capability of providing extensive hunting opportunities. Under modern wildlife management, not a single legally hunted species has been placed under jeopardy and most have shown dramatic population gains.

QUESTIONS

Answer the following questions using correct spelling and complete sentences.

1. What is population status? What are the major factors in population status?
2. What are the major limiting factors affecting animal wildlife populations?
3. What is habitat degradation?
4. What is the role of carrying capacity with animal wildlife?
5. What are the major causes of population losses?
6. What are important signs of good animal health?
7. What is parasite burden?
8. How does predation affect a wildlife animal population?
9. What are three wildlife species that have been rescued from very low population numbers by modern wildlife management?
10. What is the greatest threat to all forms of wildlife?
11. Why and how was the use of lead shot pellets a hazard to the bald eagle?
12. What has been the role of research in wildlife recovery?

EVALUATING

Match the term with the correct definition.

a. habitat destruction   e. health   i. parasite burden
b. limiting factor   f. disease   j. carrying capacity
c. land use   g. predation   d. game species
h. parasite

_____ 1. The capture and consumption of one animal by another.

_____ 2. Any condition that disturbs normal health.

_____ 3. A term used to describe the number of animals that can safely live at a given location.

_____ 4. How land is used by humans.

_____ 5. Actions that limit or have the potential to limit wildlife populations.

_____ 6. A species hunted for food or sport.

_____ 7. General body condition of an animal.

_____ 8. Parasites present on an animal.

_____ 9. An animal that lives in or on another animal.

_____ 10. The single most important cause of wildlife population depletions.

EXPLORING

1. Use the Internet to investigate the role of management in the recovery of a selected threatened species. A good source for the bald eagle is the American Bald Eagle site—www.baldeagleinfo.com/

2. Scan through old magazines or newspapers and clip pictures of various types of land use. Prepare a bulletin board or poster that shows how land use impacts wildlife populations. (Note: Be sure to use magazines or papers that are being discarded. Never take items from current issues in a library or classroom.)

3. Locate older citizens who live in your community and ask them to describe how land originally looked and how it was used when they were children. Ask them to describe what has happened to wildlife habitat in their lifetime. Prepare a written report on your findings.

4. Tour a wildlife research facility. Determine efforts underway to develop new ways of protecting animal wildlife. Prepare an oral report on your findings.

Part Four

Plant Wildlife Management

CHAPTER 12

Plant Biological Systems and Needs

OBJECTIVES

This chapter introduces plant biological systems and needs. The objectives of the chapter are:

1 List major kinds of plant wildlife and identify important species.

2 Identify major parts of a plant and explain the functions of each.

3 Describe the life cycles of plants.

4 Explain how plants reproduce.

5 Explain pest management.

TERMS

angiosperm
annuals
biennials
botany
conifer
cotyledon
dicot
deciduous

dioecious
fertilization
germinate
internode
monocot
monoculture
monoecious
node

ovules
perennials
pollen
pollination
reproductive stage
vascular plants
vegetative stage
zygote

12-1. Four popular wildflower plants are dogwood (top left), magnolia (top right), flame azalea (bottom left), and mountain laurel (bottom right). (Plants do more than just beautify our world—they convert carbon dioxide to oxygen and sunlight to food energy. Plants are the basis of the food chain.)

HOW many different kinds of plants are there? We see many different plants all around us. Each species has evolved to fill a different niche or serve a special purpose.

Think about your daily journey from home to school and back. How many different types of plants do you see? Most likely you pass by grasses, shrubs, and trees. If you live in a rural area, you also go by food crops and maybe wooded areas filled with an amazing array of different plants.

Understanding the plants in our world is important. We need to be able to identify important species and groups of plants. We also need to know the major parts of a plant, about plant life cycles, and how different plants reproduce. In addition, we need to know about basic plant pest management.

KINDS OF PLANTS

12-2. Bamboo is a giant grass. It has hollow stems as large as 1 foot (30 cm) across at the base and 120 feet (37 m) tall. There are about 700 species, with the one shown here being hedge bamboo *(Bambusa glaucescens).*

Plants fill important roles with both animal wildlife and humans. Plants are the basis of the food chain for all living things, even other plants. Human civilizations were built on the knowledge of different types of plants, their life cycles, and which parts were used for food, fiber, tools, dyes, shelter, and medicine. Animals also depend on plants for survival. The plant life in any area dictates which animals will call that area home.

The science of plants is called **botany**. As in other sciences, botanists have classified plants according to their characteristics. The following areas cover the major classifications of complex plants:

- monocots (50,000 species)
- dicots (200,000 species)
- conifers (450 species)
- cycads (65 species)
- ferns (10,000 species)
- horsetails (25 species)
- club mosses (1,100 species)
- psilophytes (3 species)
- liverworts, etc. (8,000 species)
- mosses (14,000 species)

ANGIOSPERMS

More than half of all living plants are classified as flowering plants or angiosperms. Most of these grow in the wild.

An **angiosperm** is a plant with enclosed seeds. Angiosperms are the highest forms of plant life. They are the most diversified and widespread on Earth. Their success, in comparison to other classes of plant life, is largely due to a more efficient reproductive process. Each flower usually contains both **pollen** (the male reproductive structure) and **ovules** (the female reproductive structure). **Pollination** can be completed by wind, by insects attracted to the flower, or even by the plant itself.

Angiosperms are in two broad categories: the **monocots** (or monocotyledons) and the **dicots** (or dicotyledons). Their names identify the difference between the two groups. As a rule, dicot seeds have two **cotyledons** (seedling leaves) when they first sprout or **germinate**. Monocot seeds contain only one cotyledon when they sprout.

Monocots and dicots are different in other ways, too. Dicot leaves may be all in one piece like the maple, compound like a cinquefoil, or deeply lobed like the dandelion. Monocot leaves have parallel veins, tend to be in one piece, are less varied in shape than dicots, and are less intricately edged.

Basic differences show up not only in the leaves and seeds, but also in the stems, roots, and flowers. Typical dicot stems have a center core, the pith, where food is sometimes stored; a woody portion containing the plant's plumbing system, the cortex, and the bark. The monocot stem is much simpler and often soft with vascular bundles scattered at random.

12-3. If this columbine flower is pollinated and fertilized, seeds will form, mature, and create new plants next season. (The columbine is Colorado's state flower.)

12-4. The long, thin gladiolus leaf is an example of a monocot leaf. The intricately shaped maple is an example of a dicot leaf.

Wildlife Connection

EXPLORING PINE CONES

Many people enjoy spending time in natural settings. Next time you are in an area that contains pine trees, see if you can locate cones on the trees and on the ground around the trees and compare them. Note the open cones versus those that are still closed. Try to find a cone that is just opening and still contains seeds. Also, watch for animals that might feed on the seeds, such as birds, squirrels, chipmunks, and other small animals.

This photograph shows a mother teaching her young son about pine cones.

12-5. A quaking aspen tree shimmers in a warm fall sun against a backdrop of conifers.

12-6. The tulip poplar tree has an appealing flower.

Dicot roots tend to be woody, while monocot roots, attached to nonwoody stems, may be extremely fibrous. Some monocots produce underground structures, such as bulbs or rhizomes, for reproduction and food storage. Dicot flowers generally have petals in groups of four or five, while monocot flowers have three petals or multiples of three.

Grasses are the most important monocots to wildlife. Deer, elk, and other browsing animals find sustenance in the leaves of grasses, while smaller animals, such as squirrels, chipmunks, and birds, often harvest the seeds these plants produce. Directly or indirectly, grasses constitute the main source of food for wildlife and humans alike.

Many dicots are also important to wildlife. The **deciduous** trees that green our forests in the summer and drop their leaves in the fall are all dicots, including the birches, maples, ashes, and hickories. In addition to providing a food supply, these trees also provide homes for many different species of animals. Birds nest in their branches and insects thrive in their bark. Squirrels, chipmunks, and other rodents flourish in deciduous trees, while deer and elk browse the tender shoots and buds.

CONIFERS

Another primary classification of wildlife plants is the conifers. A **conifer** typically has evergreen needles for leaves and produces cones. This class includes members of the pine, fir, cedar, and spruce families. They are so well-adapted to their environments that in the

300 million years since they first appeared on Earth, they have changed very little. They are among the most successful plants on Earth, populating about one-third of all existing forest areas. Where conditions are marginal for survival, such as in the Arctic, at high mountain elevations, and on desert borders, conifers are generally the last trees found.

Conifers produce their seeds in cones. A pine cone is really nothing more than a bunch of specialized, spore-bearing leaves or scales, concentrated into a tight stack. On each scale, one or two macrospores form. After fertilization, each macrospore will develop into a seed. The cone's structure of hard scales fitting closely in a spiral pattern protects the macrospores inside until the cone is mature.

When a cone is ripe, the tips of the scales separate and the seeds can be shaken out. Birds, rodents, and other animals count on this bounty of seeds as a food source. For example, pine seeds make up approximately 70 percent of the diet of three birds—the red crossbill, Clarke nutcracker, and white-headed woodpecker. Heavy consumption of pine and other coniferous seeds by wildlife has been known to reduce reproduction of the trees, especially during years when the crop is small. Conversely, a low seed yield may affect the size and population of many wildlife species, particularly rodents.

Another important feature of conifers is their distinct leaves. We often call these types of trees "evergreens" because most conifers stay green all year. Many, although not all, conifers can be recognized by their long, needle-like leaves, which usually grow in clusters. Each needle is a produc-

12-7. A mature loblolly pine has new vegetative growth, immature cones, and mature cones.

12-8. The cones on this pine tree have matured and shed their seeds. Notice how their scales are spread.

12-9. This pine tree has short needles.

tion unit in itself, converting carbon dioxide from the air into sugar that will nourish the plant. These small, thick-walled leaves are well-adapted to a variety of climates, from the moist tropics to the dry timberlines. Some needles are shed each year, but they usually stay on the tree until new needles are fully grown, thus creating the evergreen effect.

Conifers include about 550 species classified into seven families. Of these, the pine family is the best known, probably because of its abundance and its economic value. More than 75 percent of the lumber we use, and nearly 90 percent of paper pulp, comes from pine.

MAJOR PLANT PARTS

When you start noticing all the different kinds of plants, the variety can become bewildering. From those in our homes and backyards to the vast expanses of parks and forests, plants come in thousands of different sizes, shapes, forms, habits of growth, hardiness, and other characteristics.

Diverse as they are, plants conduct many of the same basic activities. And despite their great diversity, plants have an underlying similarity in construction. This plan or "plant blueprint" becomes evident when one looks deeper and discovers specialized cells that transport food, water, and minerals, or that provide mechanical support. Plants that have these specialized cells are called **vascular plants**. All flowering plants are vascular plants. Everything from palm trees to potatoes conforms to a similar structural plan.

THE PLANT BLUEPRINT

At their foundation, plants consist of an axis. One end of the axis becomes the root and the other end becomes a shoot. The shoot develops into stem and leaves. Together, the root and shoot form a whole unit, each with special roles. The root anchors the plant and absorbs water and minerals from the soil. The shoot, in turn, provides support, conducts water and other necessary compounds within the plant, and manufactures food.

Young stems or twigs are marked by nodes. A **node** is the place on a stem where a leaf or leaves are attached. Most stems have several nodes. The space between two nodes is an **internode**. At the base of most leaves in the angles between the leaves and the stems, buds can usually be found. Buds may grow into branches that duplicate the structure of the shoot to which they are attached. Buds that are found in the leaf axil are called lateral buds. The bud at the end of a shoot is called a terminal bud.

STAGES OF GROWTH

When plants are young, they grow rapidly by adding new tissue and storing food. This is called the **vegetative stage** of a plant's life. When a plant starts producing flowers, fruit, and seed, it enters the **reproductive stage**. Some plants, such as corn and beans, die after the reproductive phase. These plants are called **annuals**. In trees and other plants, the reproductive phase is followed by another vegetative phase. These plants are called **perennials**.

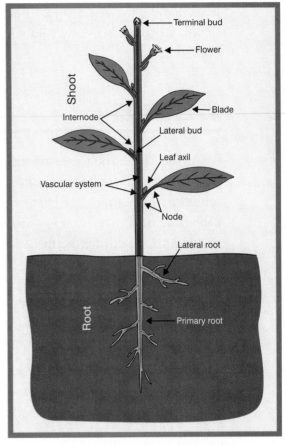

12-10. **Main parts of a vascular plant.**

PLANT LIFE CYCLES

Plants are often grouped according to their life cycle. The three categories are annuals, biennials, and perennials.

ANNUALS

Annuals are short-lived plants in which the entire life cycle, from germination to seed production, takes place in one growing season. Although they have relatively short

12-11. **The morning glory is an annual wildlife plant with an attractive flower.**

lives, many of the world's most useful plants, such as the cereal grains, peas, beans, and vegetables, are annuals. Many wildlife plants are also annuals, such as the morning glory and cocklebur.

BIENNIALS

As the name implies, a **biennial** has a two-year life cycle. Biennials do not normally bloom until the second season after the seed is planted. In the plant's second year, the plant sends up a leafy shoot bearing flowers and seeds. Many typical garden crops—beets, celery, cabbage, carrots, and turnips—are biennials. However, because most of these plants are harvested for food during the first season, the average gardener seldom sees them flower and mature.

PERENNIALS

Perennials live from year to year and have varying blooming periods. Perennials are generally divided into two categories—woody (trees, shrubs, and vines) or herbaceous. In temperate climates, the shoots of herbaceous perennials die to the ground after each growing season, but the plant's underground roots and stems survive and send up new shoots each spring. Many food and ornamental crops, including asparagus, rhubarb, peony, dahlias, and lupine, are herbaceous perennials. Most of the spring flowers in our woodlands and meadows are also perennial herbs. So are many of the desert flowers that spring up following a good rain.

12-12. Bison, as ruminants, convert the fiber of grass plants into starch, which is used for energy.

PLANT REPRODUCTION

Have you ever wondered why some plants can be grown from cuttings and others have to be grown from seeds? The key is whether the plant reproduces vegetatively or sexually. Many plants can reproduce either way.

VEGETATIVE REPRODUCTION

Vegetative reproduction is also known as asexual reproduction, vegetative propagation, or multiplication. Essentially, vegetative reproduction means plants can multiply in more ways than just by seed. Reproduction by vegetative methods happens extensively in nature and is also implemented widely by humans.

Artificial plant propagation generally involves separating a portion from the parent plant and growing it into a new plant. Almost every plant organ is capable of growing a new plant. However, many plants are designed to reproduce vegetatively and produce special structures for this purpose. Potatoes are one such plant. Each "eye" in a potato can become a new potato plant.

The ability to reproduce vegetatively occurs mostly in herbaceous and woody perennials. Some of the important structures that make this type of reproduction possible are runners (also called stolons), rhizomes, and horizontal roots. Runners, like those found on strawberry plants, send out shoots that touch the soil and produce roots at the nodes.

A rhizome is a thick, underground stem, which usually grows horizontally. Rhizomes can be distinguished from roots because they have nodes and internodes

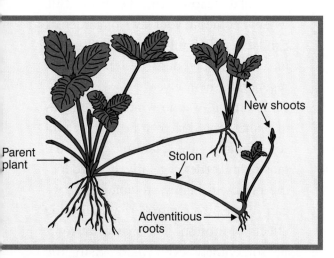

13. A sweet potato sends up shoots from several eyes. (The roots use the energy stored as sugars and starches in the sweet potato until they establish roots. Notice the tiny leaves as they begin to unfold.)

14. Vegetative reproduction in wild strawberry plants occurs when the parent plant develops runners, or stolons, which then put down roots and send up shoots.

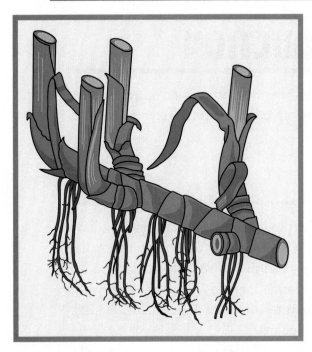

12-15. A rhizome with every node having roots.

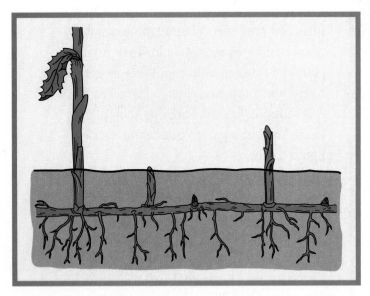

12-16. The horizontal roots of a Canada thistle send up new shoots, which will become new thistle plants. (This type of plant can spread quickly.)

and, sometimes, buds and scalelike leaves at the nodes. As a rhizome grows, it sends up new shoots from the nodes. These shoots become new plants. Each node also sends down roots to facilitate further growth and to support the shoots above the node. Many wild plants, ornamentals, and weeds spread in this manner. Most perennial grasses, poison ivy, cattails, sedges, water hyacinth, and native blueberries spread by rhizomes. These plants can spread rapidly and occupy great areas of land.

Plants like Canada thistle, dandelion, bindweed, and milkweed use horizontal roots to reproduce. The plant grows a horizontal root and then aerial stems develop along the root. These type of plants can be particularly hard to destroy. For example, if you try to dig a dandelion out of your lawn and a portion of the tap root is left in the soil, it will develop a horizontal root and, before long, new leaves appear above the ground. Thus, instead of destroying the dandelion, in all likelihood you will produce more by trying to remove it by digging it out. While this particular feature can be frustrating when it comes to your lawn or garden, it can be very helpful in nature because it means partially destroyed plants can regenerate themselves.

The rapid way in which these types of plants reproduce can be very helpful to humans. By planting perennial grasses and other vegetatively reproducing plants in highly erodible areas, we can begin to control the damaging effects of erosion. The masses of roots and below-ground stems help stabilize the soil, sometimes, even more than the above-ground parts of the plants, against the damaging effects of wind and water.

SEXUAL REPRODUCTION

Seed production is at the heart of sexual reproduction and is essential for most kinds of plants. It is also important for many species of animals that depend on the seeds for food.

Seeds are produced in flowers. Some plants produce perfect, or bisexual, flowers that contain both the stamen (male reproductive structure) and the pistil (female reproductive structure). Most plants have perfect flowers. Other plants produce imperfect, or unisexual, flowers containing either stamens or pistils, but not both. When the separate staminate and pistillate flowers are produced on the same plant, they are called **monoecious**. Wild rice is an example. When the two kinds of flowers are produced on separate plants, they are called **dioecious**. Buffalo grass is an example.

Although flowers come in many shapes, sizes, and colors, they all have common functions and parts. At the center of each bisexual flower is the female pistil. An ovary containing seeds forms the pistil's base. The top of the pistil will feature a varying number of stigmas that catch pollen released by the male stamens. Each stamen has two parts: the supporting filament and the pollen-producing anther. The stamens and the pistil are surrounded by varying numbers of petals that are, in turn, surrounded by the sepals. When the flower was a tiny bud, the sepals enclosed the entire, complex flower structure.

Beyond the showy petals of the flower, the parts that actually result in the formation of seed are the stamens and the pistils. The stamens form pollen grains. When the pollen grains reach the ovules during pollination, fertilization occurs and the ovule develops into a seed.

The critical feature in sexual reproduction is **fertilization**, which is when the male and fe-

12-17. A begonia plant has separate staminate and pistillate flowers, thus, it is classified as monoecious. The staminate, or male, flower is in the center.

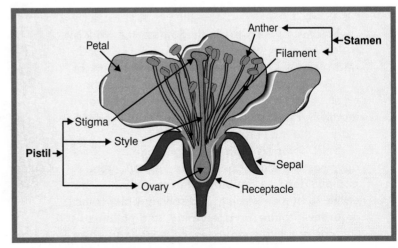

12-18. Main parts of a flower.

12-19. As bees gather nectar, a few pollen grains stick to them. They carry the pollen from an anther to a stigma and pollinate the flower. (Because bees visit many flowers, they pollinate several flowers with the pollen from other flowers.)

male sex cells join to form a **zygote**. In plants, zygotes are the equivalent of a fertilized egg in animals. It contains the genetic information from both parents and is the first cell of a new plant. The zygote grows into an embryo within the seed, and when the seed germinates, it becomes a plant.

Fertilization can only occur if pollen grains make their way to the stigma and down to the ovules. It is important to make a distinction between pollination, which is the transfer of pollen from the anther to the stigma, and fertilization, which is the fusion of the male and female sex cells.

Plants that reproduce via seed can be grouped into two pollination categories. In self-pollinating plants, the pollen in each flower can be used to pollinate that flower and other flowers on the same plant. Cross-pollinating plants, on the other hand, require pollen from another plant of the same or related species to achieve fertilization. Because of the greater diversity in the parent genetic material, cross-pollinating plants generally display more diverse offspring. This results in an

Career Profile

BOTANIST

Botanists work with plants. Some of the work is in laboratories; other work is outside in woods and meadows. Botanists develop new strains of plants by cross-breeding existing ones. Other botanists work in the field collecting samples and identifying species. Some split their time between work in the lab and field work.

Most botanists have a college degree in biology, botany, plant genetics, or related area. A botanist needs a genuine interest in plants, the ability to think abstractly and solve problems, an inquisitive nature, an open mind, and patience.

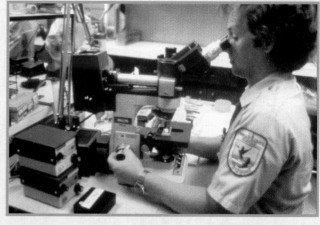

Jobs are with companies, colleges, and government agencies and in entrepreneurship. These jobs may involve extensive travel, particularly if studying plants or ecosystems that do not exist near the home work site. This shows a botanist using a microscope to study wildlife plant growth. (Courtesy, U.S. Fish and Wildlife Service)

increased ability to adapt to climate changes and new environments and gives cross-pollinating plants an evolutionary advantage.

Pollination can occur via several different mechanisms. Some plants rely on the wind to carry the pollen grains from the stamens to the pistils. Many grasses fall into this category. Other plants rely on insects, such as bees and butterflies, to carry the pollen from the stamens to the pistils. Although much less common, birds, snails, other small animals, and even water can transport pollen from one flower to another.

PEST MANAGEMENT

Nature has woven an intricate web of defenses against pests and disease. Humans have built on their knowledge of plants to develop tools to more efficiently control insect and weed pests and diseases. These tools include chemical weapons, mechanical means, and using natural plant and insect enemies.

Most plants can withstand some insect pressure and competition with other species for sunlight, water, and nutrients. In addition, all plants have structures or reactions capable of preventing fungus or bacteria from penetrating and attacking them. Plants struggling under poor growing conditions, often in places for which they are

20. A sign marks an area where pine beetles ꞁe completely destroyed the stand of trees. ꞁ surviving trees will likely have resistance ꞁhe beetles.

12-21. Many insects are beneficial! (This shows a wasp attacking a caterpillar pest.) (Courtesy, Agricultural Research Service, USDA)

12-22. Some plants can tolerate very dry conditions, such as these in an Arizona desert. (Among the plants visible here are yucca and prickly pear.)

ill-suited, are most often the ones attacked by most pests and diseases. Thus, nature has provided a way to keep each species in the areas for which they are best suited.

In addition, nature has provided a way to keep insects in balance. When one insect feeds or otherwise kills another insect known to damage crops, it can be introduced to fields as a natural way to manage pests. For example, *Trioxys* wasps are used to destroy spotted alfalfa aphids. The wasps lay their eggs in the aphids, mortally injuring the aphids. Another widely used natural predator is the green lacewing. These insects feed on a wide variety of aphids and can significantly reduce the aphid population in a given area.

Insects can also be used to control undesired plants. A weed-feeding beetle, imported to the United States from Europe, is helping destroy the Klamath weed in the western United States. The weed was, itself, accidentally imported from Europe. Without its natural enemies to keep it in check, the weed grew out of control.

The natural world was designed with a delicate balance and human interference can often produce unintended consequences. For example, when plants, such as rubber trees, grow widely spaced in the jungle, they are not particularly affected by leaf blight. However,

12-23. Benches in a nursery have experimental varieties of pine trees that are being studied for disease resistance.

when many plants are concentrated in a small area, such as on a plantation, the trees may be decimated. The same thing can happen with insects. **Monoculture** (a large area growing a single plant, such as a crop field) does not usually occur in nature. When humans artificially create monocultures, many of a plant's best defenses, such as natural insect enemies, are no longer viable because pest populations can grow out of control in these artificial food-rich environments. When this happens, humans turn to chemical, mechanical, and other means to control pests. In general, the goal is generally to manage pests rather than exterminate them, which is virtually (not to mention economically) impossible.

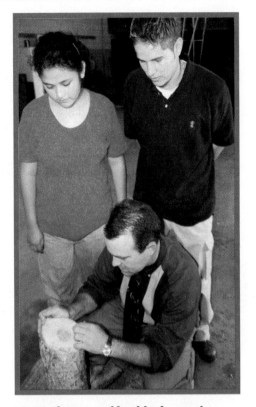

12-24. The age and health of a tree is determined by counting and assessing the size of annual rings in a cross-section of the trunk. Narrow annual rings indicate poor growth, which is likely the result of disease or insect damage, water shortage, or an environmental problem.

REVIEWING

MAIN IDEAS

Plants are the basis of the food chain for all living things, even other plants. Habitat management often involves promoting plant growth.

The science of plants is called botany. More than half of all living plants are classified as flowering plants or angiosperms. These plants are split into two broad categories—monocots and dicots—according to the number of seedling leaves they produce.

Conifers, also known as evergreens, are another important type of plant to both humans and animals. Conifers produce their seeds in cones and have needle-like leaves. These plants are well-adapted to a wide variety of climates from the moist tropics to the dry timberlines.

All plants consist of an axis. One end of the axis becomes a root and the other end becomes a shoot. The shoot develops into stem and leaves.

Plants are often grouped according to life cycles. Annuals are short-lived plants that complete their entire life cycle in one growing season. Biennials have a two-year life cycle. Perennials live from year to year and have varying blooming periods.

Plants can reproduce via vegetative or sexual reproduction mechanisms. Some important structures in vegetative reproduction include runners, rhizomes, and horizontal roots. Sexual reproduction requires seed production. Seeds are produced in flowers. The female pistil contains an ovary at its base. The male stamen sheds pollen grains. When the pollen grains reach the ovules, fertilization occurs.

Nature has woven an intricate web of defenses against pests and disease. Humans have built on their knowledge of plants to develop tools to more efficiently control insect and weed pests and diseases. These tools include chemical methods, mechanical means, and using natural plant and insect enemies.

QUESTIONS

Answer the following questions using correct spelling and complete sentences.

1. What is botany?

2. What is an angiosperm?

3. What are the two categories of angiosperms?

4. What classification do pine, fir, and spruce trees fall into?

5. What are the three life cycles of plants?

6. What two types of reproduction do plants use?

7. What function do rhizomes fulfill?

8. What are the major male and female parts of a flower?

9. What is the difference between pollination and fertilization?

10. What are three methods of pest management?

EVALUATING

Match the term with the correct definition.

a. angiosperms   e. fertilization   i. pollination
b. botany   f. internode   j. angiosperm
c. cotyledon   g. monoculture
d. dioecious   h. conifer

_____1. The fusion of male and female sex cells.

_____2. A plant with evergreen needles and produces cones.

_____3. The space on a stem between nodes.

_____4. Large areas of a single plant species.

_____5. Flowering plants.

_____6. A plant that produces enclosed seed.

_____7. Seedling leaves.

_____8. Male and female flowers are produced on separate plants of the same species.

_____9. The science of plants.

_____10. The transfer of pollen from the anther to the stigma.

EXPLORING

1. Count the different wildlife plants you pass on your way to and from school. See how many you can identify and classify.

2. To see the difference between monocots and dicots, sprout bean seeds and corn seeds. Corn is a monocot; beans are dicots. As each plant emerges from its seed, you will be able to see how the plant structures differ. To complete this activity, you will need a few corn seeds, a few bean seeds, a shallow container, paper towels, water, and a warm, sunny location, such as a window sill. Moisten the paper towel and place one layer in the bottom of your container. Place several corn seeds in a row on one side of the container. Place several bean seeds on the other side of the container. Place another moistened paper towel on top of the seeds and press down gently. Place the container in the location of choice. Check the container daily and keep the paper towels moistened. You may need to leave a little water standing in the bottom of the container to keep the seeds moist throughout the day and overnight or over a weekend. The seeds will sprout in 7 to 14 days, depending on temperature and moisture.

3. To see vegetative reproduction in action, grow a potato plant from an "eye." First cut a potato into pieces, making sure that each piece has at least one eye. Then, plant each piece in a 4-inch container of potting soil. Cover the potato piece with approximately one inch of soil. Water the planting and place it in a warm, sunny location. In 7 to 14 days, a new potato plant will emerge. If you want it to produce potatoes, you'll need to transplant it into the ground in the spring so it has plenty of root space in which to grow.

CHAPTER 13

Wildflowers

OBJECTIVES

The role and importance of wildflowers will be addressed in this chapter. The objectives of the chapter are:

1 Distinguish between a wild flowering plant and a wildflower.

2 Explain benefits of wild flowering plants to animal wildlife and the environment.

3 Explain how wildflowers are grown.

4 Describe how areas can be managed to promote wildflower growth.

TERMS

dormant	insecticide	pruning
escape cover	lime	seed
fertilizer	nectar	wildflower
fruit	nesting cover	wild flowering plant
herbicide	pest	

13-1. Wildflowers are important to insects, such as the monarch butterfly.

FLOWERING plants are the most numerous, varied, and important of the entire plant kingdom. More than 150,000 species of flowering plants have been identified worldwide by plant specialists. Many of these grow as wildflowers.

Brightly colored flowers are found in wild and open places as well as urban areas where their colors and odors are widely appreciated. Except in very cold areas, wildflowers are common throughout the year. They are especially abundant at nearly all locations in early spring after the end of winter weather. Spring, summer, and fall each have species that bloom.

Flowering plants provide food for both wildlife and humans. Bees visit wildflowers for nectar. Humans find the blossoms pleasing and schedule vacations when the flowers are blooming. Highway departments now plant them to add beauty to the roadside. Flowering plants provide a multitude of materials ranging from building materials to medicines.

WILD FLOWERING PLANTS AND WILDFLOWERS

Wild flowering plants are found nearly everywhere on Earth. A **wild flowering plant** is a plant that grows naturally without human effort. Such plants are not domesticated. They grow and reproduce on their own and have important roles with animal wildlife. Wild flowering plants range from the tiny "mouse ear" to giant pine trees. A broad group of wild flowering plants of special appeal to humans are the wildflowers.

13-2. The blossom of a "mouse ear" day flower plant is scarcely more than a half-inch in diameter. (These plants grow in moist, shaded areas of temperate climates.)

A **wildflower** is a plant that grows wild, untended and without cultivation. Wildflowers have special appeal to humans because of their blossoms, leaf color, or appealing quality. Wildflowers are sometimes planted to assure that they grow in areas of special interest. Daisies, sunflowers, dogwoods, and mountain laurel are examples of wildflowers that are often planted.

Not all wild flowering plants are listed as wildflowers. Some wild flowering plants do not have observable flowers or do not have attractive qualities that appeal to people. Only those that have special appeal are wildflowers.

BENEFITS OF WILD FLOWERING PLANTS

Wild flowering plants provide for the needs of animal wildlife and the overall quality of the earth's ecosystems. Several benefits of wild flowering plants are covered.

Jewel Weed
(Impatiens capensis)

Rosebay Rhododendron
(Rhododendron maximum)

Common Morning Glory
(Ipomoea purpurea)

Sourwood
(Oxydendrum arboreum)

Showy Evening Primrose
(Oenothera speciosa)

Running Pine (Ground Pine)
(Lycopodium flabellaform)

Blackberry
(Rubus alleghaniensis)

Wild (Indian) Strawberry
(Fragaria virginiana)

13-3. Examples of wildflowers including common and scientific names.

13-4. Wildflowers growing as a natural stand on a Texas hillside. (Courtesy, Texas Parks and Wildlife Department)

FOOD FOR WILDLIFE

Wildflowers serve as food for many animal species. Practically all animals eat vegetation. Some animals prefer roots and tubers while others eat stems, leaves, and various seeds and fruits.

Few wildlife species actually seek out and consume flowers. Most wait and consume products of those flowers—nectar, fruit, and seeds. As part of the reproduction of plants, flowers assure future generations of plants for vegetation and other materials.

Stems and Leaves

Stems and leaves are important parts of plants. They make it possible for photosynthesis and other processes to be carried out. These processes result in energy for the plant and other living organisms.

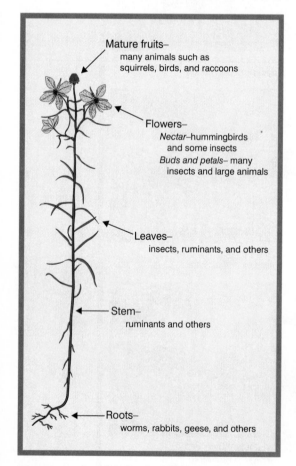

Mature fruits—
many animals such as squirrels, birds, and raccoons

Flowers—
Nectar–hummingbirds and some insects
Buds and petals– many insects and large animals

Leaves—
insects, ruminants, and others

Stem—
ruminants and others

Roots—
worms, rabbits, geese, and others

13-5. Examples of animal wildlife that feed on various parts of flowering wild plants.

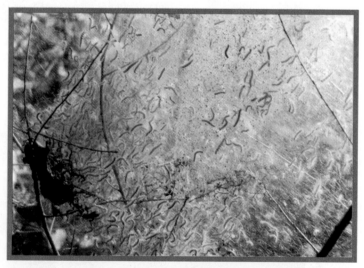

13-6. The larvae form of tent caterpillar moths (*Malacosoma americanum*) causes serious damage by eating the leaves of trees, such as cherry and gum, and other plants. (The larvae form a silk web or tent that covers the area where they eat.)

Stems and leaves are food for many animals. Tiny worms eat leaves. Deer eat small stems and leaves. In one way or another in the food chain, all life depends on stems, leaves, and other plant parts.

Buds and Flowers

Buds and flowers are foods for many species. Some prefer the developing flower bud. Others prefer flower petals, sepals, and other structures. Insects can inflict serious damage on some flower buds as well as on the flowers.

Many flowers have nectar. **Nectar** is a sugary secretion of flowers. The nectar is secreted by tissues known as nectaries. These tissues are present in many flowers and are sometimes found in other places on flowering plants.

With some animal species, nectar is used as food or to make food. Birds and insects usually get the nectar without harming the flower. Hummingbirds feed exclusively on nectar produced by flowers but consume no flower parts. Some insects, such as butterflies, feed on the nectar. Others, such as the honeybee, use nectar to make food.

13-7. A female ruby-throated hummingbird gathers nectar from a flower.

Fruit and Seed

Many animals eat the fruit and seed of trees. These form following flowers. In fact, the parts and processes of flowers result in the formation of fruit.

Fruit is a fleshy structure that results from a mature ovary. Most fruit contains seed. Fruit varies widely in shape and structure. Some are small, such as huckleberries and blackberries. Others are

13-8. The bright red fruit of the flowering dogwood (Cornus florida) matures in the fall several months after spring flowering. (The fruit, or drupe, contains two seeds and is food for wild birds and other animals.)

13-9. A white-tail deer is eating the fruits of a huckleberry plant.

somewhat larger, such as cherries and wild grapes. The largest fruits are the Osage orange, pine cones, and apples. Some are soft, such as mulberries. Others have a hard covering or shell, such as acorns and walnuts. Some fruit is shaped into pods, such as wild peas, and some into seed structures that are easily dispersed, such as the dandelion or cocklebur.

A **seed** is a container of new plant life. Seeds are formed in the ovaries of plants following fertilization. Seeds are high in nutrients because of the need of new plants as seeds germinate and grow. Many animals use seed as a primary food. Birds, squirrels, and many others eat seed.

How do animals relate to plants? Bears are commonly thought of as being carnivorous (meat eaters) but they are actually omnivorous in that their diet consists of both plant and animal materials. Bears are very fond of berries and fruits and as a result, vegetation makes up an important part of their yearly diet.

Wildlife Connection

BEWARE THE POISON IVY!

Some wild flowering plants are poisonous. Learn the plants in your area. Know those that have juices, seeds, or other parts that can cause injury or disease.

Poison ivy (*Rhus radicans*) grows in many areas of the United States. It is usually as a vine on trees or spread over the ground. The leaves of poison ivy consist of three leaflets attached to a main steam. This helps identify the plant and distinguish it from others that are not poisonous. Small green flowers grow on the stem where the leaves are attached. Afterward, small, whitish berry-like fruit may form.

The tissues of poison ivy contain an oil that can result in an itchy skin irritation and blisters. Avoid contact with the plant. If you do accidentally touch it, wash immediately with plenty of soap and water. Some herbicides are effective in controlling it on a small scale.

This shows how poison ivy grows on a tree trunk and the shape of its leaflets.

Deer, squirrels, turkeys, ducks, and wild hogs are especially fond of acorns and make special efforts to seek out this food item. Many other animal species, especially birds, feed almost exclusively on small seeds produced by flowering plants. This group includes mourning doves, quail, and many duck species.

Animals sometimes cause losses to crop producers. In large numbers, these animals can be pests. Raccoons may attack mature ears of corn. Opossums are known for their fondness for ripe persimmon fruits, and coyotes love ripe watermelons. Squirrels eat pecans and are disliked by pecan growers because these small animals can consume large numbers of valuable pecans and reduce profit to the farmer.

Roots

Roots are the underground structures of plants. They anchor the plant, take up moisture and nutrients, and store food a plant has made. This stored food makes roots particularly desirable to some wildlife animals.

Some species, especially geese, grub and dig for succulent plant roots and tubers (potato-like portions of roots). Wild geese are also fond of peanuts and feed in agricultural fields looking for peanuts left after harvest.

COVER

Flowering plants provide necessary cover for various wildlife species. Cover is the vegetation thick enough to allow animals to safely perform their daily, seasonal, or yearly activities.

Ground nesting birds must have ample *nesting cover*. This is vegetation that allows concealment against predators while the female is egg laying and incubating her eggs. Most female birds are brownish—drab in color. Nature provides this color pattern to allow them to better remain hidden in their nesting cover to avoid disturbance, possible egg loss, or loss of the female to predators. As a general rule, the taller and more dense the nesting cover, the more secure the nest.

Escape cover is needed by all wildlife species. This is a form of vegetation sufficiently dense to allow an animal to escape

13-10. Daisies provide cover for a mule deer fawn. (The white flowers and white spots on the fawn camouflage the animal.)

13-11. A brightly colored butterfly blends in with the color of a sunflower.

13-12. Kudzu *(Pueraria lobata)* **rapidly grows long vines that virtually stop soil erosion on a hillside or road bank.**

danger. To a cottontail rabbit, escape cover might be thick brush and briars where the animal can run a short distance and blend in among the vegetation. Escape cover for a whitetail deer is generally a screen of brush or trees that allows the animal to move away unseen from danger.

OTHER BENEFITS

Wild flowering plants have many other benefits. A few examples are:

- Protect soil—Wild flowering plants protect the soil by preventing erosion. Roots and material from dead plants cover the ground and keep wind and water from carrying away soil particles. Some have been planted especially to protect the soil. Kudzu, for example, covers many eroded hillsides and prevents further soil loss.

- Clean the environment—Wild flowering plants help by removing harmful substances from the environment. They may take carbon dioxide and other pollutants from the air, and, in some cases, release them in desirable forms. Some have special qualities in removing pollution from the soil. A few take heavy metals from the soil and reduce soil pollution.

- Economic value—Some wild flowering plants are used to make products of value to people. Cane may be used to make fishing poles or weave baskets. Palmetto may be used to make fans and other woven products. Some vines are used to make decorative wreaths and other display materials.

- Food for humans—A few wild flowering plants produce berries, nuts, and other products used for human food. Wild blackberries and hickory nuts are two examples. Many people enjoy going into wooded or natural areas in search of these foods. (Of course, never go "hunting" for berries and nuts on restricted land. Private land that has been posted is off-limits without permission of the owner. Government owned lands are also off limits unless permission has been officially granted.)

GROWING WILDFLOWERS

Wildflowers come in many colors, sizes, and shapes. Some flowers are so small they must be observed with a magnifying glass, while some tropical flowers grow to 3 feet in diameter. Most flowers have a fragrance that attracts insects and birds to aid in pollination. Flower fragrance ranges from pleasant to very unpleasant. Some plants have fragrances that are undetectable by humans.

Flowers vary greatly at different locations. Each flower is designed to fit a particular set of growing circumstances. As an example, flowers growing in a cool alpine meadow of the Rocky Mountains are quite different from those growing in sub-tropical regions of southern Florida or those growing in the desert southwest.

Most wildflowers are either annuals or perennials. Annual wildflowers are those that live one growing season. Typically, annual wildflowers come up in the spring, grow and flower in the summer, and die in the fall. They grow again the next year from seed produced in earlier growing seasons. Perennial wildflowers continue their life span for several years from the original roots established when the plant first sprouted from the earth.

13-13. Wildflowers have been planted in the median of this North Carolina highway.

13-14. The oxeye daisy (*Chrysanthemum leucanthemum*) is an often planted wildflower throughout the United States and Canada.

ANNUALS

Annual plants usually re-seed themselves. Annual plants generally produce an abundance of seeds in late summer or fall. Mature seeds fall to the ground where they remain until good growing conditions return. Most annual plants germinate in the spring, but when poor conditions occur, seeds can remain in the soil for several years before they sprout and create living plants exactly like the original parent plant.

Many of the weeds in cultivated crops, such as wheat, corn, rice, and peanuts, are annuals. A number of the brightly colored wildflowers and grasses are annuals. The morning glory is a weed with an appealing flower that can create big problems in crops.

Areas where wildflowers are desired may be artificially seeded. The area to be planted is typically cleaned of any old plants and brush. The soil is lightly tilled, fertilized, and seed are planted. In areas where erosion is likely, the soil may be covered with straw or weed-free hay. Wildflower seed are available from commercial seed stores. Many areas along highways have been planted to annual wildflowers. In some cases, the wildflowers produce adequate seed for the next year. This means that it is not always necessary to plant an area each year. Table 13-1 lists a few examples of common wildflowers.

Career Profile

ENVIRONMENTAL EDUCATOR

Environmental educators plan and deliver programs to educate people about the environment. They often speak to groups of children, youth, and adults. Skills in organizing and making presentations are essential. They must also know about the living and nonliving ecosystems where they work. This shows an environmental educator explaining the structure of part of a cross-section of a pine tree—a flowering plant!

Environmental educators need a college degree in environmental science, agricultural education, agricommunication, or a related area. The education should include areas of written and broadcast media as well as teaching skills.

Most jobs are with agencies involved in conservation education or private industry, such as large paper companies.

Table 13-1. Examples of Common Wildflowers

Common Name	Scientific Name	Life cycle/type
Bachelor's button	Centaurea cyanus	Annual/forb
Black-eyed susan	Rudbeckia hirta	Perennial or biennial/forb
Common sunflower	Helianthus annus	Annual/forb
Dandelion	Taraxacum officinale	Annual/forb
Flowering dogwood	Cornus florida	Perennial/small tree
Golden asters	Chrysopsis mariana	Perennial/forb
Horse nettle	Solanum carolinense	Perennial/forb
Jimpson weed	Datura stramonium	Annual/forb
Morning glory	Ipomoea trichocarpa	Annual/vine
Multiflora rose	Rosa multiflora	Perennial/shrub
Oxeye daisy	Leucanthemum vulgare	Perennial/forb
Plains coreopsis	Coreopsis tinctoria	Annual or perennial/forb
Prickly pear	Opuntia humifusa	Perennial/succulent
Rocky Mountain columbine	Aquilegia caerulea	Perennial/forb
Wild strawberry	Fragaria virginiana	Perennial/stoloniferous
Yucca	Yucca flaccida	Perennial/nonwoody

PERENNIALS

Perennial plants are generally long-lived. Many perennial plants shed their leaves and become **dormant** during fall and winter. A dormant plant goes through a time of rest when little or no growth occurs. They sprout new leaves and continue growth again in the spring from the same roots and branches. Some perennial plants, especially those in warmer regions continue to grow through fall and winter and some even produce flowers in December and January. Perennial plants produce seeds and fruits. New plants are commonly formed when those mature seeds and fruits drop to the ground and germinate. Some trees and shrubs have brightly colored flowers and grasses.

13-15. Small packets of wildflower seed are available for planting in the backyards of homes. Always select species adapted to your climate.

13-16. The blossoms on black-eyed susan plants are commonly seen along roadsides in some parts of the United States.

Perennials are planted as seed, root structures, or living plants. Once established, the plants will likely live for several years. Root structures are used for propagating various kinds of lilies, yucca, and several common wildflowers. Large masses of perennial lilies are planted along some highway right of ways.

Wildflower trees and shrubs are transplanted to the location where desired. This is typically done in the late fall, winter, or early spring, depending on the climate. In some locations, inadequate water in the summer makes it difficult to get transplanted trees to live.

MANAGING WILDFLOWER HABITAT

Some individuals, groups, and government agencies have programs to maintain or increase wildflowers for the public enjoyment, wildlife benefits, and improved agricultural output. The management of wildflowers involves activities similar to growing farm crops.

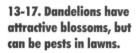

13-17. Dandelions have attractive blossoms, but can be pests in lawns.

OBTAINING SEED

Seed may be bought from commercial sources or saved from one year to the next. Good, pure seed should be used. If not, a poor stand of wildflowers will be the likely result.

Agencies, forestry companies, individuals, and others collect wildflower seed. Some highway departments collect large volumes of wildflower seeds and store them to be eventually spread along roadsides to provide color for travelers in spring and summer. These are mainly annual plants that reproduce from year to year by relying on annual seed production. Mowing is generally discouraged until after wildflowers have matured and dropped their seeds. This ensures a crop of plants the following year.

Wildflower plants may be planted to provide forage for wildlife. Homeowners often maintain flowering plants to attract and feed hummingbirds. Beekeepers promote large fields of flowering plants, such as clover. This allows bees to collect and store nectar to eventually be sold commercially for human consumption. Hunters and other wildlife enthusiasts often plant sunflowers, winter rye grass, peas, honeysuckle, and other plants to provide food for various wildlife species.

13-18. Parks, nature trails, and other public facilities ban the picking of wildflowers.

PRUNING

Perennial wildflowering shrubs and trees in special locations, such as near a home, may need pruning. **Pruning** is cutting off limbs and branches to assure the plant has the desired shape. Dead or diseased limbs are also removed. Most wildflowering perennials are not pruned but allowed to grow naturally.

In most trees and shrubs, flowers and fruits are produced on new growth at the tips of limbs. Pruning is an excellent way to increase production of flowers and fruit. Late fall or early winter is the ideal time to cut away unwanted limbs and give shape to trees. Pruning is not widely used with wild flowering perennials except in special locations, such as near power lines or buildings.

Fire can be a tool for gaining prairie flowers. Late winter or early spring burning removes old or dead growth and provides space for seeds to sprout, grow into adult plants, and complete their flowering process. Prairies that have been properly burned often produce a brightly colored landscape that provides much needed food and cover for wildlife.

Using Soil Additives

With small wildflower plots, it is a good idea to have a sample of soil analyzed. This will indicate the kind and amount of *fertilizer* and lime to use. Fertilizer is any substance used to add plant nutrients to the soil. Most fertilizer used with wildflowers is in a dry, pelleted form. *Lime* is a soil additive used on soils that are high in acid. Some wildflowers grow best in soils that are not acidic. The form to apply is known as agricultural lime—a product usually made of crushed limestone high in calcium. Without adequate nutrients in the soil, most wildflowers will fail to grow properly.

Controlling Pests

In some cases, wildflowers must be protected from pests. A *pest* is a plant or animal that is growing where it is not wanted or is causing damage. Pests cause injury or loss to wildflowers. Insects and weeds are common pests.

Insects may attack the plants. An appropriate insecticide or biological control should be used. An *insecticide* is a chemical product used to control insect pests. If not, large numbers of insects will quickly eat a small plot of wildflowers.

Having a pure stand of the desired species is important. Unwanted plants sometimes grow in wildflower areas. These should be controlled by cutting, pulling, or spraying with a

13-19. This caterpillar has eaten the leaves, leaving only stems.

13-20. Honeysuckle (*Lonicera japonica*) is a common wildflower that grows as a vine, has an attractive fragrance, and produces considerable nectar.

13-21. Joe-pye-weed (*Eupatorium purpureum*) is an appealing wildflower often seen in the fall along roadsides in the Eastern two-thirds of the United States.

herbicide. A ***herbicide*** is a chemical product used to control undesirable plant vegetation. Herbicides should be selected properly. Using the wrong herbicide can kill the desired wildflowers! Several precautions should be followed. Always use only approved insecticides and herbicides. Use these materials properly and only when needed. Avoid polluting streams and ponds. Do not spray materials on plants susceptible to injury.

REVIEWING

MAIN IDEAS

Flowering plants are the most numerous, varied, and important of the plant kingdom. Wild flowering plants produce flowers and grow naturally without aid from humans. Those that are admired for their special beauty are known as wildflowers. They are found in wild and open places as well as urban areas. Their colors and fragrances help create a special human fondness for them.

Wildflower plants vary widely and come in many different shapes and sizes. The parts of wild plants include roots, stems, leaves, flowers, fruit, and seed. Some flowers are so small they must be observed with a magnifying glass, while others may grow up to 3 feet in diameter. The petals are generally the largest part and most often are brightly colored.

Most wildflowers are in one or two groups: annuals and perennials. Annuals complete a life cycle in one year. Perennials live for several years.

Flowering plants are important to animal wildlife. These plants provide food and cover. Practically all animal species eat vegetation. Some eat roots, others eat stems, leaves, and various flowers, seeds, and fruits. Plants provide cover for ground nesting birds and allow females to remain hidden while laying and incubating eggs. Plants also provide escape cover which allows animals to avoid danger.

Most wildflowers grow without aid from humans. Some are planted to assure the beauty in desired locations. Hunters and other wildlife enthusiasts often plant sunflowers, peas, honeysuckle, and other plants to provide food and cover for various wildlife species. Some roadways are planted with wildflowers to add beauty for travelers in spring and summer.

QUESTIONS

Answer the following questions using correct spelling and complete sentences.

1. What is a wild flowering plant? Wildflower?

2. What are the benefits of wild flowering plants?

3. How is nectar important to insects?

4. How are seed and fruit important to animal wildlife?

5. What is the role of wild flowering plants in providing cover?

6. How are annual wildflowers grown?

7. How are perennial wildflowers grown?

8. What management practices may be needed to assure the growth of wildflowers?

9. What are two examples of annual wildflowers? List both common and scientific names.

10. What are two examples of perennial wildflowers? List both common and scientific names.

EVALUATING

Match the term with the correct definition.

a. wildflower   d. seed   g. dormancy
b. nectar   e. nesting cover   h. fertilizer
c. fruit   f. escape cover

_____1. A chemical added to soil to promote plant growth.

_____2. A time of rest when little growth occurs.

_____3. A wild flowering plant with appealing flowers.

_____4. A sweet liquid produced by some flowers.

_____5. A container of new plant life, including food to support the germination of the new plant.

_____6. A fleshy structure on some plants that is formed by the mature ovary and that contains seed.

_____7. Plant vegetation sufficiently dense to allow an animal to hide.

_____8. Plant vegetation that allows birds to hide from predators to reproduce.

EXPLORING

1. Obtain a packet of wildflower seeds available through local plant nurseries or mail-order catalogues. Follow instructions and plant seeds at a location that can be viewed over time. Record planting date, plant emergence date, and date of maximum flowering.

2. Visit a plant nursery during spring and compile a list of annual and perennial wildflowers that are for sale. Record the price and growing information that is available.

3. Locate a rural or semi-rural location where wildflowers bloom. Use a resource person to help identify the wildflowers. Take a field trip around the school grounds and note any wildflowers that are growing. Identify the plants by common and scientific names. (Information on wildflowers is available from the Cooperative Extension Service or a state natural resources agency.)

CHAPTER 14

Native Forests

OBJECTIVES

This chapter introduces the importance of native forests, including important species, forest regions, animal wildlife habitat, and simple management techniques. The objectives of the chapter are:

1 Explain the importance of native forests.

2 Describe the physical structure of a forest.

3 Describe how trees are named and identified.

4 Name the major forest regions of the United States.

5 Explain the relationship of forests to animal wildlife.

6 Describe management practices with forests.

TERMS

canopy
commercial forest
crown
forest
forester
monoculture

native forest
old-growth forest
regrowth forest
seedling
selective cutting
silviculture

story
tree
trunk
urban forest

14-1. Young foresters are using a compass in studying woodland.

Vast forests once covered the North American continent. This valuable natural resource helped make the growth of our nation possible. Today, millions of acres are still in forests and many of these continue to grow native species.

The availability of quality timber was one of the major factors that eventually led to the colonization of the United States by England in the 16th century. England's economy was dependent on the shipping trade and American forests provided tall, straight timber for ship masts, ribs, and planking.

Since early times, forests have provided Americans with housing, tools, and a wide variety of foods, ranging from maple syrup to hickory nuts. Native forests are important to large wildlife populations. In addition, they provide important recreation benefits for outdoor enthusiasts.

IMPORTANCE OF NATIVE FORESTS

14-2. The "cradle of forestry" near Asheville, North Carolina, provides a wealth of information on the forest industry.

14-3. Old-growth forests have never been cut and contain a wealth of native species that support animal wildlife. (This shows an old-growth forest area in Oregon.)

A *forest* is where trees and other plants grow in a community that is ever changing. Large trees dominate the land area. Animal wildlife may live in association with the forest community.

A *native forest* is one where the species are voluntarily growing and comprised of numerous species that are naturally present in the area. This is contrasted with tree farms that have been planted to selected and improved species. Only selected species are allowed to grow in improved timber stands on tree farms.

ORIGINAL NATIVE FORESTS

The original native forests in the United States covered 822 million acres of land (1,284,975 square miles). For comparison, the State of Oklahoma contains 69,919 square miles. The original American forested area would have made up an area about 18 times the size of Oklahoma!

Native forests have been used in many ways. Over 200 million acres of forest land have been cleared for crops and pastures, factories, and residential areas. Another 489,555,000 acres of the original forest land remain as *commercial forest*. A commercial forest is where trees are grown to be harvested for wood products. The forest on a tree farm is a commercial forest. It is estimated that 247,126,000 acres of standing timber exist in non-commercial forest areas. These are ranch and farm wood lots and small wooded areas scattered throughout the original forest area.

The majority of the forest area east of the Rocky Mountains has been cut from one to several times. This area is generally referred to as *regrowth forest*. Only a few areas remain with uncut forests. The uncut forests are known as *old-growth forests* (ancient forests). Most of the old-growth forest is in the Pacific coast states.

14-4. A banyan tree in Hawaii has roots that form interesting structures above the ground. (The banyan *(Ficus benghalensis)* is a type of fig tree.)

14-5. Older trees in urban areas are valuable and often protected from damage by lightning with a ground wire as shown here.

URBAN FORESTS

Urban forests are areas found in cities where trees and other species grow that are normally found in forests. The trees may be in parks, on areas surrounding factories and office buildings, along streets, and in residential areas. The presence of trees results in lower summer temperatures on city streets. Shade on buildings reduces the energy consumed for air conditioning. Trees also help people like urban areas and enjoy life.

Maintenance is sometimes needed with urban trees. Carefully prune away limbs that should be removed. Cut the limbs to avoid injury to the standing tree.

6. Never "bob-off" (cut short) the limbs of a tree. Selectively ove weak or diseased limbs at their base.

TREES FORM A COMMUNITY

14-7. Sequoia trees may live for 2,000 years and grow to be the largest living things on Earth!

Individual trees form a community as they grow in a forest. They support each other and help make the overall community stronger. Good evidence of how trees support each other is demonstrated when some trees are cut and others are left. Those that are left cannot resist wind and ice to the same extent as they could when the community of trees was untouched. How trees relate begins with a study of their parts and is followed by how they form a structure in a forest.

TREES OR SHRUBS

Many plants often look alike to the casual observer. It is sometimes difficult to separate young trees from shrubs. However, shrubs are most commonly low, woody plants with numerous stems only a few inches in diameter.

A *tree* is a woody plant generally having one well-defined stem and a definite top of small branches. The stem

Career Profile

LOGGER

A logger is a person who harvests trees as logs. The work involves using power and hand equipment to cut (fell) and trim (remove limbs), skid logs through the woods and load them onto trucks, and drive trucks loaded with logs to a mill. Many loggers are specialized in a particular area of equipment operation.

Loggers need skill in safely using equipment, tree identification, making measurements, and other areas associated with logging. Most have high school degrees and many have some education beyond high school. Experience in forestry is very important.

Jobs are found where trees are grown and harvested. The photograph shows equipment being used to load harvested logs onto a semi-trailer for hauling to a mill.

may grow to be 30 inches or more in diameter, depending on the species of tree. Trees are a minimum of 8 feet tall. Most reach heights 30 to 100 feet or more. Any woody plant less than 8 feet tall is generally a shrub, though some shrubs grow to greater heights.

PARTS OF A TREE

Trees have three major parts: crown, trunk, and roots. These three parts function together to provide for the life processes of a tree.

The **crown** is the top part of a tree with limbs, leaves, and, perhaps, flowers and fruit. The crown often provides good nesting sites for animal wildlife, such as squirrels and birds. The nature of the growth in a crown varies with tree species.

The **trunk** is the main stem connecting the crown with the roots. It performs important roles in transporting raw materials upward to the crown for photosynthesis and manufactured food downward to the lower trunk and roots. Stems are often strong and valued for the wood products they can produce.

Roots are the part of a tree that is in the ground. Roots take water and nutrients from the soil. They store manufactured food for the plant. Roots anchor a tree in position and help it withstand wind and other weather conditions. Some trees have shallow root systems and fall over easily. Others have deep root systems that allow them to resist more wind.

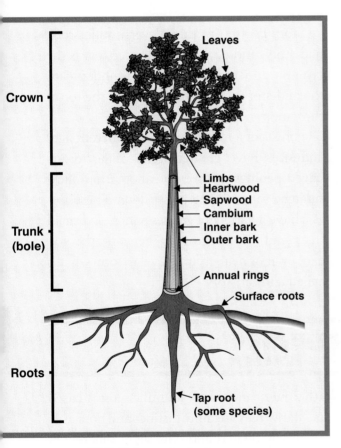

14-8. Major parts of a tree.

PHYSICAL STRUCTURE OF A FOREST

Forests are made of trees and other plants that form fairly definite structures. The structure is formed by the size, age, and species of trees and shrubs that are present.

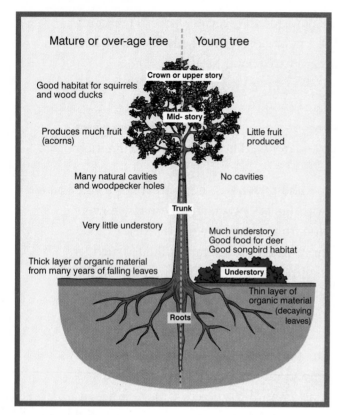

Mature or over-age tree   Young tree

Crown or upper story

Good habitat for squirrels
and wood ducks

Mid- story

Produces much fruit
(acorns)

Little fruit
produced

Many natural cavities
and woodpecker holes

No cavities

Trunk

Very little understory

Much understory
Good food for deer
Good songbird habitat

Thick layer of organic material
from many years of falling leaves

Understory

Thin layer of
organic material
(decaying
leaves)

Roots

14-9. The values of a mature tree and a younger tree to animal wildlife based on story.

Some forests are composed of a single species that spread large, dense canopies. A **canopy** is formed by the upper part of trees by limbs and foliage.

The physical structure is often described by story. A **story** in a forest is a horizontal layer of vegetative growth. The layers are often fairly easy to distinguish. Layers are based on the species and age of the plants that are growing.

Story is often in three layers: understory, mid-story, and upper story. Understory is the layer on or near the ground. It is underneath the mid-story. The upper story is at the top of the canopy.

Forests of a mixed species of different ages and sizes have greater story. Some forests have openings in the top canopy that allow sunlight to reach the forest floor. These forests have a variety of grasses, vines, and small trees and shrubs growing beneath the top canopy at or near ground level to form what is called a lower story.

TREE SPECIES

Over 250 species of trees are found in North American forests. Identification is based largely on leaf shape and types of seeds and fruits. Many trees are quite distinct and not easily confused with others. However, some trees are closely related and only slight differences separate one species from another.

NAMES OF TREES

Trees are known by common and scientific names. Common names are those used by people in their every-day work. This sometimes leads to confusion. People in different regions may use different common names for the same species. For example, water oak is known at different locations as "possum oak, red oak, pin oak, swamp oak, and spotted oak".

The scientific name of water oak is *Quercus nigra*—a name that communicates exact species to foresters.

To avoid confusion over common names which vary in different sections of the country, botanists and scientists agreed to give each plant or animal a single scientific name derived from the Latin language. Scientific names typically have two parts; others have three parts. The first two parts are written in italics or underlined. The first part of a scientific name is the genus, with the first letter capitalized. The second is the species name and is uncapitalized. The third, if used, is an abbreviation of the name of the person who first described the species. Thus, the scientific name for water oak is *Quercus nigra* L. The capital "L" is the abbreviation for the Swedish botanist Linnaeus who first identified and named the tree.

A few examples of common and scientific names of trees are listed in Table 14-1.

Table 14-1. Examples of Trees*

Common Name	Scientific Name
bald cypress	*Taxodium distichum*
black walnut	*Juglans nigra*
blue spruce	*Picea pungens*
boxelder	*Acer negundo*
buttonbush	*Cephalanthus occidentalis*
California sycamore	*Plantanus racemosa*
eastern hemlock	*Tsuga canadensis*
jack pine	*Pinus banksiana*
loblolly pine	*Pinus taeda*
pin oak	*Quercus palustris*
ponderosa pine	*Pinus ponderosa*
post oak	*Quercus stellata*
quaking aspen	*Populus tremuloides*
red maple	*Acer rubrum*
sweetgum	*Liquidambar styraciflua*
sycamore	*Platanus occidentilis*
white oak	*Quercus alba*

*Some species listed may be known locally as shrubs.

TREE IDENTIFICATION

Most common trees are fairly easy to identify; others may require careful examination. The major identifying characteristics of trees are leaves, twigs, bark, flowers, and fruit. All of these may not be present. Bark and twigs are usually always present. Evergreen trees have leaves all of the time.

With leaves, shape, type, size, arrangement, color, and odor may be used in the identification process. Some leaves are shaped as long, slender needles. Other leaves are large, flat, and have lobed or serrated edges. Leaves can often be used to make accurate identification. Fruit is also helpful in the identification process. For example, the leaf of a post oak has distinct shape differences when compared to the white oak.

Contact the forest service or local office of the Cooperative Extension Service in your state for specific information on trees that grow in your local area.

14-10. Leaves and fruit of selected trees often found in native forests.

MAJOR FOREST REGIONS OF THE UNITED STATES

Temperature, moisture, and soil type are factors that influence the type of native forests that grow at different locations. As an example, forests in Florida are quite different from forests in Montana. This is because temperatures in Florida are very mild, the land is relatively flat, and soils are deep and often saturated with water. In Montana, the land is often steep and mountain-like, soils are more dry, and winter temperatures are quite low.

The United States can be divided into six major forest regions based on the species of trees present and their growth characteristics. Two regions are restricted to the eastern half of the nation and two are restricted to the western part. The remaining two forest regions are found from coast to coast.

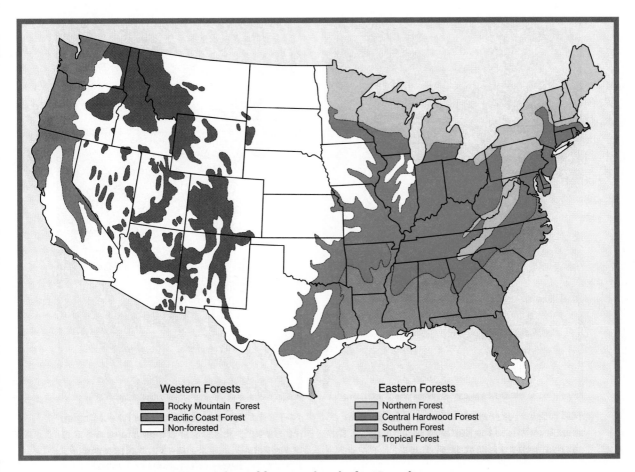

Western Forests

- Rocky Mountain Forest
- Pacific Coast Forest
- Non-forested

Eastern Forests

- Northern Forest
- Central Hardwood Forest
- Southern Forest
- Tropical Forest

14-11. Locations of forest regions in the 48 contiguous states.

1. NORTHERN FOREST REGION

The Northern Forest Region is the largest of the six forest regions. It extends from northeastern Georgia, north along the Appalachian Mountains, to New England and the northern portions of the Lake States. This region extends through Canada and the interior of Alaska.

The northern portion of this region produces small-size trees that are primarily black and white spruce, balsam fir, larch, paper birch, aspen balsam, poplar, and willows. The southern portion is characterized by highly valuable timber species, such as spruce, birches, beech, basswood, maples, and red oak.

2. SOUTHERN FOREST REGION

The Southern Forest Region covers the coastal area from Maryland southwest to Texas. It extends north from Texas along rivers into Oklahoma, Arkansas, and Missouri. This forest region is one of the most important timber producing areas in North America. This

14-12. Snow cover much of the year is found in some locations in the Northern Forest Region. This shows a wolf pack near small trees.

14-13. Oak trees in the Southern Forest Region may have Spanish moss (*Tillandsia usneoides*) growing and hanging down in their crowns. As a parasite, heavy infestations of Spanish moss may kill a tree.

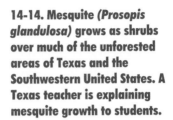

14-14. Mesquite *(Prosopis glandulosa)* grows as shrubs over much of the unforested areas of Texas and the Southwestern United States. A Texas teacher is explaining mesquite growth to students.

region produces seven species of pine, bald cypress, tupelo gum, sweetgum, beech, ashes, elms, oaks, hickories, and others.

3. CENTRAL HARDWOOD REGION

The Central Hardwood Region covers the central portion of the eastern United States, with the exception of the Appalachian Mountains, and extends into Canada. Oaks are the dominant species but important species include hickories, ashes, elms, maples, gum, beech, yellow poplar, walnut, cottonwood, sycamore, and dogwood.

4. TROPICAL FOREST REGION

The Tropical Forest Region is found in Arizona, California, southern Florida, and extreme southern Texas. Trees are small and often shrubby and generally lack commercial value. Florida and Texas represent the extreme northern range of plants from the deep tropics of Central and South America. Arizona and California provide a desert climate with brushy plants capable of living under extremely dry conditions. Palms, ebony, mesquite, huisache, and other thorny species are typical of this region.

5. ROCKY MOUNTAIN FOREST REGION

The Rocky Mountain Forest Region is spread over the mountains and high plateaus from Mexico into northern Canada. It is bordered on the east by the Great Plains and on the west by the Pacific Coast Forest. The primary tree species are spruce, lodgepole pine, aspen, poplar, ponderosa pine, Douglas fir, various oaks, pinyon pine, junipers, and cottonwood.

6. PACIFIC COAST FOREST REGION

The Pacific Coast Forest Region includes the Pacific coast states and is bounded on the east by the Rocky Mountain Forest and on the west by the Pacific Ocean. This region supports the largest and tallest trees in the world (giant sequoia and redwood).

The single most important timber species in the world (Douglas-fir) is also common to this forest region. Trees tend to grow in dense stands and this region contains the major portion of the United States supply of saw lumber.

ANIMAL WILDLIFE AND NATIVE FORESTS

Animals and native forests often have special relationships. For example, the kind of tree in a forest determines the food that is naturally available, such as acorns from various oak trees.

A popular belief among some is that timber harvest has had a totally disastrous impact on all wildlife populations. In truth, various forest-dependent wildlife species have shown both gains and losses since timber harvest was first begun.

At many locations, white-tailed deer have shown dramatic gains as the virgin forest was replaced with new growth. At some locations, populations are at all-time highs.

Some forest-dependent wildlife species were eliminated where large expanses of forest were cut and replaced with farmland. However, in many cases, other wildlife species began to prosper when the forest was removed. As an example, when the forest was replaced with pastures, wood lots, and grain fields, a different set of wildlife species began to live on the converted land. This included brush and grassland species, such as rabbits, quail, pheasants, and numerous songbirds that could not prosper in dense forests.

MAMMALS

The forest provides ideal habitat for many kinds of mammals. A mammal is a species in which the female gives birth to

14-15. Lynx prefer forested areas.

14-16. A mature bull moose at the edge of a forest clearing.

babies and has mammary glands that produce milk as food for the baby. The white-tail deer is likely the most important game mammal in the United States. Although, deer are often found on lands classed as grasslands, this species reaches maximum abundance in forested areas with small canopy openings or in forests that have been cut over and are in the process of growing back.

Elk occupy forested mountain areas but use valley openings during winter when snow is deep at higher elevations. Moose are forest dwellers but often feed in openings along lakes and streams.

Squirrel populations (grey and fox squirrels) are dependent on large, old trees. Generally, squirrels prosper in hardwood timber stands where trees are at least 60 years or older.

Although, the cotton tail rabbit is primarily thought of as a grassland-brush dependent animal, it does remarkably well in forest openings and along edges of standing timber.

Most furbearing mammals are forest dependent. These include raccoon, mink, opossum, weasel, otter, beaver, and skunks. Red and gray fox populations are highest in forest areas. Bobcats and lynx also reach maximum abundance in forested areas.

The larger predators, such as wolves and bears, are forest dependent. Bears remain almost entirely in densely forested areas but wolves have large hunting ranges and often frequent areas outside the forest. Originally, the coyote was considered a predator of open areas and brushland but in recent years this mammal has prospered in heavily forested areas, particularly in Texas and Louisiana.

A number of less visible small mammals are also forest dependent. These include wood rats, moles, shrews, pine mice, white-footed mice, jumping mice, ground squirrels and flying squirrels. Many of these small mammals live primarily on the forest floor where they forage for food and burrow among root systems. Some use tree cavities or fallen logs to bear their young and escape cold weather and predators.

BIRDS

Only a small number of bird species spend their lives completely in open land and do not depend to some degree on forested areas. Most birds owe at least part of their existence to wooded areas, either as nesting areas, feeding areas, or night-time roosts.

14-17. A pileated woodpecker feeds young nesting in a dead tree habitat.

The spruce grouse and band-tailed pigeon prefer dense, mountain forest habitats. Woodpeckers are strongly linked to mature or maturing forests since they nest in cavities and feed on older, often diseased and insect-laden trees. Most other birds prefer to periodically use openings and margins of wooded areas. This is especially true of turkeys, quail, and mourning doves.

Eagles build huge nests in tall trees and generally return to the same nest from year to year. They often hunt for food around rivers, lakes, and streams and are commonly observed perching in trees when not hunting.

Mallard ducks build their nests on the ground and raise their young each summer in the northern prairie states and Canada. However, these birds have a strong tendency to utilize flooded oak forests during winter where they feed on acorns and rest during the day under the dense canopy of tree branches. Wood ducks are strongly oriented to forest areas. In the spring and early summer, they nest in tree cavities and frequent dense woods in winter.

The forest supports a wide variety of nongame birds. Throughout the United States, these birds are most abundant in forests with openings and small streams. Warblers, nuthatches, vireos, chickadees, jays, hawks, owls, and many others rely on the rich mixture of vegetation, and the insects it supports, as found in forests.

FISH, REPTILES, AND AMPHIBIANS

With the exception of the desert portion of the Tropical Forest Region, forests are associated with water. Southern forests generally have an abundance of slow, sluggish-moving water, while northern forests have running water associated with mountainous or hilly terrain. Northern streams are likely to be clear and cold, while southern waters are more likely to be warmer and slightly turbid.

Trout streams are almost always associated with forests where rain and snow melt runoff cause the water to remain clear, cold, and with high levels of dissolved oxygen. In warmer forest areas, black bass, sunfish, and catfish become the major fish species where dissolved oxygen is lower and water more turbid (less clear) and warmer.

Alligators, snakes, turtles, frogs, and small amphibians reach great abundance in warm, slow-moving streams, lakes, and swamps. The organic material in these areas from decaying woody vegetation provides a fertile and secure environment for these slow moving animals.

14-18. A green tree frog is perched and ready for making a quick move.

14-19. Snakes are adapted to particular environments. For example, the Mojave rattlesnake prefers hot, dry climates.

FOREST MANAGEMENT

Practically all commercial forest areas are managed by professional specialists called foresters. A *forester* is a college-trained individual charged with the responsibility of ensuring that forests produce maximum profits and timber reserves are provided for the future. In addition, they have the responsibility of ensuring that forests provide recreational opportunities and meet environmental needs.

Income from forest lands comes primarily from the harvest and sale of wood products, which include posts, piling, dimension lumber, pulpwood, plywood, turpentine, and wood chips for the manufacture of paper products. Additional income is often derived from hunting leases, livestock grazing, mineral leases, and oil and gas production.

14-20. A diameter tape is being used to measure a tree trunk.

SILVICULTURE

Silviculture is managing tree stands to increase productivity. A number of cultural practices may be used. These often begin with planning the practices that are to be implemented.

14-21. A pine seedling of adequate size for planting.

14-22. A 4-inch high yellow poplar that grew from seed.

Major areas of silviculture work include:

• Planting trees—Planting involves preparing the land, selecting the species to plant, and properly planting the seed or seedlings. In some cases, the land is cleared and/or burned in preparation for planting. The trees planted should be of the desired species adapted in the area. Many people prefer to plant seedlings. A **seedling** is a young tree 15 to 18 inches tall. It is set in the ground so the roots are properly covered. Most trees are planted in winter or early spring. Moisture must be available for a seedling to live. In some cases, native forests are managed so mature trees are left to produce seed. These seed will germinate and produce new trees.

14-23. This tree has a canker disease and should be removed by cutting from the forest.

• Thinning—Thinning is used to reduce the number of trees in a woodlot. In some cases, the trees are large enough for posts or poles. Trees may be removed to promote the growth of understory for wildlife.

14-24. A tree that was killed by a lightning strike may be removed or left standing as habitat for woodpeckers and other species.

14-25. Log-size trees are being harvested to liberate the growth of younger trees.

- Cleaning—Cleaning is removing diseased or defective trees. It may occur along with thinning or as a separate process. Be sure to consider the species of animal wildlife that is desired. Some prefer to live in dead or defective trees.

Wildlife Connection

THE AGE OF A TREE

As the stem of a tree grows larger, annual rings are formed by the growth of the cells that form the wood. Usually, one ring is formed each growing season or year. By counting the number of rings, we know the approximate age of a tree.

An annual ring has both dark and light-colored rings. The dark-colored part of a ring is harder and gives wood strength. The width of annual rings varies with the species of the tree and conditions of growth.

Studying the annual rings in the cross section of a tree can tell much about the environment in which the tree has been growing. Rings smaller than usual indicate dry weather, lack of nutrients, or other conditions not favorable to growth. Rings of an older tree will even indicate if the tree has been damaged by fire!

Look at this cross section of a pine tree. How old is the tree?

14-26. A forest destroyed by fire will require years to grow again.

- Liberation—Liberation is a kind of cutting that removes older trees so younger trees can grow. Trees with large canopies can shade much ground and prevent the growth of young trees, shrubs, and understory.

- Harvesting—Harvesting is used to take out trees that are of adequate size for poles or logs. Older trees may be cut if they are of sufficient quality for the market.

- Protecting forests—Trees are subject to attack by insects, disease, human activity, fire, and weather. In some cases, trees that are diseased or that have been damaged by insects need to be removed. Removing diseased trees tends to protect other trees from the disease or insect problem.

14-27. Signs are used to alert people to the level of fire danger that exists.

PROMOTING ANIMAL WILDLIFE

The production and maintenance of animal wildlife populations can be incorporated into the process of growing timber for eventual harvest and sale. Wildlife management costs are generally quite small and revenues derived from hunting leases add to the profit.

Major wildlife management actions for foresters to consider are:

1. Where economically possible, avoid clear-cutting practices that involve the harvest of all trees on a given site.

2. If clear-cutting is necessary, reduce the size of clear cuts and make a checker-board configuration of clear-cut and mature forest.

3. Prohibit clear-cutting along margins of streams to avoid erosion and siltation and to provide stream-side belts of mature trees.

4. Quickly replant clear-cuts with a variety of trees rather than creating monocultures. A **monoculture** is a forest planted with only one species of trees. A mix of trees will result in better food variety for animal wildlife.

5. Harvest timber through **selective cutting** where individual trees are marked for sale before cutting, thus leaving many desirable trees.

6. Avoid cutting den trees during timber harvest.

7. Limit livestock grazing activities to well-planned grazing programs where grazing can be used to control vegetation to the improvement of both timber and wildlife production.

8. Initiate well-planned burning programs where fire can be used as a management tool to improve both timber and wildlife production.

9. Regulate the annual harvest of game species to keep population numbers in check to avoid vegetative damage by over-utilization (consuming too much vegetation).

10. Leave examples of diverse natural areas. Exclude timber harvest that would impact marshes, bogs, haw flats, deep sands, steep slopes, and other special places.

14-28. A mature, overage pine tree is being checked as a possible nesting site for the endangered red-cocaded woodpecker.

REVIEWING

MAIN IDEAS

North America has been recognized as a continent with vast forests. Forests provide Americans with a wide range of food, building supplies, paper, and many other products. The forestry industry provides jobs for a strong economy. Native forests also provide important recreational benefits and habitat for fish and wildlife.

Forests are generally described as areas dominated by thick growths of tall trees. Some forests have never been cut and are called old-growth or ancient forests. Other forests have been cut several times and are called cut-over or regrowth forests.

Temperature, moisture, and soil type are major factors that control the type of forests that grow at different locations. Forests in North America are separated into six major types based on kinds of trees growing there. Over 250 species of trees are found in North American forests.

Native forests provide for a number of wildlife species that rely on trees for their survival. This includes large and small mammals, a wide variety of birds, fish, reptiles, and amphibians. Fish and wildlife produced in forests provide much hunting and fishing recreation. Hunting leases provide important revenues to forest owners.

The production and maintenance of wildlife populations can be incorporated into the process of growing timber for eventual harvest and sale. These actions generally involve the method in which timber is harvested.

QUESTIONS

Answer the following questions using correct spelling and complete sentences.

1. What is a forest? Distinguish between a native forest and a commercial forest.
2. What is an old-growth forest?
3. What is the difference between a tree and a shrub?
4. What are the three major parts of a tree? What are the functions of each?
5. What is story? What three stories are often used in forest development for animal wildlife?
6. What are the major identifying characteristics of trees?
7. What are the six forest regions?
8. How does a forest provide habitat for mammals?
9. How does a forest provide habitat for birds?
10. What is silviculture?
11. What are the major forest management practices in silviculture?
12. What forest management practices promote animal wildlife production?

EVALUATING

Match the term with the correct definition.

a. selective cutting
b. monoculture
c. forest

d. urban forest
e. canopy
f. story

g. seedling
h. silviculture

_____1. A forest planted to only one species of tree.

_____2. Taking out certain trees and leaving others.

_____3. Practices used in managing trees to increase production.

_____4. A horizontal layer of vegetative growth.

_____5. Trees and forest areas in cities.

_____6. A young tree used for planting forests.

_____7. A covering formed by the crowns of trees.

_____8. A place where trees and other plants grow in a community relationship.

EXPLORING

1. Use a separate sheet of paper or poster paper and make a sketch of a typical tree and label the various parts.

2. If there is a commercial, national, or state forest nearby, make arrangements to visit and have the resident forester discuss job opportunities and forest management practices that result in favorable conditions for wildlife. Ask the forester to compare the species found in native forests with those on tree farms.

3. Visit a lumber yard or large hardware store and make a list of items for sale that originated in the forest.

4. Carefully examine your home and classroom and make a list of items constructed of wood. Be sure to include all paper items since paper is made of chemically processed wood.

5. Make a list of wildlife species that you have seen or can identify that are dependent on the forest.

Browse, Herbage, and Mast

This chapter will help you understand the roles of browse, herbage, and mast in sustaining animal wildlife. It will provide help in identifying major browse, fruit, and nut plants and cover basic practices in their production. The following objectives are included:

1 Identify plant food sources for animal wildlife.

2 Explain browse production.

3 Explain herbage production.

4 Explain mast production.

TERMS

acorn	herbage	nut
berry	legume	ripe
controlled burning	mast	

15-1. Deer often eat tender leaves and stems at the edges of forested areas.

WHEN we visit a grocery store, we can select from many kinds of fruits, vegetables, and nuts, along with thousands of other items. Many of the foods we see are from different plant species. People and animals have used plants as food since life began.

Trees, vines, and herbs are prominent in the habitats of many animals, including deer, squirrels, turkeys, ruffed grouse, quail, and ducks. These plants grow leaves, shoots, berries, nuts, and other popular animal foods. Fortunately, steps can be taken to ensure adequate foods for wildlife.

Using land wisely is a good beginning. Allowing space, for wildlife and the growth of needed foods is essential. A first big step is knowing what plants are needed and how their growth is promoted.

293

PLANT FOOD SOURCES

Animals must have food. Food provides important nutrients for health, movement, growth, and reproduction. Without adequate food, animals are unhealthy and fail to grow and reproduce. Many animals use plants for food. Where animals are found, sufficient plants of the right kind are necessary if the animals are to be healthy.

Three common groups of plant materials used by terrestrial animals for food are browse, herbage, and mast.

15-2. Browse grows at a wide range of elevations. (This shows scrub oak at the lower elevations, aspen and pine in the middle range, and pine and spruce at the upper levels.)

BROWSE

Browse is the tender growth of shrubs and trees. Small trees with leaves, shoots, and stems near the ground are ideal for most animals that eat browse. Shrubs are particularly good because of the pattern of their growth. Most shrubs are small, woody plants with many branches near the ground. These are accessible by most animals that eat browse.

Ruminants (animals with stomachs of several compartments) make the best use of browse. Their digestive systems can handle the fibrous materials. Deer are particularly known as good at eating browse. Some monogastric animals make limited use of browse, with beaver being an example.

Many plants that grow as browse are perennials. A perennial browse plant lives for several years. Some are green year round. Others are green only in the warm seasons of the year.

The nature of browse often varies with the time of year and species of animals. In the spring, tender leaves and shoots are available as plants grow. As summer ends and fall approaches, the leaves and shoots have matured and are no longer as tender as they were earlier.

During the winter, many shoots and stems are dormant. Dormancy is a time when the plant is not growing. It has typically lost its leaves and is not tender and succulent. Animals eat the slightly larger materials, including twigs or small limbs and bark. Plants that keep

-3. Open areas adjacent to woodland provide
od habitat growth of browse and herbage for
ne wildlife species.

15-4. An Atlantic salt marsh has good growth of native herbage. (Courtesy, L. Childers, U.S. Fish and Wildlife Service)

their leaves year round are important in providing forage in the winter. Winter-growing plants are important in the survival of certain animal wildlife.

Herbage

Herbage is the succulent nonwoody leaves and stems of herbaceous plants. These are plants of small to medium height that do not grow woody stems. Grasses are common herbs consumed by animals. Some broadleaf and vine-type plants would be included as herbage. In fact, many of the weeds that grow in crops and lawns make good animal wildlife food!

Ruminants have digestive systems that allow them to make the best use of herbage. The large digestive systems of bison, caribou, elk, and moose make consumption of relatively large amounts of herbage possible. As with all ruminants, the lower quality grasses are converted to higher quality food materials by the action of bacteria in the digestive system.

Mast

Mast is the fruits and nuts of trees and shrubs eaten by animal wildlife. A vast array of foods are included. Hickory nuts and acorns are common nuts. Fruits include berries and other forms of fruit, such as wild plums, pokeweed berries (also known as poke salet or inkberry), and blackberries.

The nutrient materials are more concentrated in mast. Animals with monogastric stomachs, such as squirrels, bear, rabbits, and birds, are more likely to eat mast. Some ruminant animals also eat mast. For example, deer sometimes eat acorns.

15-5. The pokeweed (poke salet) grows succulent broadleaf plants, 3 to 4 feet tall, that produce berries during the summer. (When ripe, the berries are dark purple.)

15-6. Wild persimmon fruit matures each fall. (When ripe, the fruit is sweet and a favorite of opossums!)

Fruits

A fruit is the developed ovary of a flowering plant. Some fruits are very fleshy; others tend to be dry. For example, wild plums, wild grapes, and persimmons are fleshy. Fruits in a pod or shell are dry. Dry fruits include pods on locust and catalpa trees.

Career Profile

HABITAT TECHNICIAN

Habitat technicians help animal wildlife have good places to live. The work may involve assessing habitat conditions, preparing sites, and planting trees. People in this work may be known as wildlife technicians.

Habitat technicians need practical experience with wildlife and the outdoors. They also need appropriate education for their level of work. The education may be at a high school or post-secondary level. Some have college degrees. Those with more education typically make better pay.

Jobs are found where wildlife are managed and habitat is established and maintained. Many are with state and federal government agencies. Some are with private forestry companies and wildlife associations.

This photograph shows a small tree seedling being examined before planting. (Courtesy, U.S. Department of Agriculture)

The ovary (fruit) contains one or more seeds. The structure and number of seeds in fruit vary with the species of plant. Some have only one seed, such as a plum. The persimmon is a fleshy fruit with several seeds.

Fruits are rich in carbohydrates and vitamins and are especially important foods for wildlife. Fleshy fruits are mainly produced on woody plants, such as bushes and trees. Fruit crops generally ripen during the warm summer days and into the early fall. Some hardier species, such as holly, grape, snowberry, mountain-ash, and persimmon, are also available to wildlife in the winter.

Berries

Smaller fruits having seeds and without hard outer coverings are known as berries. A **berry** is a fleshy fruit with seeds embedded inside. Each berry may have several seeds. The skin of berries is often soft and easy to damage. Most berries have a rounded or oval appearance. Many are small, which makes it easy for birds to use them as food. Immature berries may not be appealing to animal wildlife.

Berries typically go through stages of development from immature green fruit to **ripe**. When ripe, berries may be red or black with an increased amount of juice and sugar. Many berries are popular wildlife food. Huckleberries, hackberries, wild strawberries, and blackberries are common berries eaten by animal wildlife.

15-7. Huckleberries are important food for some birds and other animals.

Nuts

A **nut** is a mature, dry fruit enclosed in a shell. The inside, or "meat," is a kernel that, when planted, is capable of growing into another plant. Most shells have either a woody or leathery texture. Nuts with woody shells include hickory nuts, acorns, and wild pecans. The **acorn** is likely the most important nut that grows. It is the dried fruit

15-8. Wild strawberries are food for some animals.

15-9. Acorns will serve as important food for some animals.

or seed of a wide number of oak trees. Sizes and shapes of acorns vary with the species of oak. Many river bottoms in the southern United States have good stands of oaks that produce big crops of acorns.

Some woody-shelled or hard nuts grow inside of fleshy fruits, such as the seed of peaches and almonds—a close peach relative. Rodents have strong teeth. This makes it possible for them to crack and use the food material inside nuts.

BROWSE PRODUCTION

15-10. Browse in this area of the Sierra-Nevada Mountains includes a variety of plants adapted to dry, cold climates.

In managing wildlife habitats, most browse consists of the native shrubs and nonwoody plants that grow in an area. In some cases, browse plants can be planted. Planting is not as widely used as practices to promote the growth of browse plants that naturally exist. Shrubs, canes, and some types of vines can be planted, but usually only on a limited basis.

Management practices promoting the growth of browse are more likely to be used. Leaving unplowed areas between fields and woods allows small shrubs and herbs to grow. Deer and other animals that feed on browse are often seen in these areas in the early morning or late evening. Sometimes, deer will bed down in the area if sufficiently secluded by brush, briars, and trees.

Most of the browse that grows in a wildlife area occurs naturally from native plant species. To help browse mature, avoid burning young growing areas. After maturity, **controlled burning** may help promote browse. Controlled burning is using fire to remove unwanted debris and enhance new plant growth. Only people who are well qualified should be in charge of controlled burning. One accident can result in a large wildfire that destroys large areas of habitat, homes, and businesses. Controlled burning is more likely to be used in areas with greater precipitation. Controlled burns in dry areas of the western United States may pose particular dangers.

In timber harvesting, strips can be cut next to larger wooded areas. With plowed fields, strips along creeks, wooded areas, and in the middle of fields can be left unplowed.

Logging and construction activities often damage small trees and shrubs. This results in additional sprouting. For the short run, the tender sprouts are good browse. With more growth, such trees and shrubs tend to be poorly shaped and of no economic value. If you have seen the cluster of sprouts from a small tree stump after cutting, you are well aware of how some species send up multiple stems. These will not usually grow into good timber even if thinned to a reasonable population size and spacing.

In trying to establish browse plants, use only those that are adapted to the climate, altitude, and other site features. Plants that are not adapted will not grow well. They will not produce much food for animal wildlife. In some cases, certain plant species may be controlled or undesirable. For example, establishing certain types of aquatic weeds can lead to the weed taking over a water facility. This will destroy the use of the pond, stream, or lake.

15-11. Some animals, such as deer, eat mushrooms.

15-12. Planning habitat development has resulted in several types of food and cover on this Wisconsin farm.

HERBAGE PRODUCTION

15-13. Crested wheatgrass (herbage) was seeded on desert land in Nevada 45 years before this photograph was made.

As grasses and small broadleaf plants, herbs are more likely to be planted than other food-producing plants. Most often, these are planted using seed, but sprigs, cuttings, and other means could be used. In some cases, domesticated crops that serve well as animal wildlife food may be planted.

Small areas near where wildlife species now congregate can be planted. Select a site that wildlife will use. Consider the general characteristics of the animals. Shy animals would not want to be in public areas!

Planting may involve clearing brush and undesirable weeds from the area. The land is disced and otherwise prepared as a seedbed. Fertilizer and other soil amendments may be used according to the results of soil tests. Seed can be distributed over the area. The seed should germinate and grow plants that are important as animal wildlife food. It is also beneficial to plant species that are perennials or will naturally reseed themselves. If not, the area will need to be planted each year. Clovers and perennial grasses are likely best. Common herbage planted includes rye grass, sunflowers, wheat, clover, fescue, and milo. The grass-type forages are used by ruminant animals as good food sources. Of these, sunflower and milo are summer annuals. Rye grass, wheat, fescue, and clover are often planted in the fall in the southern United States. These cool-season plants grow in the winter providing food for wildlife. Seeds produced by summer-growing plants are used as food during the winter and at other times.

In planting herbage, use care to prevent soil erosion. Soil erosion is the loss of fertile topsoil. The soil is washed

15-14. Fescue grass seed can be spread by hand over small open areas near woodland to grow herbage in climates with sufficient rainfall.

or worn away. Most is lost to running water from rains or melting snow. Some is lost because of wind. Plowing hillsides can result in considerable soil loss in the event of heavy rains. It is best to avoid any kind of activity that destroys the existing protective cover on hilly land. Soil particles from erosion degrade water quality in streams. Soil particles are first suspended in the water, making it appear muddy. Later, they settle out, forming delta areas and filling up lakes and oceans.

15-15. Lespedeza is commonly used in some areas as legume cool season herbage.

In choosing the species to plant, select those that improve the soil. Good choices include the legumes. A *legume* is a plant that improves soil fertility. In the presence of soil rhizobium bacteria, a legume fixes nitrogen from the air as nodules on its roots. These tiny nodules provide increased soil fertility for other plants. Examples of legumes used as herbage include all clovers, vetch, and lespedeza.

Wildlife Connection

FIRES AND HABITAT

Fire! Smoke!

Fires can quickly destroy animal wildlife habitat. Some fires burn only the ground. Others burn the ground and the tops of trees. Those that get into trees are very hot. Food, small plants, twigs, and nesting areas are destroyed by fire. Fires also kill young and old animals. With wind, a fire can travel faster than some animals.

Not all fires are bad. Habitat managers and foresters have learned that small controlled burns can improve habitat over a growing season. Careful planning is needed. Good fire control measures must be in place to keep a planned burn from becoming a wildfire.

A person should never try a controlled burn unless they have been trained. Adequate control equipment and people must be on hand. Fires are dangerous!

This shows a well-monitored controlled burn. Note that firefighters are on hand with a hose to keep the fire under control. (Courtesy, U.S. Department of Agriculture)

MAST PRODUCTION

Most fruits and nuts grow on trees. Several years may be required for a crop to be produced. The tree must reach sufficient maturity. For example, a young oak tree will not produce acorns until a certain size has been reached. Several years (perhaps, 20 years) will be needed for an oak tree to begin acorn production. Even longer will be needed for the tree to produce very large amounts of acorns. Since getting plants to produce mast may require years, good long-term planning is essential.

15-16. When these black walnuts reach maturity, they may be eaten by squirrels.

Some fruits, particularly berries, are herbaceous perennials; others are woody shrubs. Plants store large amounts of readily consumable energy in fruits and nuts. The seed will grow to form new plants under normal conditions. This energy—fats and carbohydrates—is what animal wildlife species need to be healthy.

MAJOR FRUIT AND NUT PLANTS

Wildlife specialists have long been intrigued by native fruit and nut crops and their influence on wildlife. One of the most important groups is the wide-ranging rose (*Rosaceae*) family. Members of this family produce a large proportion of the most important fleshy fruits, including blackberry, strawberry, raspberry, cherry, rose, serviceberry, hawthorn, apple, and mountain-ash. Other fleshy fruits important to wildlife include grapes, holly, blueberry, persimmon, sassafras, and blackgum. These are valuable to many kinds of birds and some mammals, such as the raccoon, deer, bear, fox, squirrel, skunk, and opossum.

Botanically speaking, nuts are fruits with a dry, hard coating. Animals—especially rodents—use these

15-17. Many wildlife use rosehips as a food. (They are high in energy and vitamin content.)

Table 15-1. Important Woody Plants for Wildlife*

Species	Tree	Vine	Shrub	Other
Oak	X			
Pine	X			
Blackberry			X	
Wild cherry	X			
Dogwood	X			
Grape		X		
Poison ivy		X		
Cedar	X			
Prickly pear				X
Maple	X			
Blueberry			X	
Hackberry	X			
Birch	X			
Mesquite			X	
Elderberry	X			
Serviceberry	X			
Sumac			X	
Aspen	X			
Fir	X			
Sagebrush			X	
Beech	X			
Willow	X			
Spruce	X			
Manzanita			X	
Alder	X			
Mulberry	X			
Snowberry	X			
Gooseberry			X	
Douglas fir	X			
Saltbush	X			
Persimmon	X			
Greenbrier (cat brier)		X		
Black gum	X			
Virginia creeper		X		
Holly	X			

*Ranked in order of importance.

hard-shelled fruits extensively. Nuts are unusually high in fats and proteins and are available over long periods. Of all the nuts, acorns are the most widely available and the most commonly eaten by wildlife. Next in order of importance come pecans, beechnuts, and cultivated walnuts. Hickory nuts, hazelnuts, black walnuts, and butternuts, because

Table 15-2. Important Upland Broadleaf Herbs and Grasses for Animal Wildlife

Species	Broadleaf Herb Non-Legume	Legume	Grass
Bristle grass	X		X
Ragweed	X		
Pigweed	X		
Panic grass			X
Oats			X
Sedge			X
Knotweed	X		
Sunflower	X		
Goosefoot	X		
Crabgrass			X
Clover		X	
Russian thistle		X	
Brome grass			X
Dove weed	X		
Turkey mullein	X		
Grama grass			X
Tar weed	X		
Bluegrass			X
Deer vetch		X	
Fescue grass			X
Chickweed	X		
Dropseed grass			X

Table 15-3. Important Marsh and Aquatic Plants for Animal Wildlife

Species	Broadleaf Plant	Grass or Grass-like
Pondweed	X	
Bulrush		X
Smartweed	X	
Widgeon grass		X
Spikerush		X
Musk grass		X
Wild rice		X
Wild millet		X
Cord grass		X
Naiad	X	
Wild celery	X	
Duckweed	X	
Horned-pondweed	X	
Salt grass		X
Water lily	X	
Bur reed		X
Arrowhead	X	

of their especially thick, hard shells, are important only to squirrels, chipmunks, and other rodents capable of cracking them.

Nuts are particularly important to small rodents. Squirrels, for example, are very energetic and require high-calorie diets. A squirrel requires about 100 pounds of food per year. Although squirrels are omnivorous, wild nuts play an important role in squirrel diets, particularly in the late winter and early spring. In fact, scientists have related poor acorn yields with poor squirrel production and heavy acorn yields with high squirrel production.

Information has been collected to determine which are the most important plants used by wildlife. Though far from perfect, this information can help in planning wildlife habitat developments whether on a farm, in an urban greenbelt, or in wildlife refuges.

MANAGEMENT PRACTICES

The supply of available foodstuffs for animal wildlife can be increased by planting and maintaining fruit and nut plants. Location is a very important factor to consider when establishing plants for this use. Although animals will travel considerable distances in open areas to obtain food, they are often deterred by the exposure to predators and humans.

With woodlands used for both wildlife and timber production, several management practices are beneficial in harvesting timber. Always selectively leave a few large trees that produce food for animal wildlife. For example, leave a few large oaks that produce good crops of acorns. Another procedure is to leave untouched areas, where no trees are cut, as wildlife habitat. Allow the cut area to grow and then harvest the uncut area in a few years. This provides an acceptable habitat on a long-term basis.

When establishing plants to enhance a wildlife habitat, the new area should be adjacent to an existing wildlife habitat. If not, a **greenbelt** should be used. A greenbelt is a strip of grasses, shrubs, and other plants that serve as cover leading from the existing habitat to the newly established area. This allows wildlife organisms to enter the new area without exposing themselves to danger. You can provide relatively safe access by creating or making use of existing draws (ditches and gullies) or fence rows with woody vegetation leading from forested areas. Nut trees can be planted along the draw or spaced appropriately along the fence row. However, it is critical that at least one of the rows is tied to a forested area that provides adequate cover. Also, keep in mind that animals that consume wild nuts can be costly nuisances if they are in the wrong place.

Nut trees prefer moderately fertile soil that is well drained. They can use stony land or slopes that are too steep for cultivated crops. When establish-

15-18. Lush herbage provides good protection for a young fawn.

ing trees, weeds and grass should be controlled with mulch, and watering may be necessary during dry periods. On a large scale, watering and mulching may be impractical. In addition, livestock and wildlife should be kept away from young trees until they are well established. Fertilization needs will depend on soil fertility and the type of crop being produced. More information on plants suited to your local area is available from a game warden or other wildlife specialist.

*T*YPES OF TREES TO PLANT

Plant species of trees, shrubs, and others that provide a food material suitable for the wildlife in the local area. Begin by studying the food preferences of wildlife. Next, identify the kinds of plants that are adapted in the areas that provide food. Many people also view a wildlife habitat as land that produces marketable timber. If so, be sure to plant trees that produce wildlife food and have value as timber.

Keep in mind, the species of animal wildlife to be attracted when selecting what to plant. Smaller nuts are generally more useful to wildlife, particularly birds. Plants

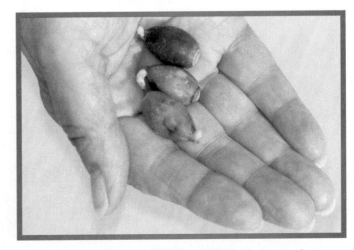

15-19. These acorns were found under moist leaves and were beginning to sprout.

15-20. Mulberries are favorite foods with blue jays, crows, and other common birds. (They are produced on trees that mature to be medium in size.)

15-21. Muscadine grapes form in clusters each fall and are typically dark purple when ripe.

that produce seed are also attractive to birds. Pecans, shagbark hickories, and small pignut hickories are top foods for the fox and gray squirrels. Black walnuts are readily taken, but are usually second choice to hickories and pecans. Pinon pine and other pine trees produce cones with seed that are popular with squirrels and other rodent-type wildlife.

The bulk of natural nut food comes from acorns, in part due to the wide distribution of oaks. It is wise to include both white and black oaks in any plan that is designed to encourage squirrels and other wildlife.

USING DOMESTICATED CROPS

Farm crops are good sources of animal wildlife food. Small plots of crops can be planted in wildlife habitat areas. Wheat, milo, and others are sometimes used. Native plants may often provide better food nutrients than farm crops. Since most crops are seasonal, foods from other sources must be available when the crops are gone.

In some cases, wildlife can be a pest in crop fields. Animal wildlife species eat and destroy valuable crops. A good

15-22. Birds often like farm-raised raspberries and may be pests when the berries ripen.

example is deer. A small herd of deer can consume leaves, pods, stems, and other plant structures. Some soybean fields have been wiped out by deer! A few producers plant areas just for wildlife with the notion that if they are fed elsewhere, they will not get into the fields of crops.

Table 15-4. Cultivated Plants Often Used as Wildlife Food

Corn	Barley	Apple	Grape
Wheat	Sorghum	Rice	Rye grass
Oats	Cherry	Alfalfa	

Note: Nearly every cultivated plant is a food source for some animal species; be it deer browsing in a field, or rabbits eating tender lettuce in a garden.

REVIEWING

MAIN IDEAS

Plants provide food for many animal wildlife species. The kinds of plants animals consume and an adequate quantity must be available to support the animal population.

Animal wildlife food plants are often divided into three main groups: browse, herbage, and mast. Browse refers to tender shoots that animals may eat. Herbage includes succulent nonwoody plants, including legumes and grasses. Mast is the fruits and nuts produced by plants. The fruit may be in various forms, including wild berries, plums, and cherries.

Steps can be taken to promote the growth of plant food materials. A range of habitat management practices may be used. This includes planting trees that produce nuts or fruit, grasses, and legumes. When harvesting timber, important trees that produce foods may be left without cutting. Only species of plants suited to the area should be planted. If they are not, resources will be wasted and food will not be produced for the animal wildlife.

QUESTIONS

Answer the following questions using correct spelling and complete sentences:

1. What is browse?

2. Which animals make the best use of browse? Why?

3. What is herbage? Give three examples.

4. What is mast? Give three examples.

5. What is the difference between a berry and a fruit?

6. What is a nut? Give three examples.

7. What is soil erosion? How is it important in establishing a wildlife habitat?

8. Why are nuts rather than grasses better suited as food for rodents?

9. What type of land is best for trees that produce nuts?

10. With habitat, why is it important to have plants that are available all seasons of the year?

EVALUATING

Match the term with the correct definition. Write the letter by the term in the space provided.

a. acorn
b. legume
c. berry

d. ripe
e. nut
f. herbage

g. controlled burning
h. mast

_____1. Fruits and nuts of trees and shrubs eaten by animals.

_____2. Plant that fixes nitrogen from the air in soil.

_____3. Using fire to improve habitat.

_____4. Dried fruit of a wide variety of oak trees.

_____5. A small, fleshy fruit with seed embedded inside.

_____6. Condition of a mature berry that is juicy and sweet.

_____7. A mature, dry fruit with a shell.

_____8. Plants with succulent nonwoody stems and leaves.

EXPLORING

1. Make a field trip to an area that has been improved to provide better animal wildlife habitat. Ask the person in charge to explain what was done and the results that have been obtained. Determine the kind of animal wildlife the area is intended to attract.

2. Identify an area in your community that could be developed and improved as an animal wildlife habitat. Determine the native plants now in the area and the species of animal wildlife that may be present. Prepare a plan for installing and maintaining the improved habitat.

3. Tour an area of woodland or other habitat. Make a collection of fruit, nuts, and other plant materials that animal wildlife can use as food. Caution: Be careful not to touch plants that may be poisonous, such as poison ivy.

Part Five

Enjoying Wildlife: Citizen Responsibilities

CHAPTER 16

Hunting

OBJECTIVES

This chapter explains sport hunting. It traces hunting from early times and describes how it relates to modern wildlife management. The following objectives are included:

1 Explain hunting as a sport.

2 List important regulations that govern hunting.

3 Describe the kinds of firearms used in hunting.

4 Explain hunter safety.

5 Describe how common species are hunted.

6 Describe how harvested game is prepared.

7 Explain landowner and property rights.

TERMS

ammunition	hunter orange	rifle
bag limit	hunting	season length
bowhunting	hunting gear	shell
broadhead	hunting license	shooting
cartridge	landowner rights	shooting hours
choke	marksmanship	shot
firearm	muzzleloader	shotgun
firearm safety	primitive hunting device	

16-1. A duck hunter with her daily bag limit.

HUNTING is popular with many people. They enjoy being outdoors, walking in the woods or meadows and experiencing nature. Some people hunt animals while others hunt mushrooms, berries, nuts, and many other living and nonliving things.

Most sport hunting is about taking animals—rabbits, squirrels, deer, bears, ducks, and many others. People get good equipment and practice using it. They study the game and the laws that relate to hunting. Hunters learn and practice safety in all that they do while hunting or handling firearms. They respect the rights of landowners and treat non-hunters with courtesy.

Sport hunting is sometimes controversial. Not all people agree that killing animals in this manner is a good thing. Hunters as well as non-hunters need to appreciate the ideas of other people. A little understanding can go a long way in overcoming differences.

HUNTING AS A SPORT

16-2. A hunter with a trophy caribou.

16-3. Shotgun skills are improved by practice at a skeet range.

Hunting is killing game for food and/or recreation. Today, the emphasis is on the enjoyment that is gained from hunting. In most cases, the game is used as food or, in some cases, as trophies. Sport hunting is a tradition in many families. They look forward to hunting trips with great anticipation. Family schedules are often set around open hunting seasons!

The term, shooting, is sometimes used synonymously with hunting but a distinction is often made. ***Shooting*** is non-hunting firing of guns to develop skills in aiming, firing, and accuracy. The shooting may be at a skeet range with a shotgun and involve firing at swiftly moving clay targets. The number of shots fired is often greater than in an actual hunting situation.

HUNTING HERITAGE

All people were hunters at one time. Before animals were domesticated, hunting and gathering were used to get food. The methods used were simple. No guns were available. People had to outsmart the animals and use traps, clubs, or rocks to kill the game. Modern sport hunting is a carryover from the time when taking animals for food and clothing was required for human survival.

Game is a crop. It is produced by the land and harvested by hunters. Game animals are more abundant some years than others. In good years, plenty of game is available. In lean years, hunters limit their take or may refrain from hunting all together.

16-4. Sport hunting is an important recreational activity to many people.

Table 16-1. Common Game Species

Large Mammals	Small Mammals	Waterfowl	Upland Birds
Caribou	Fox squirrel	Ducks—	Turkey
Mule deer	Gray squirrel	Mallard	Mourning dove
White-tailed deer	Swamp rabbit	Wood duck	Bobwhite
Moose	Cottontail rabbit	Pintail	Ruffed grouse
Black bear		Blue-winged teal	Ring-necked pheasant
Pronghorn		Canvasback	Mountain quail
		Ringneck duck	

Note: This table lists a few examples of game animals. Some may be protected in certain states and local areas. Always know and follow the law.

Hunting can be viewed as an important wildlife management tool. Hunting is used to reduce wildlife populations and help keep a balance between the number of animals in an area and the ability of the area to provide food. Restrictions on taking some wildlife species may result in population increases.

HUNTER RESPONSIBILITY

Good hunters are responsible people. They strive to protect and improve the areas where wildlife species grow. They

16-5. Hunters should transport unloaded guns in approved cases that prevent damage to the gun and equipment and provide safety.

HUNTER CODE OF ETHICS

1. I will consider myself an invited guest of the landowner, and get permission before using their land.
2. I will obey rules of safe firearm handling and encourage others to do so.
3. I will obey game laws and regulations and insist that my companions do so as well.
4. I will acquire good shooting and hunting skills to ensure sporting kills.
5. I will support conservation efforts to ensure hunting in future years.
6. I will help other hunters learn skills and attitudes necessary to allow them to become true sport hunters.
7. I will securely store my firearms and ammunition when not in use.

Adopted from *North Carolina Hunter Education Manual*, Wildlife Resources Commission, Raleigh, 1996.

16-6. Code of Ethics for Sport Hunters.

learn and follow all laws related to hunting. Hunters know that safe use of hunting equipment is essential.

Hunter education is required before sport hunting. The education covers important safety and legal areas. Many states offer hunter education as classes in schools, through the local office of the Cooperative Extension Service, and in other ways.

Hunters should hunt only in approved locations. They should never trespass. They always respect the property of others. A farm is the private property of another person, just as you own certain things. You would not want another person to use your property without permission!

Hunters should always exhibit ethical behavior. This means that they know and do the right things. A code of ethics has been developed to guide the behavior of hunters.

HUNTING CONTROLS

16-7. Mourning doves are popular game birds in some areas.

Hunting is a highly regulated sport. State and federal regulations tightly control hunting procedures. In addition, many hunting clubs or individual hunters add extra restrictions and rules.

LICENSE

All hunters must have a hunting license. A **hunting license** is a small written document that indicates that an individual has paid a fee and is legally entitled to hunt. Hunting licenses are issued by an agency of the state government. They are often sold through local sporting goods stores.

Waterfowl hunters must have a federal duck stamp in addition to the state hunting license. Many states have a mandatory state duck stamp. There are additional special stamps for hunting of certain species in some locations. Examples include turkeys, bear, doves, and elk, depending on applicable laws.

Money derived from hunting licenses and stamps is used by conservation agencies to improve wildlife. Research and conservation areas are developed to benefit wildlife, sport hunters, and the general public.

LEGAL SPECIES

Laws vary from one state to another and within states. Always keep up-to-date on the species that can be hunted. Game agencies use hunting to help regulate wildlife populations. Severe fines can be assessed to individuals who take game illegally. Some species are never hunted. These are protected animals. (See Appendix F for names of state agencies with information on hunting laws.)

BAG LIMITS

Bag limit is the number of animals that can be taken in one day or season. This is the maximum number of animals that a person can kill. In some cases, limits are set on the number that a person can kill in a season. Taking more than the bag limit is illegal.

Bag limits may be based on the species of the animal within a broad group. This is often used with ducks. For example, the bag limit for ducks may be a total of four, but only two wood ducks can be included.

SEASON LENGTHS

Season length is the number of days that a species can be hunted in one year. For example, a deer season may be 62 days in length to begin on a specified day in

16-8. Binoculars may be used to locate and identify legal game.

16-9. A hunter has had a successful day.

16-10. Hunting is often restricted to the daylight hours and may begin at sunrise. (Courtesy, U.S. Fish and Wildlife Service)

November and run until the number of days is up in January. Other season limits are much shorter, such as 7 or 14 days. Any hunting before or after the season is illegal.

In some cases, seasons may be split. A week of open season could be in November and another in January. Just as hunting before or after is illegal, hunting between the open weeks is also illegal.

SHOOTING HOURS

Shooting hours (hunting hours) is the time of the day when hunting can take place. Hunters can go into the woods or field before or stay afterward, but they cannot fire their guns. For most species, legal shooting hours are from 30 minutes before sunrise to sunset. Some hunting may run from noon to sunset. Hunting, before or after the shooting hours, is illegal.

HUNTING GEAR

Hunting gear is all of the devices used in taking game and protecting the hunter. This includes devices known as firearms. A **firearm** is a tool that propels a projectile (bullet) by burning gun powder. Laws regulate the kinds of firearms that can be used with various species. Here is a brief summary:

- Migratory game birds can only be hunted with shotguns that hold no more than three shells. Examples include doves, ducks, geese, rails, swans, and sandhill cranes.

- Most big game is hunted with rifles. Local exceptions exist. Examples of wildlife animals hunted with a rifle include deer, elk, moose, antelope, and sheep.

- In some areas, bows and arrows can be used to hunt animals, such as deer.

It is illegal to use the improper firearm in hunting a species. Never take a gun to a school or other place where people could be injured.

Note: More information on firearms is presented in another section of this chapter.

AMMUNITION

Ammunition is any combination of powder, shot, or bullets used in shotguns, rifles, or pistols. Laws closely regulate some aspects of ammunition use in sport hunting. Always determine and follow the laws in the area where you are hunting.

Nontoxic ammunition is generally required in hunting waterfowl. This ammunition is made from steel or bismuth rather than lead. Lead is poisonous to waterfowl. The problem is with the pellets that fall to the ground. Waterfowl will sometimes eat the pellets as food or grit. Lead is poisonous to wildlife and humans. Many hunters are moving away from using lead shot.

FIREARM DISCHARGE

Firearm discharge regulations deal with where and when firearms can be discharged. Most towns and cities have ordinances that restrict the discharge of firearms. Areas near roads, homes, businesses, factories, animals in pastures or feedlots, and other places where people or property may be damaged by shots are restricted. Wildlife refuges and management areas restrict firearm discharge except during special hunts. Violating a firearm discharge law is illegal and punishable by fine.

CLOTHING

Hunting is an outdoor activity. The weather is often cold. The woods and meadows often have thorns, insect pests, snakes, and other hazards. Proper clothing is needed to protect the body under the conditions of the hunt.

One requirement in most areas is to wear hunter orange. This is a bright, fluorescent color that enables other hunters to clearly see you. No natural woods, field, or animals are the color of hunter orange. Hunters know that they are never to shoot in the direction of hunter orange. This prevents being mistaken for game and being shot. States often have regulations on the number of square inches of hunter orange fabric a hunter must wear.

16-11. Proper dress on a cold day includes warm clothing, hunter orange, proper personal protective equipment, and a backpack for other items.

HUNTING EQUIPMENT

Many kinds of devices can be used in hunting. These devices are generally in two groups: primitive and modern. Laws about wildlife vary somewhat depending on the device being used. For example, primitive devices can be used for extended seasons with certain species in some locations.

PRIMITIVE DEVICES

A *primitive hunting device* is a device with less power and, hence, less capacity to kill. The group is not well defined, but includes the bow and arrow, crossbow, and muzzleloading guns. Using these devices is sometimes known as specialty hunting.

Bowhunting

Bows and arrows were used for hunting before firearms were developed. In recent years, bowhunting has increased in popularity. **Bowhunting** is using a bow to propel an arrow. The bow has a string that is stretched tightly to propel the arrow into the game. Hunting seasons are usually longer for bowhunting than with modern firearms.

Bowhunting requires a commitment to learn what is involved. Practice, using the equipment, is essential. Safety must be followed to avoid injuring others as well as self-inflicted injuries. Special courses are available to teach hunters how to use bows and arrows.

The basic equipment needed includes: a bow, arrows, a quiver, a spare bowstring, proper clothing, finger and hand protection, and a license. Select equipment that feels good in your hands. Different types of bows are available: a straight limb or long bow, recurve, and compound bow. Arrows average 28 inches long. The tip on an arrow is known as a **broadhead**. Practice shooting skills with the same kind of broadhead as will be used in hunting. The quiver is the container in which the arrows are carried. The quiver should cover the broadheads securely.

The seven basic steps in shooting with a bow and arrow are:

16-12. Parts of a straight limb or long bow.

- Nock
- Upper limb
- String
- Serving
- Grip
- Lower limb

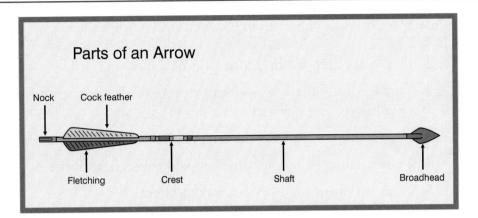

16-13. Parts of an arrow.

1. Position—Get the bow and arrow in position to shoot. Hold the equipment properly.

2. Nocking—Nocking is placing the nock (base of the arrow) against the string.

3. Drawing—Drawing is pulling the bowstring and nocked arrow back to generate force to propel the arrow when it is released.

4. Aiming—Aiming is carefully aligning the arrow in the bow to hit the object or animal.

5. Holding—A short pause occurs after drawing and aiming before the arrow is released.

6. Releasing—Releasing is letting go of the bowstring so the arrow reaches the target.

7. Follow-through—Follow-through is a brief opportunity to pause and observe the procedure followed in shooting the arrow.

Wildlife Connection

FOR ALL WHO ENJOY IT

Sport hunting is for all people who enjoy it, including those who are differently abled. The way they go about hunting may need some adaptation to meet their needs. Access to some areas of terrain may be somewhat limited. In some cases, hunting devices may need to be modified so individuals with certain disabilities can use them.

This photograph shows a group of successful hunters with their game. (Courtesy, U.S. Fish and Wildlife Service)

Safety is extremely important in bowhunting. Here are a few rules:

1. Get instruction in the proper use of a bow and arrow.

2. Practice using the bow and arrow properly. Know the safe way to use it. Keep broadheads well covered.

3. Always properly identify the target and be sure the path to the target is clear.

4. Be sure no obstructions interfere with operation of the bow or bowstring.

5. Nock an arrow only when ready to shoot.

6. Never shoot over a hill where you cannot see.

Crossbow Hunting

Crossbows were a major innovation some 2,500 years ago in China. The later invention of gunpowder replaced the important role of crossbows. The crossbow makes use of a bow, string, and an arrow, which is held in position and released by a device similar to a gun.

Anyone attempting to use a crossbow should get thorough instruction in its use. Crossbows may not be legal in all places, so check state laws. Know the safety rules. Practice using the crossbow to gain proficiency.

Muzzleload Hunting

A **muzzleloader** is a firearm that is loaded through the barrel (muzzle). Muzzleloaders are not considered modern firearms.

Career Profile

HUNTING GUIDE

Hunting guides take sports hunters on hunting expeditions. They help hunters find, shoot, and retrieve game safely. Hunting guides must know the local area and study where wildlife animals gather or are found in the area. They must be well informed on applicable laws.

Hunting guides need experience with wildlife, the outdoors, and hunting. High school education with specific education in wildlife will be very beneficial. They must be good communicators and prepared to handle safety problems.

Jobs for hunting guides are found in areas where hunting is important. This photograph shows a guide taking hunters into the back country on horseback.

Powder and shot will be needed to fire the gun. Shot is selected based on the size needed for a particular game animal. For example, #6 or #7½ size shot is used for pheasant and other small and medium game.

Hunting with a muzzleloader is challenging because only one charge is in the gun at a time. Powder and shot must be loaded between each firing. This takes time and allows game to escape. Thus, the challenge of muzzleload hunting!

Learn about the muzzleloader you will use before hunting. Practice using it safely. Never violate a safety rule.

MODERN FIREARMS

Firearms became common tools throughout much of the United States in the second half of the 1800s. Muzzleloaders had been the major firearms available. Much progress occurred with the development of the percussion cap. This made it easy to load and reload guns with shells or cartridges.

Firearms were used on farms to protect the livestock from predators and other property from poachers. Firearms were also used in game hunting and for other recreational uses.

Sporting firearms are divided into smooth-bore and rifle-bore. The smooth-bore firearms are shotguns, while the rifle-bore are rifles.

Shotguns

A **shotgun** is a firearm that fires several small pellets in a pattern at a target. Most use shells containing powder and pellets typically made of steel or lead.

The inside of the barrel has a smooth bore. The size of the bore is known as gauge (caliber). Common gun gauge sizes are 10, 12, 16, 20, 28, and .410. The smaller the gauge number the larger the size of the bore and, hence, of the shell that is used. Gauge is based on the size of a pure lead ball that is the exact diameter of the bore. Lead balls are sized on the basis of the number required to weigh one pound. For example, a 16-gauge shotgun would take a lead ball that weighed one-sixteenth of a pound (one ounce).

16-14. Using a 20-gauge pump-action shotgun.

16-15. Common types of shotguns are (from the left): side-by-side or double barrel, over-under, semiautomatic, and pump or slide action.

Shotguns, however, do not shoot pellets that are the size of the gauge. Pellets are much smaller.

Shotguns are available with a variety of features. Some hold only one shell at a time. Others are pump-action or semiautomatic guns, which means that a shell that has been fired can be rapidly replaced with a new shell. Shotguns may have one or two barrels. Those with one barrel are known as single barrel guns. Those with two barrels may be known as double barrel (barrels side by side) guns or as an over-under gun (one barrel on top of the other). Shotguns typically have longer barrels than rifles. This helps the shooter hold and balance the gun better when shooting.

Guns are known by choke. **Choke** is a constriction at the muzzle (end of barrel). Choke influences the pattern that the shots take after being fired from the gun. Most guns have a built-in choke. The kind of game being hunted determines the benefits of a choke. A broader shot pattern is more likely to kill small birds at close distance. Less choke is needed to get a broader shot pattern. A full choke is used with ducks and turkeys because they are larger birds and fly away at greater distances from the hunter. A gun without a choke is known as cylinder choke.

A **shell** is the container that holds the shot, powder, and other parts needed in the ammunition of shot-

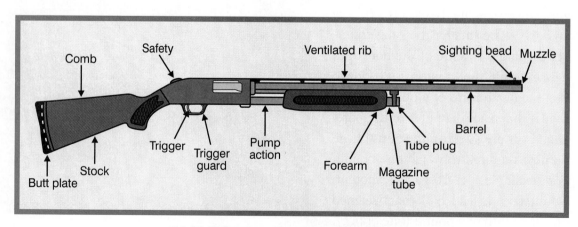

16-16. Major parts of a pump-action shotgun.

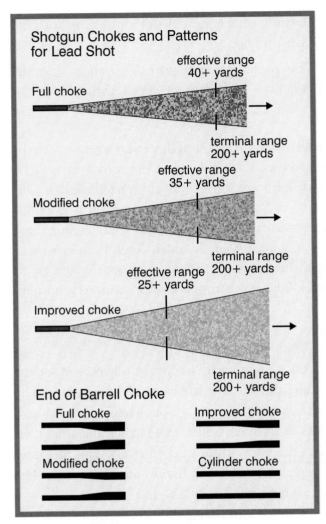

16-17. Chokes and patterns of shot.

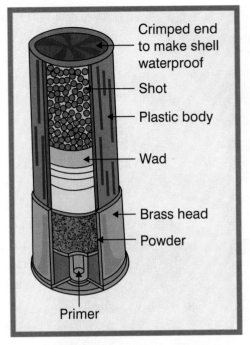

16-18. Major parts of a shotgun shell.

guns. Most are manufactured to be used one time and discarded. Some people reload shells for future use. Shot comes in various sizes.

A **shot** is a pellet of lead or steel (sometimes other material) used in shotgun shells. Shot size is determined by the diameter of the pellet. Each size is given a number. Standard shot sizes range from 12 to 1. The larger the number, the smaller the pellet. The smaller shot sizes, such as 7½ or 8, are used when hunting squirrel and small birds, such as bobwhite quail and dove. Shells with buckshot are used with large game. A shell has more small pellets than large pellets. Buckshot are the largest pellets, ranging from size 4 to 00.

All the parts of a gun must be in place to work properly. In general, the following occurs when a gun is fired:

1. The trigger is pulled to release the hammer.

2. The hammer drives a firing pin into the primer area.

3. The primer explodes setting the gunpowder on fire.

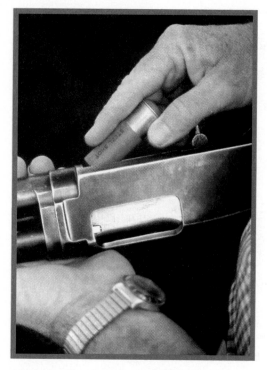

16-19. Loading a nontoxic shell into the magazine of a pump-type shotgun.

4. Burning of the gunpowder causes instant high pressure gas.

5. The intense pressure pushes the shot out of the gun at a high rate of speed through the air (toward your target).

Marksmanship is the ability to hit a target with the shot from a gun. With a shotgun, the end of the barrel is pointed toward the target (as contrasted with a rifle, which is aimed). A good shooting position is essential. Face the game or target. Bring the shotgun to your cheek and rest it against your shoulder. Keep both eyes open and align the barrel on the target. When ready, gently and firmly squeeze the trigger. Do not use a jerky motion.

Rifles

A *rifle* is a firearm with a spiral or rifle bore inside the barrel. Rifles fire one shot from a cartridge at a time. The spiral bore causes the bullet to spin when it goes through the barrel. A spinning bullet goes farther and straighter. Rifles are selected based on the diameter of the bore (inside of the barrel). This measurement is known as caliber. Caliber is reported as millimeters or hundredths of an inch. The most popular caliber rifle is the .22 caliber. Others are .270, 30.06, and 6 mm.

Some rifles have features so several firings can be made in rapid succession. Such features on a rifle describe it as a repeater or automatic rifle. The trigger must be pulled each time a shell is fired.

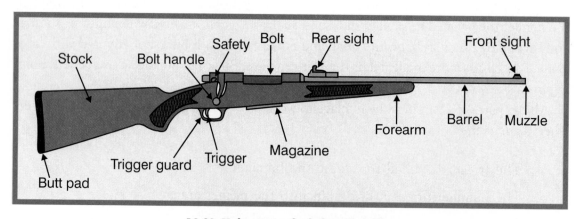

16-20. Major parts of a bolt-action rifle.

16-21. Three types of rifles commonly used in sport hunting are (from the left) lever action, semiautomatic, and bolt action. (Each rifle shown has a telescopic sight.)

16-22. Safely using a powerful rifle with scope involves knowing the potential hazards. Consider the distance the bullet will travel and be sure there is nothing in the distance that could be an unknown target.

Ammunition manufactured for a rifle is known as a **cartridge** or round. The size cartridge to buy depends on the bore of the rifle. Cartridges can be manufactured as centerfired or rimfired. Rimfired cartridges have solid or hollow points and are made only for smaller rifles and pistols. Ammunition must be properly selected and cared for. Never use ammunition in a firearm for which it was not designed.

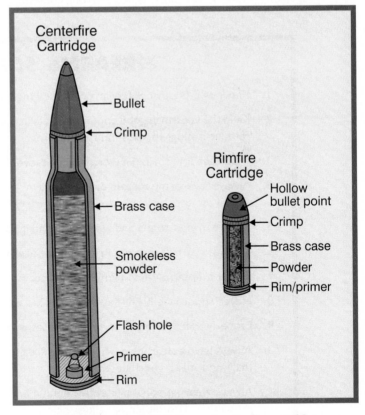

16-23. Major parts of rimfire and centerfire cartridges.

HUNTER SAFETY

Firearm safety is preventing accidents and injury by using a firearm in a responsible manner. This requires safe behavior as well as thinking to anticipate possible dangers. Respect other people as well as their property. Most accidents occur because people violate safety rules. Other accidents occur because hunters make poor judgments and lack the skills to operate the firearm properly.

16-24. Most accidents occur when guns are handled in a dangerous way. (This shows the proper way to go through a fence when two people are hunting together.) (Courtesy, Bob Hines, Winchester-Olin Corporation)

FIREARMS SAFETY RULES

1. Know your firearm. Safety involves knowing how to load, shoot, and care for the firearm.

2. Keep the firearm in good condition. A clean firearm is safer. Be sure the barrel is open. (A barrel that is clogged with mud is extremely dangerous.)

3. Treat each firearm as if it were loaded. Never load a firearm until you are ready to use it.

4. Always control the muzzle of your firearm. Never point the barrel toward an individual, farm animal, or property. Always properly carry your gun when walking.

5. Be sure of your target and what is beyond it. Objects behind a target are a part of the target.

6. Unload firearms when not in use. Never have a loaded firearm in a motor vehicle or building.

7. Empty a firearm when climbing a fence or crossing a ditch.

8. Never shoot at a hard, flat surface. This will result in the bullets ricocheting.

9. Properly store firearms so children cannot get them.

10. Always have a clear mind when using a firearm. Never use substances that alter your ability to think and make good judgments.

11. Always wear personal protective equipment when shooting. This includes hearing and eye protection. Use either ear plugs or muffs to protect hearing. (Most firearms make noise above 130 decibels, which is the level at which hearing damage occurs.)

16-25. General Safety Rules with Firearms.

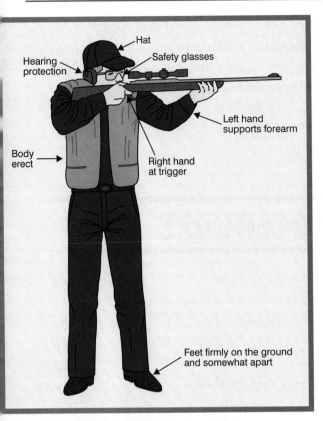

Hat

Safety glasses

Hearing protection

Left hand supports forearm

Body erect

Right hand at trigger

Feet firmly on the ground and somewhat apart

16-26. How to properly hold a gun for shooting right-handed from the standing position. (Note: The butt of the stock is against the shoulder, the left hand supports the gun at the forearm, and the right hand is around the trigger guard with the index finger on the trigger.)

16-27. Training in safe gun use is available for hunters and target shooters. This shooter is holding her shotgun in a correct and safe manner while she listens to instructions. Note that the gun is unloaded and the breech is open making accidental discharge impossible.

Always have emergency telephone numbers in your wallet and at the place from which you began the hunt. A cellular telephone or two-way radio can be useful.

Safety requires that individuals understand the fundamentals of shooting and handling firearms. Good vision is necessary for accurate shooting. Safety is everyone's responsibility!

16-28. Hold a gun properly when you are carrying it.

Shoulder

Trail

Cradle

Bullets from guns can travel great distances. Bullets also travel a great deal farther at elevations above sea level. For example, a .22 short rifle bullet will travel about one-half mile at sea level but nearly a mile at elevations of 12,000 feet. Some rifle bullets can travel three miles or more. Shotgun pellets do not travel as far as rifle bullets. No. 9 shot fired from a 12-gauge gun will travel about 750 feet at sea level and 900 feet at 12,000 feet altitude. No. 2 shot fired from a 12-gauge gun will travel more than 1,000 feet. Always be alert to what might be in the direction in which you are shooting.

HUNTING PROCEDURES

Once a firearm is mastered, successful hunting requires understanding the animal being hunted. Animal activity is greatest during early morning and late evening hours. Animal characteristics and laws may influence hunting hours. Be sure to have the proper license and follow bag limits and other laws. Have the proper firearm and ammunition. Respect all safety rules.

General guidelines for hunting selected species are presented here.

QUAIL

Hunting procedures vary with geographic location and the species of quail being hunted. It is helpful to know the general habitat of quail and where they can be found. The hunt begins by approaching one edge of the area where the quail will likely be found. The hunt

16-29. Small covey of valley quail.

moves across the area so as to locate any game. Bobwhite, for example, are hunted in grassy areas near wooded land.

Quail hunters often use trained dogs known as bird dogs. The dogs move ahead of the hunters and freeze into a statue-like pose when they smell or see birds on the ground. The birds remain hidden and motionless near the dog. Hunters walk to the dog with shotguns held at ready. When the birds fly, the hunters shoot. Downed birds are retrieved by the bird dogs and the hunt resumes. Quail hunting generally requires much walking during the course of the hunt.

16-30. Quail hunting with a German shorthaired pointer.

DEER

Many deer hunters walk slowly in the forest in an attempt to see the deer before the deer sees or smells them. Other deer hunters sit on elevated platforms (stands) or in box blinds (small structures that offer concealment) and wait for deer to move toward them. Blinds may be constructed of lumber, canvas, grass, shrubs, or tree limbs. Blinds are located at travel lanes called deer crossings. Most deer are shot with rifles, but, at some locations, par-

16-31. A big white-tailed deer buck (mature male) eats leaves from a twig. (Courtesy, George Hurst, Mississippi State University)

16-32. A proud hunter shows a wild boar he killed on Cumberland Island, a National Seashore off the coast of Georgia.

ticularly in the South where vegetation is very thick, shotguns are used. Be sure to only take the legal animals—never shoot a doe (female deer) or fawn (young deer) unless it is legal.

DUCK AND GOOSE

Duck and goose hunting is generally done in harvested fields or shallow-water areas along streams. Most waterfowl hunters hide in blinds made of vegetation and set out numerous decoys made of wood, plastic, or rubber. Decoys either float on the water or are placed on the land. Waterfowl hunters commonly use calls that, when blown correctly, sound like ducks or geese. Hunters try to imitate sounds made by birds when they are feeding.

The combination of decoys and calling (imitated bird sounds) is used to attract flying birds. When birds respond to the decoys and calling and fly into range, they are taken with shotguns. Many hunters use highly trained dogs, called retrievers, to swim out and fetch downed birds or find birds that fall into dense vegetation.

All hunters, but especially waterfowl hunters, need specialized equipment. Since waterfowl hunters often hunt in water, they need rubber boots, called waders, waterproof gloves, caps, and warm clothing. They also frequently need boats to reach remote areas or to cross deep water.

16-33. A mallard drake. (Courtesy, U.S. Fish and Wildlife Service)

TURKEY

Turkeys are hunted at different times of the year, depending on the legal season. Some are hunted in the fall and winter; others are hunted in the spring. During the spring season, the male turkey (gobbler) is very active and often travels alone looking for hens (female turkeys).

Turkey hunters locate areas that turkeys are known to frequent. Hunters sit quietly against trees or in brush blinds. Because of the wariness of the male turkey, many turkey hunters wear camou-

16-34. A turkey hunter aims at a wild gobbler.

flaged clothes with a minimum of hunter orange. Hunters periodically use calling devices to imitate the calls of female turkeys. Hunters tempt the gobbler to investigate the calling sounds. When the turkey is in range and completely visible, the bird is shot with a shotgun, or in some cases, with a rifle.

RABBIT AND SQUIRREL

Rabbit and squirrel may be hunted with a shotgun or rifle. Rabbits are hunted in brushy, grassy areas near woodland. Squirrels are hunted in wooded areas. Squirrels are especially fond of large trees with foods, such as hickory and oaks with acorns. Most squirrel hunters

16-35. A rabbit hunter flushes a Cottontail on a hunt.

walk through the area, being careful to keep noise to a minimum. They keep on the alert for the game. Once visible and within range, the shotgun or rifle is used to kill the animal.

PREPARING HARVESTED GAME

Harvested game should be used as food and for other products. Not using it is a huge waste!

The goal is to have wholesome food prepared in a tasty manner. This requires processing or dressing the animal to remove hair, skin, internal organs, and other parts that are not used. All of the work should be done to keep the meat clean. Refrigeration is needed to chill the meat and prevent spoilage.

Proper cooking enhances the flavor of game. Many recipes are available for cooking game. Families often have favorite recipes that are passed down from one generation to the next.

BIG GAME

Assuring quality food from game begins during the hunt. Big game animals are handled differently from small animals. Big game animals, such as deer (venison), are almost always field dressed as quickly as possible. Field dressing involves splitting the animal from the pelvis to the neck with a sharp knife to expose the body cavity. The heart, lungs, and other internal organs are removed. The animal's carcass is hung from a tree limb or other point to allow the blood to drain out and the body to lose its heat.

After field dressing, the animal is taken home or to a processing plant. Home processing begins with skinning the animal. Care must be taken to avoid getting hair and dirt on the flesh. The carcass is then quartered, which is detaching front and rear legs from the body. The dressed quarters are cut into steaks and roasts by slicing the muscle tissue from the bone of the thighs. Tender steaks are cut from the loin (large muscle at the base of the ribs). Roasts are cut from the neck area. The remainder of the usable flesh is ground into sausage or used as ground meat.

Some hunters take game to processing facilities where skilled butchers skin, fabricate, wrap, and freeze the meat. These businesses charge a fee for their work. Processing facilities are available at nearly all major hunting areas.

Processed meats must be frozen or otherwise preserved to prevent spoilage. The quicker this occurs, the better the quality of the game as food. Always keep the meat clean and refrigerated or frozen to prevent spoilage.

SMALL GAME

Dressing small game varies by species. Animals with fur are obviously different from those with feathers.

Small mammals, such as squirrels and rabbits, are skinned and eviscerated (gutted) in the field or immediately upon returning from the hunt. The skinned animals are usually cut into quarters before cooking. Some may be cut into individual parts, such as legs or back. A few people keep the brain and certain internal organs, such as the liver and kidneys, for cooking.

Most birds are picked in the field. Picking removes the larger feathers. After the large feathers have been removed, many hunters place the rough-picked carcass over a small open fire to singe the smaller feathers and soft down. This process removes all of the feathers. A properly picked and singed bird looks as neat and clean as a packaged fowl bought at the

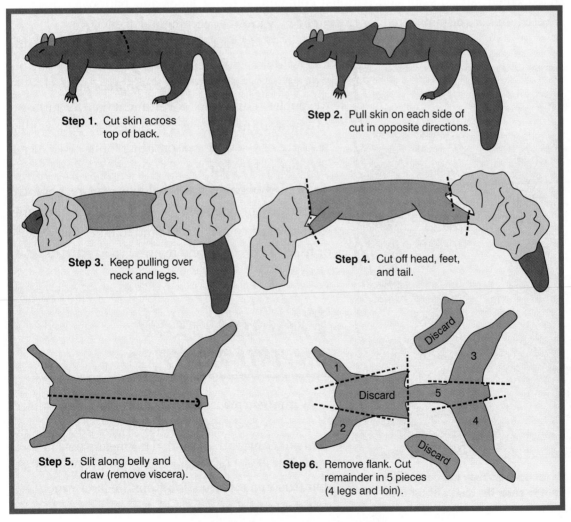

Step 1. Cut skin across top of back.

Step 2. Pull skin on each side of cut in opposite directions.

Step 3. Keep pulling over neck and legs.

Step 4. Cut off head, feet, and tail.

Step 5. Slit along belly and draw (remove viscera).

Step 6. Remove flank. Cut remainder in 5 pieces (4 legs and loin).

16-36. How to dress a squirrel or rabbit.

store. The next step is to remove the internal organs, head, wings, and feet. Thoroughly wash the carcass. Many hunters keep the gizzards and hearts. Birds can be cooked whole or cut into halves or smaller pieces.

LANDOWNER AND PROPERTY RIGHTS

All land and water in the United States and Canada is either publicly or privately owned. Farms, ranches and residential sites make up the majority of privately owned lands. Businesses, large corporations, private universities, and private land trusts own and manage large tracts of land scattered across the country.

Public lands usually consist of rivers, lakes, coastal bays, parks, wildlife refuges, wildlife management areas, state and national commercial forest lands and national grasslands. These lands are administered for the public by various governmental agencies.

16-37. Private landowners may use posted signs to warn people not to enter the land without permission.

Despite the fact that the vast majority of our fish and wildlife resources live on private property, our laws clearly state that these resources are owned by the public. This means government has the authority to control the harvest of those fish and wildlife resources by setting seasons, bag limits, and means and methods of harvest.

Even though fish and wildlife resources are the property of the public, landowners have the authority to control who enters their land to hike, camp, hunt, or fish. This is generally referred to as *landowner rights*.

TRESPASS LAWS AND PROPERTY RIGHTS

With some few exceptions, most lands are subject to trespass laws and all landowners have certain rights to control their land. This means that in most cases, it is illegal for anyone to enter upon land unless that person has permission from the landowner. The vast majority of private landowners enforce the trespass laws and keep gates locked to prevent unwanted use of their land. The law punishes those guilty of illegal trespass. In most cases, the courts assess a simple fine for this violation but in some cases, the punishment can involve imprisonment.

In the case of public lands, the government generally sets up specific regulations governing the use of those lands. State and Federal Parks usually allow public entry at specific entry points where permits can be purchased. Some public areas have unlimited access and individuals can enter and leave at their own discretion. This is particularly true of national forests, rivers, lakes and coastal bays.

A small number of private landowners allow unlimited access to their properties but the vast majority either allow entry upon permission or lease their land to individuals or groups. In many rural areas, it is possible to gain access to lands to hunt, fish, hike or otherwise use that land simply by seeking out the landowner and asking permission to enter. In those cases, most landowners do not charge for permission to enter. However, it is becoming more common for landowners to lease their land for a fee. This allows individuals to have complete access to the land for recreational purposes

OBLIGATIONS TO THE LANDOWNER

Everyone using either private or public lands has an obligation to provide common courtesy and to respect the rights of the landowner. Examples of common courtesies are:

1. Keep gates closed and avoid damaging fences.
2. Keep vehicles on improved roads and avoid making ruts on wet or unimproved roads.
3. Pick up all trash and litter.
4. Use extreme care with fire. Extinguish all fires when leaving.
5. Be extremely careful with firearms. Watch for livestock and other hunters. Do not hunt near buildings or roads.
6. Obey all local, state or national laws.

REVIEWING

MAIN IDEAS

Present-day sport hunting is a carry-over from the early history when humans hunted and gathered food and clothing. Today, hunting is a favorite pastime with some people. It provides food for the table, as well as hours of enjoyment.

Hunting is a regulated sport. Both federal and state laws apply. All hunters must know the laws and have valid hunting licenses. Bag limits, seasons, hours of hunting, and other laws apply.

A wide variety of devices are used in hunting. Some people like the primitive devices, such as bows and arrows or muzzleloaders. Most people use modern firearms, with the two main types being shotguns and rifles. A hunter must know the firearm used in hunting. Practice is needed to develop skill in safely using firearms. The firearm and ammunition are selected based on the kind of game to be hunted.

Safety is essential in sport hunting. Always handle and use firearms in a safe manner. Never get careless. Know the rules of hunting safety before handling a firearm and beginning a hunt.

Before any hunt, always have approval to go onto the land. Never trespass on private property. Always respect other people and their property.

QUESTIONS

Answer the following questions using correct spelling and complete sentences:

1. What is hunting? How has the nature and purpose of hunting changed?
2. What is the code of ethics for sport hunters?
3. What are the areas in which laws apply to hunting? Briefly explain each.
4. What is hunter orange? Why is this color important?
5. What primitive hunting devices may be used?
6. What are firearms?
7. What is the distinction between shotguns and rifles?
8. What is marksmanship?
9. What is firearm safety? Name four important safety rules.
10. What procedures are followed in hunting game? (Select one of the game animals described in the chapter and briefly describe how it is hunted.)
11. How is game prepared for consumption?
12. Game is sometimes considered to be a crop. Why?
13. What are landowner rights?
14. What obligations does a hunter have to a landowner?

EVALUATING

Match the term with the correct definition. Write the letter by the term in the space provided.

a. hunting license   e. ammunition   i. firearm safety
b. bag limit   f. bowhunting   j. shooting hours
c. hunting gear   g. shell
d. firearm   h. cartridge

_____ 1. Number of animals that can be taken in a day.

_____ 2. Time of the day when hunting can take place.

_____ 3. Written document indicating that a person has paid a fee and is entitled to hunt.

_____ 4. Devices used to hunt animals and protect the hunter.

_____ 5. A combination of powder, shot, and bullets.

_____ 6. Manufactured ammunition for use in a rifle.

_____ 7. A tool that propels a projectile by burning gun powder.

_____ 8. Preventing accidents in using firearms.

_____ 9. Manufactured ammunition for a shotgun.

_____ 10. Sport hunting with a bow and arrow.

EXPLORING

1. Go to a store or office that sells hunting and fishing licenses. Obtain a brochure that lists hunting regulations. Summarize the regulations in a report to the class.

2. Take a field trip to a shooting range. Have the proper way of firing a rifle or shotgun demonstrated to you. Practice holding, loading, aiming, and firing firearms. Be sure to use ear muffs or plugs and shooting glasses.

3. Arrange to take a hunter safety education class. This could be at your school, a local office, or other location. Complete the instruction and gain certification.

CHAPTER 17

Fishing

OBJECTIVES

This chapter introduces the important area of fishing, both as a sport and commercially. The following objectives are included:

1 Explain commercial and sport fishing.

2 Explain aquaculture.

3 List legal regulations that apply to sport fishing.

4 Describe sport fishing equipment and supplies.

5 Explain important safety practices in fishing.

6 Describe how fish are prepared for use.

TERMS

aquaculture	fishing	fry
bait	fishing hook	line
cane pole	fishing season	lure
commercial fishing	fishing tackle	sinker
fee lake	float	sport fishing
fingerling	food fish	stock enhancement

"LET'S go fishing!" is often heard across North America. Sport fishing is a popular activity. Millions of people spend many hours fishing each year. They enjoy being around water, in fresh air, and scheming of ways to catch the "big one."

In addition to the enjoyment of fishing, sport fishing contributes jobs and income in many areas. Boats, tackle, bait, fuel, food, lodging, and many other areas benefit from the money spent in sport fishing.

Fishing also includes commercial fishing. This is harvesting large quantities of fish from lakes, oceans, and streams for human food. In recent years, fish farming has emerged to have a prominent role in some areas.

17-1. A sport fisher shows a nice size largemouth bass that was caught with a casting rod and lure.

THE FISHING INDUSTRY

Fishing is capturing fish using seines, nets, hooks, or other means. Fishing can be an occupation or a leisure-time activity. As an occupation, fishing involves capturing fish for use as food and other purposes. It forms a commercial fishing industry. As a leisure-time activity, it is sport fishing.

The fishing industry has two major areas: commercial fishing and sport fishing.

COMMERCIAL FISHING

Commercial fishing is capturing wild fish from oceans and inland waters for use as human food and in making other products. The fish are caught in large quantities using sophisticated equipment. They may be marketed fresh, canned, or frozen.

Commercial fishing is an important industry in the waters around North America, especially in the ocean areas. It is even more important in other countries where fish account for a greater share of human food. Expensive and often complicated equipment, plus large amounts of human effort, are expended to catch fish for sale. Commercial fishers sell their catch for human consumption or other commercial uses, such as fish oil, fertilizer, and pet food. Most of the products produced through commercial fisheries are known as seafood. They are organisms that live primarily in saltwater.

17-2. Commercial fish processing is carried out in large automated facilities.

Commercial fishers typically use large, nylon mesh nets to catch a variety of seafood, ranging from shrimp to codfish. Lobsters, crabs, and crawfish are caught in wooden or wire mesh traps that are baited with fish scraps or prepared fish products. Some commercial fishers use lines with hooks baited with small fish, shrimp, squid, or crabs. A fish commonly caught with a hook and line is the red snapper. Many regulations apply to commercial fishing. Most of these are designed to prevent over-fishing and assure a supply of fish for the future.

Practically all commercial fishers operate from boats. Commercial boats range in size from 14-foot flat bottom boats to diesel-powered boats more than 100 feet long. The large boats have engines to power seines, brailling bags (large net used to hold captured fish), and

17-3. Commercial fishing cannery in Alaska.

other equipment. These boats are capable of capturing thousands of pounds of fish at one time.

By most standards, the life of a commercial fisher is strenuous and demanding. The work includes occupational dangers. Bad weather is a serious threat to people working on boats in large bodies of water.

SPORT FISHING

Sport fishing is capturing fish for relaxation and enjoyment. The number of people in sport fishing is far greater than the number in commercial fishing, but the volume of fish caught by the commercial fishers is much greater. Sport fishers cannot usually sell the fish they catch. Some of the species of fish they catch are game fish and protected by law. The fish are often eaten at home or are released back into the water if not injured while being caught.

The nature of sport fishing varies widely. It may be a quiet trip to a creek or a larger trip for a deep-sea fishing expedition. It may involve fishing through holes

17-4. The first fishing experience for a three-year-old keeps mother and daddy busy!

17-5. Setting a crab trap is one form of sport fishing in the Gulf of Mexico.

in the ice or using spears to capture fish. All of these are sport fishing, though they are carried out differently. The equipment used may be a simple pole with line and hook or a more sophisticated rod and reel or fly rod.

AQUACULTURE

Aquaculture is the production of aquatic organisms. It is sometimes said to be "water farming." The crop is not wild. Careful management is used to assure a wholesome food just as with other food products produced on farms.

Water environments are managed in ways that promote the growth of fish, shellfish, aquatic plants, and beneficial algae. Most of the emphasis is on fin fish, though shrimp, oysters, clams, crawfish, prawns, and lobster are among the species that are cultured. The major species of fin fish cultured include catfish, salmon, Tilapia, hybrid striped bass, trout, and bait fish minnows. Aquaculture is viewed as providing foods when the earth's oceans and streams fall short. In fact, many natural waters have been over-fished to the point that no wild fish can be harvested from the water.

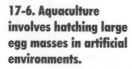
17-6. Aquaculture involves hatching large egg masses in artificial environments.

The conditions in aquaculture are different from those of wild fish living in streams and lakes. Improved stocks of fish are kept in a carefully controlled environment and provided nutritionally-complete feed. The crops grown can be freshwater, saltwater, or brackish water species.

Water Facilities

Most aquaculture occurs in ponds, tanks, or raceways. A pond is a body of water that is carefully managed to assure a good environment for the fish. Tanks are often used where additional control is needed over the environment. The population density in tanks is much greater than in ponds. Raceways are water facilities that use flowing water. Pens and cages are sometimes used in natural bodies of water. These confine the fish to one area of the water.

Aquaculture requires a good supply of water. The water must be managed to assure adequate oxygen and remove wastes. The major wastes are solid materials and ammonia formed by the action of the bacteria in the water on certain waste materials.

17-7. Raceways are used to grow trout at this Virginia farm.

7-8. Round tanks are used to raise prawns on this quaculture farm.

17-9. An aerator is being used in this pond to add oxygen to the water.

PRODUCTION CYCLE

Aquaculture production involves hatcheries where young fish are raised to adequate size for stocking. Young, newly-hatched fish are known as *fry*. Most fry hatch with a yolk sac attached. The sac provides nutrition for the fry for several days. Fry are raised to fingerling-size. A *fingerling* is a small fish used to stock ponds or tanks. Fingerlings are typically 4 to 8 inches long. Under good conditions, the fingerlings become food fish size in a few months.

A *food fish* is one that is large enough to provide a quality food product. In the case of catfish or Tilapia, food fish size is typically 1 to 2 pounds. The fish are harvested in large quantities and sent through automated processing plants. The plants prepare the fish for selling in stores or to restaurants.

17-10. Food-size fish are being lifted from a pond for hauling to a processing facility. (Courtesy, Fish Farming Experimental Station)

RECREATIONAL AQUACULTURE

A few cultured fish are released into sport fishing facilities. This practice is increasing in popularity.

A *fee lake* is a small lake or pond where people are charged a fee to fish. Fee lakes are stocked with an abundance of fish to assure that customers will catch fish. People who fish are charged by the day, by the weight of the fish, or on some other basis. Many sport fishers enjoy going to fee lakes.

Another area of recreational aquaculture involves releasing cultured fish into a stream. This is often referred to as stock enhancement. *Stock enhancement* improves the number and quality of fish in a stream. Cultured fish are placed in the stream along with the wild fish that may currently live in it. State and federal government hatcheries often exist for the purpose of stock enhancement.

17-11. This fee lake has an attractive sign and easy way for fishers to display their catch.

A good source of additional information is *Aquaculture: An Introduction*, which is available from Prentice Hall/Interstate.

LEGAL REGULATIONS

Both commercial and sport fishing are regulated by state and federal laws. In some cases, fish and other species in the oceans are regulated by international laws. Most regulations are designed to prevent depletion of the fish population. The goal is to have fish available for future sport fishers and consumers.

SPECIES

Catching certain species of fish may be restricted. The restrictions may apply to the species at all times

17-12. Sport fishers line the edge of this popular river in Mississippi.

Career Profile

FISH FARM TECHNICIAN

A fish farm technician works on a fish farm. The work involves a variety of duties, such as monitoring water, repairing water systems, feeding fish, treating eggs and fry for disease, operating boats and seines, and harvesting fish.

A fish farm technician needs considerable practical experience in the work. High school education is needed and postsecondary education is beneficial, especially training in aquaculture and fish hatchery management. Continuing to learn and use new techniques on the job is essential.

Jobs are found on fish farms and at hatcheries. State and federal government hatcheries have opportunities. Private farms and hatcheries in areas where aquaculture is carried out also have opportunities. This photograph shows a small boat and a person in waders moving a seine across a pond in harvesting fish.

or to certain seasons of the year or sizes of fish. If it appears that the number of fish in an ocean or other body of water is getting low, restrictions may make it illegal to harvest that particular species for a while. This allows the population to naturally replenish itself. Commercial fishers are often restricted to certain areas and species of fish. Table 17-1 lists examples of species that are often favorites with sport fishers. Laws on these species vary. Always determine what is legal at the time you are planning to sport fish.

Table 17-1. Selected Freshwater Sport Fish in North America

Species	Location, Season and Best Method
Rainbow trout *Oncorhynchus mykiss*	Prefer clear, cold streams and lakes; best fishing is in spring and summer during legal season; fly fishing is used in streams, but using hooks with worms or salmon eggs is good; typical weight is ½ to 8 lbs.
Largemouth bass *Micropterus salmoides*	Prefer slow-flowing streams and lakes; like areas with weeds; cool to warm water; most active at dusk and dawn; casting with lures and natural bait, such as minnows, plastic worms, and grasshoppers; fish all year in the South, and summer and fall in the North; 4 to 7 lbs. common.
Bluegill *Lepomis macrochirus*	Generally prefer lakes and ponds; use cane pole and line with worms, insects, or crawfish on a small hook; active and fun to catch with a light-weight cane pole; fly fishing can be used; year-round, including ice fishing; ¼ to 1 lb. common.
Walleye *Stizostedion vitreum*	Found in northern rivers of United States and Great Lakes area; night feeders that are most active in the spring and fall; trolling at night with an eel or minnow or still fishing with live minnows is best; casting is also good; 2 to 7 lbs.
Channel catfish *Ictalurus punctatus*	Common in clear-water streams and lakes in eastern and southern United States and in cultured fee lakes; use stink baits, chicken entrails, and baits with dried blood; may use treble hook for holding bait, but single hook is most popular; fish with line on cane pole weighted to near bottom of water; fish most any depth in well-stocked fee lakes; all year, but warmer weather preferable in daytime or night; popular eating fish; common 1 to 8 lbs., but can be much larger.
Black crappie *Pomoxis nigromaculatus*	Found over much of the United States, black crappie are popular sport fish; prefer clear water; spring and fall are best times to fish; use cane pole with worms, crickets, or small minnows, or fly casting with streamers, jigs, or spinners; 1 lb. is common size.
Yellow perch *Perca flavescens*	Found along the upper Atlantic coast, in the Great Lakes, and Mississippi Valley; prefer lazy streams and lakes; fishing in summer and winter using live minnows on a line and pole; fly fishing and casting with jigs works; can ice fish; typically no more than 1½ lbs.
Northern pike *Esox lucius*	Found in northern United States and Canada in shallow lakes and streams where weeds and grass grow; bite all year, but fall and spring are best; bait casting is best method using spinners or spoons; small perch may be used as bait with still fishing; commonly 10 to 15 lbs.

Note: This table lists only a few species. Regional selections have been used to depict national appeal.

SIZE

The size of fish that a sport fisher can keep may be regulated. Fish that are too small are to be returned to the water. For example, the regulation may state that only fish more than 15 inches long can be kept.

NUMBER

Somewhat like bag limits in hunting, the number of fish that a person may take in one day may be limited. The number restrictions are intended to protect the fish population. Restrictions may allow only three trout per day per sport fisher from a particular stream. In some cases, number is used in combination with the size and species of fish. The regulation may state that only three fish can be caught in one day and these must be over 15 inches long.

17-13. Sport fisher with a 14-pound coho salmon.

SEASON

A **fishing season** is the time of the year when it is legal to catch a particular species of fish. For example, trout fishing may be legal between set dates in April and August. Fishing at other times of the year would be a violation of the law. Catching cultured fish in fee lakes is not regulated by the season of the year, other than the natural influences of warm and cold weather patterns.

EQUIPMENT

Some types of fishing equipment are designed to harvest large numbers of fish without regard to leaving an adequate population in the water. Nets have often been used to deplete fish populations on rivers. Using nets in certain places is now illegal. Commercial fishers are restricted to certain kinds of seines and nets to protect fish species. Using simple poles and lines is usually not restricted.

17-14. A largemouth bass has been hooked by a sport fisher.

17-15. A sport fisher is selecting a new fly.

FISHING LICENSE

Just as a hunter must have a hunting license, a sport fisher must have a fishing license. A license allows an individual to catch certain species of fish from natural water areas. A license may not be needed to fish at fee lakes stocked with cultured fish. The income from fishing license fees often goes to research programs to improve the quality of fish. Most license are valid for a year.

Commercial fishing licenses are more costly and the number issued may be carefully controlled. This is sometimes known as a limited entry program. The goal is to protect fish populations from over-fishing.

LOCATION

Regulations often restrict where people can fish. Private ponds and facilities are posted. A sport fisher must have permission and pay a fee to fish in private fee-lake facilities. Fishing

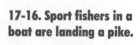

17-16. Sport fishers in a boat are landing a pike.

17-17. Fly fishing in a cool mountain stream.

from an aquaculture pond without permission is illegal and amounts to theft of a valuable crop.

Public streams, lakes, and oceans may have restrictions on where fishing can take place. For example, fishing is usually restricted from bridges that pass over water.

SPORT FISHING EQUIPMENT AND SUPPLIES

Fishing equipment and supplies are needed to assure a good catch. The nature of what a sport fisher needs varies widely. Some people enjoy a simple pole, line, hook, and bait. Others want elaborate rods with expensive bait. A big investment in equipment and supplies is not needed to enjoy fishing.

FISHING TACKLE

Fishing tackle is the equipment that people take when going sport fishing. It includes a variety of devices for attracting fish, getting the fish to bite or attack a baited hook, and landing the fish from the water after biting. It may also include items to keep the fish fresh until it is dressed and afterward.

The simplest tackle is a **line** (string) with a hook on one end and a pole attached to the other end. Lines may be monofilament or braided nylon, Dacron, or silk. Lines are sized on the basis of diameter of the string and weight of material the line is designed to lift, known as test weight. Lines on one end of a pole are about the same length as the pole. A line longer than the pole is hard to use and get the hook placed out in the water.

Cane poles are the most common types of poles, though metal and glass poles are used. Poles range from 7 to 15 feet long. A small float or cork is attached to the line to hold the hook at the desired depth below the water surface. A *sinker* or small weight may be on the line near the hook. Some sort of bait or attractant is used on the hook.

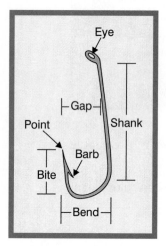

17-18. Parts of a hook.

A *float* is a small piece of cork, plastic, or other material lighter than water used to see movement of the fishing line. The float is usually attached so it can be moved up and down the line to regulate the depth of the hook in the water. The hook may have a barb that securely holds a fish that takes the baited hook into its mouth. Up-and-down or sideways movement of the float on the water is evidence of a bite—a fish is taking, or has taken, the baited hook. The pole is sharply moved upward to "set" the hook and the line lifted from the water to remove the fish.

A *fishing hook* is a curved piece of metal for holding bait and sticking into and holding fish. Hooks vary in size and design. Most are single hooks, though some are double and treble. The kind of hook needed depends on the species and size of the fish. Hooks are made of various metal wire materials that have been shaped for the best success in fishing. The better hooks cost a little more because they may be coated to prevent rust.

Hooks are sized by number and length of shank. Two numbering systems are used, though the systems merge. Sizes range from 32 to 13/0 or larger. Generally, the smaller hooks and lighter lines and rods are used with freshwater fish, because they are intended to catch smaller fish. Small hooks are sized with larger numbers. Numbers for large hooks are given as numerators. The larger hooks have larger numerators. Table 16-2 shows common hook sizes and the species they are used to catch.

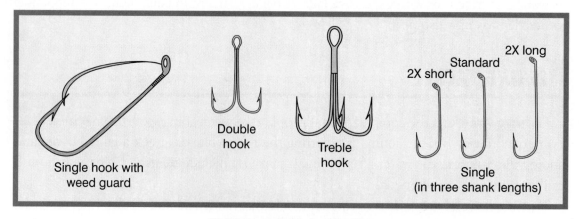

17-19. Common kinds of hooks.

Table 17-2. Common Hook Sizes*

Hook Size (Number)	Length (Inches)	Species of Fish	
		Freshwater	**Saltwater**
Small Hooks			
14	11/32		
12	7/16	Sunfish	
10	9/19	Bluegill	
8	11/16	Crappie	Smelt
6	13/16	Trout	Snapper
4	15/16	Perch	Kelp Bass
Medium Hooks			
2	1⅛	Bullhead	
1	1¼	Bullhead	
1½	1⅜	Pickerel	Pompano
1/0	1½	Channel catfish	Flounder
2/0	1⅝	Walleye	Croaker
3/0	1¾	Walleye	Croaker
4/0	1⅞	Bass	Bluefish
5/0	2	Pike	Striped bass
6/0	2¼	Muskie	Channel bass
Large Hooks			
7/0	2½		Barracuda
8/0	2¾		Tarpon
10/0	3¼		Marlin
12/0	3¾		Tuna

*Round hooks with standard length shanks. Shanks vary in length from short to long.

Some sport fishers use more expensive poles or rods. Many rods are made of graphite and have been carefully manufactured to withstand force in landing a fish. Rods may be in various lengths, but 6 feet is most common. Reels are often attached to rods near the rod handle. A reel has a winding of several feet of line that can be used to reach a distance out into the water. Some reels may have 100 or more yards of thin monofilament line. Skills in casting are needed to make the most efficient use of lines.

Both expensive and economical equipment rely on similar hook designs. Most hooks have a barb that ensures that the hook is "set" and does not come loose from the fish. Some

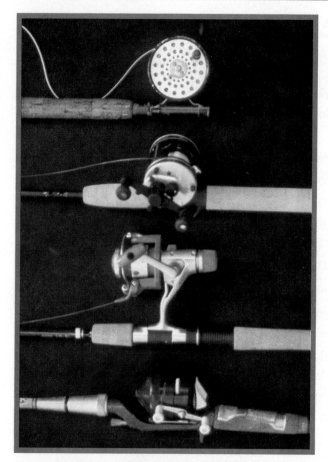

17-20. Examples of different types of fishing reels are shown here (from the top): fly reel, bait casting reel, open face spinning reel, and closed face spinning reel.

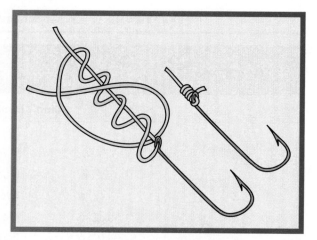

17-21. Improved clinch knot.

hooks are designed with weed guards to keep the hook from getting caught in vegetation in the water. A hook must be securely tied to the line. Several kinds of knots are used, with the improved clinch knot being popular.

Tackle includes tools and equipment to make fishing comfortable. Examples are cord or chain stringers, creels, live bags, bait containers, tackle boxes, pliers, dressing knife and other cleaning equipment, insect repellant, and safety equipment.

BAIT AND LURES

Bait is live or dead material put on a hook to entice fish to bite. Bait may be natural or artificial. Natural bait is used more often to catch fish than is artificial bait. Artificial baits are also known as lures.

Bait is a material that is attractive to the fish being sought. The nature of bait varies with the species of fish. Worms, minnows, and crickets may be used for bass and other sunfish. Chicken livers and stink-bait may be used for catfish. Salmon eggs, small pieces of fish, and frozen squid, shrimp, or crawfish are sometimes used as bait. With some fish, hot dog pieces are all that they need to bite. The most common live baits are minnows. They are widely used because they are the principle natural food of many fish.

A **lure** is an artificial "bait" that is pulled through the water with the notion that the fish will mistake it for something to eat. The fish will strike the lure, which has one or more

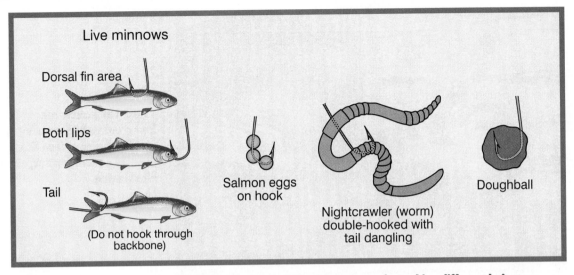

17-22. Bait should be securely attached to the hook. (This shows ways of attaching different baits to a hook.)

hooks on or around it. Lures are made of wood, metal, feathers, or plastic. Various kinds of lures are used, with flies, spoons, spinners, plugs, and jigs being common. Lures are typically used with rods and reels and cast a distance out into the water. Some lures stay near or on the surface; other lures sink into the water. Lures are selected for their particular appeal to certain species of fish. Some have moving parts to give added appeal in attracting a striking fish.

SAFETY

Fishing poses several potential safety hazards. These relate to the equipment used, animals caught, and the water environment. Sport fishers should always have a small first aid kit on hand and emergency telephone numbers handy. More sport fishers today have cellular telephones and two-way radios to keep in touch.

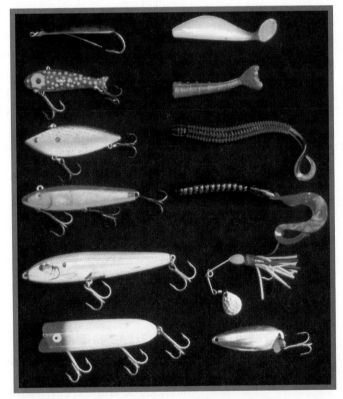

17-23. Different types of lures are used to entice fish to strike and bite.

17-24. Life jackets are being worn while standing on a float pier to feed fish in cages on Willapa Bay, Washington.

EQUIPMENT SAFETY

A wide range of equipment is used in fishing. Some of these pose hazards to the sport fisher.

Fish hooks are sharp and can stick into the skin and flesh. Because of the barb, hooks that stick in deeply may be hard to get out. Medical attention may be needed to remove a stubborn hook. Sport fishers should have a current tetanus shot. Wounds caused by hooks should be cleaned and protected. Infections can develop from the water and fish and bait fluids on hooks. Use hooks cautiously to prevent snagging yourself or other people.

Knives, pliers, and other tools are potential sources of injury. Use them properly and with safety in mind. Some jobs require wearing eye safety goggles or glasses.

Boats and motors pose particular hazards. The equipment should be operated properly and only after being trained in how to use it. Never operate boats in a reckless manner. Never overload a boat—too many passengers creates more weight than the boat can safely carry. Do not stand in a small boat or tilt it. The boat might turn over. Always wear a life preserver. Have extra preservers for other people, as needed.

HANDLING ANIMALS SAFELY

Fish and other aquatic animals can inflict wounds. Sharp spines and fins can make punctures in the skin that are hard to heal. Handle fish properly and use gloves to protect the skin. Some fish, especially certain saltwater species, can bite and create severe wounds. Place fish that have been caught in the proper container or on a stringer.

Snakes, turtles, and other animals may pose hazards. Poisonous water snakes, such as water moccasins, may bite and create life-threatening situations. Watch out for snakes and have a health safety plan in mind in case of a bite.

Take insect repellant along to keep mosquitoes and other pests away.

ENVIRONMENT

Sport fishing is usually outdoors where a variety of safety hazards exist.

The water environment poses many safety hazards. Many sport fishers, unfortunately, fall into the water and drown each year. Wear a life preserver. Learn how to swim. Do not take unnecessary risks.

Stormy weather can result in lightning, water waves, and other conditions. Seek shelter in the event of lightning. Stay out of lakes where high winds may create unsafe waves. Be able to get to high ground quickly if a sudden downpour results in rapidly rising water in a stream.

Sun and wind can damage the skin and eyes. Wear clothing to protect the skin. Use sun screen to keep the ultraviolet rays off the skin. Have extra clothing to stay warm. Take plenty of drinking water along to prevent dehydration. The protection needed varies with the season of the year. Summer weather is often hot and protection is needed from the heat and bright rays of the sun. Take precautions to avoid getting too hot and having a sunstroke.

Wildlife Connection

COUNTING FRY

Fry are very small, newly-hatched fish. Counting large numbers of fry in a tank or other container is difficult.

Fry are often handled with small dip nets and beakers. Once the number of fry a beaker will hold has been determined, the beaker can be filled to that level each time. The number of fry is found by multiplying the number of beakers filled to the measure mark by the predetermined number of fry it will hold.

To find the number of fry in a beaker, weigh a sample of 10 fry using grams. Weigh the beaker empty and filled to the mark. Subtract the empty weight from the filled weight to get the total weight of the fry. Divide total weight of the fry in the beaker by the weight of the 10 fry and multiply by 10. This indicates total number of fry every time the beaker is used.

This photograph shows fry being emptied into a beaker. The beaker has two measuring marks. Using this system allows for quick counting within a range that is consistent with fry of the same species and age. These are catfish fry about 10 days old.

Winter weather may be cold and windy. Protection from extreme cold is needed to prevent hypothermia and frostbite.

Poison ivy and other plants that create allergic reactions may be along banks and levees in the fishing area. Learn to identify these plants and avoid touching them.

PREPARING FISH FOR HOME USE

17-25. Keep fish in a chest with ice after leaving the fishing site and before cleaning. Ice should be under and above the fish.

Fish can be used to make tasty dishes and are good sources of needed nutrients. Proper care is needed to assure that they are safe to eat and not wasted.

Once caught, a fish should be kept from spoiling until it is cleaned. After removal from a hook, a fish can be placed on a stringer and returned to the water or in a container. Injured fish that are not living should be placed on ice.

Carefully dress fish as soon as possible. Depending on the species, this usually involves removing the scales and/or skin, head, and internal organs. How fish are dressed varies with the species. Larger fish can be cut into steaks or fillets. In cleaning fish, avoid puncturing and letting contents of the entrails get onto the flesh. After cleaning, thoroughly wash fish before it is refrigerated or frozen.

Dressed fish can be kept safely for three or four days in a refrigerator at 34 to 38°F before cooking. Product wholesomeness deteriorates rapidly above 40°F. If fish are kept longer, they should be frozen at temperatures well below freezing.

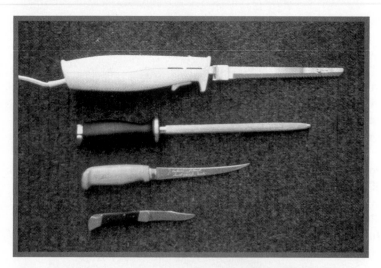

17-26. Typical equipment often used to process fish includes (from top) electric fillet knife, butcher's steel for sharpening knives, thin blade fillet knife, and stout blade knife.

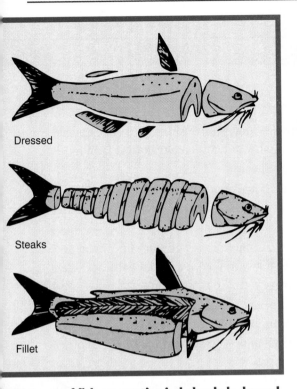

17-27. Forms of fish preparation include whole dressed, steaks, and fillets.

Dressed

Steaks

Fillet

17-28. Preparing to remove the pectoral fins is the first step in processing a common carp.

In cooking, fish can be prepared in a variety of ways—frying, broiling, and other ways. Be sure the flesh is heated and thoroughly cooked. Cooking will kill any bacteria or other microorganisms that are present. Avoid overcooking, however, as this destroys nutrients. People who eat raw or under-cooked fish are often taking health risks.

17-29. The body cavity of a trout may be opened with sharp-pointed scissors inserted at the vent and moved toward the head.

REVIEWING

MAIN IDEAS

Fishing is capturing fish for sport or commercial purposes. Most sport fishing is to capture wild fish. Commercial fishing is largely with species that grow in saltwater. Aquaculture (fish farming) is increasingly being used to produce freshwater and saltwater species.

All fishers should be aware of the appropriate legal regulations. Sport fishers must have a license to fish in natural streams and lakes for wild fish. They must also abide by the rules on species, size, number, season, equipment, and location.

Sport fishers use a wide range of equipment and supplies. A simple cane pole with line, float, and hook is satisfactory with many species. Baits may be natural or artificial. Artificial baits are often known as lures. Fly fishing and casting may involve expensive rods, lines, and lures.

Safety is essential. Water poses safety hazards for sport fishers as well as commercial fishers and aquaculturists. Fish should be handled carefully to avoid wounds from fins and spines. Always take steps to protect skin, eyes, and the entire body from injury by sun rays, wind, temperature, and other elements.

Fish can provide good nutrition. It is important that they be properly stored to prevent spoilage before dressing. Afterward, they must be placed in a refrigerator or freezer. Thorough cooking is needed to prevent health hazards associated with undercooked fish.

QUESTIONS

Answer the following questions using correct spelling and complete sentences:

1. What is the distinction between fishing as an occupation and fishing as a leisure-time activity?

2. How does the nature of sport fishing vary?

3. Why is aquaculture said to be "water farming?"

4. What production cycle is typically followed with fish aquaculture?

5. How is aquaculture a part of sport fishing?

6. What are the major legal regulations on sport fishing?

7. What is the simplest fishing tackle used by many sport fishers?

8. What is bait? What kinds are used?

9. What safety practices should be followed with sport fishing?

10. How is the wholesomeness of fish maintained after catching?

EVALUATING

Match the term with the correct definition. Write the letter by the term in the space provided.

a. commercial fishing   d. food fish   g. fishing tackle
b. aquaculture   e. fry   h. bait
c. sport fishing   f. fee lake

_____1. Material put on a hook to entice fish to bite.

_____2. Capturing wild fish from oceans and streams for human food and other uses.

_____3. Newly-hatched fish.

_____4. Fish cultured especially for use as human food.

_____5. Fish farming.

_____6. Equipment used in sport fishing.

_____7. Lake where sport fishing takes place for a fee.

_____8. Capturing fish for relaxation and enjoyment.

EXPLORING

1. Plan a field trip to a fee lake. Investigate the operation of the business. Determine the species of fish available, how fishing charges are assessed, safety procedures, assistance provided to sport fishers, and other details of operation. Prepare a report on what you observe.

2. Contact a local game warden or state wildlife conservation department and obtain copies of regulations about fishing in your state. Summarize the regulations and prepare a report for your class.

3. Arrange for an experienced sport fisher to demonstrate methods and procedures in sport fishing. This includes tackle selection; fishing procedures (especially catching wild fish); handling fish; and dressing fish, including making fillets.

CHAPTER 18

Trapping

OBJECTIVES

This chapter provides an overview of trapping with emphasis on animal well-being. The following objectives are included:

1. Describe the importance of trapping.
2. Explain why trapping is used today.
3. List legal regulations that apply to trapping.
4. Describe trapping equipment, procedures, and pelt preparation.
5. Explain live trapping.

TERMS

animal well-being
arresting trap
capture gun
confining trap
exterminating trap
fur
fur farming
live trapping
nuisance animal
pelt
propelled net
trap
trapline
trapping
trapping season

DIFFERENT methods are used in managing and taking animal wildlife. Trapping is one method that is sometimes used. In some cases, it is the best way to achieve our goals. Trapping is often an effective way to protect people from certain animals, manage animals for their well-being, and derive products from animals.

Many of the products humans use in their daily living have an origin with either domesticated or wildlife animals. A variety of ways are used to take the animals. Though trapping has been used a long time, people sometimes disagree about its use.

All people need to understand how trapping can be used properly. People that trap animals need to be aware of the importance of animal well-being. Following the proper procedures helps assure that trapping is an appropriate method to use.

18-1. A box trap used to capture a pesky rabbit is baited with carrot. The trap does not injure the rabbit and is used to carry it elsewhere for release. Cut pieces of carrot are good bait.

IMPORTANCE OF TRAPPING

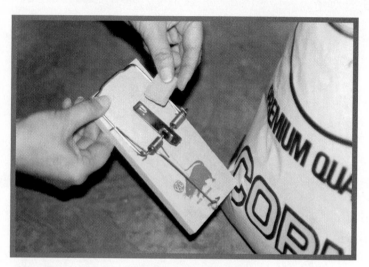

18-2. Handy snap traps are used to remove pesky rodents from our homes, barns, and businesses. Cheese, wadded bread, peanut butter, and bacon are used as baits.

18-3. A fur trapper is skinning a muskrat in front of his trapping camp on the edge of a large marsh. (Furs are drying on stretchers in the background.) (Courtesy, Dan Lay, Texas)

Trapping is capturing animals using traps. A *trap* is a mechanical device used to capture animals. Most traps have mechanisms that suddenly spring shut, such as a mouse trap. Some traps have barriers that the animal cannot get around once inside, such as a crab trap.

Trapping is sometimes controversial. Using practices that provide for the well-being of animals is essential. Only legal methods should be used.

HISTORY

Trapping began in ancient times when people developed skills to obtain materials for food, clothing, and shelter. Early European interests in the North American continent were in part due to fur resources that were present in great abundance.

French and English fur traders sent explorers and trappers into what is now Canada and the United States. They trapped and traded with the Native Americans. This resulted in huge profits for the fur companies. Early exploration by trappers and traders made the eventual settlement of the North American wilderness much easier. Beaver, mink, fox, and rabbit were frequently trapped for their fur.

The occupation of fur trapper played an important role in some areas of rural America prior to the large-scale movement of people into the cities in the 1900s. Because demand was high for fur products, many people were full-time trappers. Many farm families relied on

18-4. Two fur trappers are posing with their weekly catch of raccoons, mink, and muskrat. (These trappers lived the entire winter trapping season in a one-room cabin and returned to their families after the season was over.) (Courtesy, Dan Lay, Texas)

trapping for extra income. Furs were easy to sell by mail or to fur buyers who had permanent places of business at various locations. In some cases, buyers traveled the countryside offering to buy furs from individual trappers.

ALTERNATIVES

Trapping has changed considerably in the last 50 years. Fewer animals are trapped for their fur. Some of these changes are due to concern about animal well-being. **Animal well-being** is using practices that provide the best environment and situation for an animal. The practices result in a minimum of pain and bodily injury.

Artificial furs are manufactured to replace natural fur products. In some cases, the artificial furs have advantages over natural furs. Artificial furs are usually more economical to produce. They are often easier to store and use in manufacturing.

Fur farming has emerged to take the place of trapping. **Fur farming** is the raising of animals for their furs and other products. It is sometimes known as fur ranching. The animals are raised in carefully controlled environments that provide for their needs. Animals, such as mink and chinchillas, that were formerly only trapped, are now grown on fur farms.

Trapping animals for their fur continues in some areas where fur-bearing species are present. Of course, trapping is still widely used throughout the world to get animals for their products.

TRAPPING TODAY

Trapping serves several important purposes today. A few of the major uses of trapping are described here.

PRODUCTS

Products are obtained from trapped animals. This has been the longstanding purpose of trapping. People are able to get fur or hides, food, ornaments, and other products from animals.

Fur is the soft, fine hairy coat that covers mammals. It consists of the top or outer hair that is oily and often known as guard hair. Thicker underfur is finer in texture and serves as a good insulator against cold weather. Both the outer and fine underfur are attached to the skin. Today, most fur is from beaver, nutria, foxes, minks, muskrats, rabbits, raccoons, squirrels, skunks, lynx, ermine, coyotes, otters, and seals.

A **pelt** is the fur and skin of an animal. The pelt is skinned from an animal and dried by the trapper. From the trapper, the pelt goes for processing. This involves dressing, dyeing, and manufacturing. Dressing is softening and cleaning the pelt. Dyeing is used to obtain the desired color. Manufacturing is cutting, sewing, and otherwise preparing pelts into coats, gloves, hats, rugs, and other products.

A hide differs from fur in that it does not have hair or, if it does, the hair is removed. Hides are used to make a product known as leather. Alligators are trapped for their hides. Many alligators today are farmed. Boots, belts, and other products are made from alligator hides.

Food is obtained from a number of trapped animals. These include rabbits, lobster, crabs, fish, squirrels, alligators, raccoons, and antelopes. Food safety is important. Only animals that are kept alive in traps should usually be used for food, such as lobster and fish. Once an animal dies, it can quickly deteriorate and be unsafe to eat.

18-5. Valuable furs are on display at this store.

18-6. This alligator trap involves using a baited hook that is suspended above the water and is attached to a line and pole.

Bones, teeth, claws, and other parts are used for making clothing and ornaments. By-products may be made from animal oils and other materials.

SAFETY

Animals are trapped to protect them from danger. Some animals may stray from their habitat and be trapped to return them to a safe environment. This may be the case with bear, wolves, alligators, and deer. These animals are relocated to an environment that is more suitable for their well-being. Bears are often trapped in towns, near campgrounds, and other places and moved to remote locations in a forest. Trapping methods are used to prevent injury to the animals.

18-7. A bear is being released in the remote Sarah's Creek area of Rabun County, Georgia, after becoming a nuisance in a residential area. (Trapping is often used in relocating animals.) (Courtesy, Susan Gober, Tiger, Georgia)

NUISANCE ANIMALS

A **nuisance animal** is an animal living in a place where it creates problems for humans. The most common nuisance animals are bears, rats, mice, squirrels, alligators, deer, and some kinds of birds. Nuisance animals may be trapped and relocated or killed.

Animals are trapped to protect humans from danger. Traps are used to catch rats, mice, snakes, birds, squirrels, and other pests in homes. These pests may carry disease and damage food and home furnishings. They sometimes attack people, especially small children and infants.

Some species of birds can cause major crop losses on farms. Crows, blackbirds, and others can eat large amounts of grain. Cormorants can eat large amounts of fish from ponds. Predators can attack small animals, such as a hawk that attacks a small dog or chicken.

Animals damage property, especially if present in large numbers. Pigeons damage buildings by roosting on rafters and in other places. Geese can create unpleasant conditions with their droppings on golf courses and in parks.

Some nuisance animals are protected by law. These animals should not be trapped without approval in the form of a permit.

18-8. A captured bird is being fed as part of a rehabilitation work. (Courtesy, Matthew Perry, U.S. Fish and Wildlife Service)

RESEARCH AND EDUCATION

Animals are trapped to collect information about their behavior and growth. Fish, birds, and other species may be trapped, tagged, and released without harm. The animals are later captured again and information collected from the tag. Bands on the legs of birds help track migration habits. Radio transmitters may be used in place of tags or bands on some species. The waves sent by the transmitters allow wildlife biologists to keep track of animal wildlife on a continual basis. Whereas, tags are only good if the animal is captured.

Animals are sometimes trapped to study their health condition. This may provide information to help in habitat management, as well as protect domestic animals from disease carried by wildlife animals. Only people who are trained and authorized to trap animals for research and education should do so.

LEGAL REGULATIONS

18-9. Entering this area for trapping or other purposes is prohibited.

Much as hunting and fishing, trapping has legal regulations. Anyone who traps animals should know and follow the regulations. Always determine the regulations in your local area. Contact the state game and fish or wildlife agency for information. A local game warden or wildlife conservation officer will also have the information.

LICENSE

All trappers must have a valid license for trapping game and protected animals. States set the requirements of the license, including the fees. In some cases, federal permits may be needed before attempting to trap protected animals, such as birds. A license is not needed to trap certain nuisance animals, such as rats and mice.

TRAPPING SEASON

Certain times of the year may be designated as trapping seasons for some species. A **trapping season** is the time of the year when it is legal to trap animals. All trappers should know and follow these regulations. Trapping seasons for fur-bearing animals coincide with cold weather when the fur is in prime condition. Fur taken from animals in the summer is not marketable. (Animals naturally grow fur to its best condition in cold weather as protection against unfavorable weather.)

SPECIES

Legal regulations specify the species that can be trapped for fur and meat. Some species are protected and should not be trapped. Major fur species included in legal trapping regulations are muskrats, badgers, wolves, fishers, nutria, mink, otter, beaver, raccoons, opossums,

18-10. The large nutria (left) and smaller muskrat are two important fur-bearing animals that are trapped in some areas.

Wildlife Connection

CONFISCATED PRODUCTS

Animal products that have been taken illegally are confiscated by law officers. Such products may be taken by trapping, shooting, or in other ways that violate laws. Individuals with such products are subject to fines and jail sentences.

This shows furs, hides, and other products that have been confiscated by one law enforcement agency. Some of these products are from endangered species of animals. Study the photograph and see the kinds of products you can identify. (Courtesy, U.S. Fish and Wildlife Service)

18-11. Peanut butter is the most often recommended bait for catching nuisance squirrels in a box trap.

skunks, bobcats, weasels, martens, foxes, and coyotes. State and local regulations vary and should be followed.

With some species, special tags must be attached to the hide or fur. An example is the alligator. Numbered tags are issued to trappers according to the number of alligators living at specific locations. To protect alligators from excess trapping, each hide must have a tag attached. A trapper can take no more alligators than he or she has tags. Tags remain on the hides until processed into leather products.

EQUIPMENT

Regulations often relate to the equipment used in trapping. This includes the kinds of traps that can be used and how the traps are set and monitored. These regulations relate to the well-being of the animals. No animal should be allowed to suffer needlessly in a trap.

Checking traps regularly is essential. This protects an animal from starvation if captured in a trap. It also allows the release of animals that accidentally were caught, such as a pet dog that wanders into a trap.

TRAPPING EQUIPMENT AND PROCEDURES

A variety of trapping equipment is used. These should be used safely and legally. The major equipment is the trap. Other equipment is used in processing trapped animals.

KINDS OF TRAPS

Traps vary in how they capture animals. Some kill animals immediately; others safely confine the animal. Four kinds of traps are commonly used: exterminating traps, arresting traps, confining traps, and glue traps.

Exterminating Traps

An **exterminating trap** is a kind of trap that grips and kills an animal. Death of the animal is usually quick and instant. These traps are often used to control pests. Everyone is familiar with rat and mouse traps. These traps are baited with a food material that attracts the animal. As the animal attempts to remove the bait, a trigger releases a spring-loaded, metal rod that snaps shut on the animal, breaking its neck and causing instant death. Exterminating traps should be used properly and never in a way that ignores animal well-being.

Arresting Traps

An **arresting trap** grips an animal without causing death. The most common kind of arresting trap is the steel trap. A powerful spring holds the jaws of the trap open. Upon release by the trigger, the jaws snap shut and hold the animal's foot, leg, or other part in the trap. Steel traps with teeth are illegal in many areas. Steel traps have been widely used in capturing some fur-bearing animals. Some people feel that steel traps should not be used. Steel traps are set near areas where animals live. They may be in paths near stream banks where animals run. Steel traps should be checked (run) regularly and frequently.

Confining Traps

A **confining trap** is one that captures an animal in an enclosed area. It is used so the animal suffers no physical harm. A common kind of confining trap is the box trap. These traps are baited to entice the animal inside. Once inside, the animal may try to eat or move the bait. This results in a trigger being released that causes the animal to be confined in an enclosed area. These traps are used to remove animals to areas to

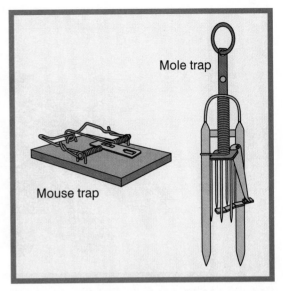

18-12. The mousetrap and mole trap are two kinds of exterminating traps.

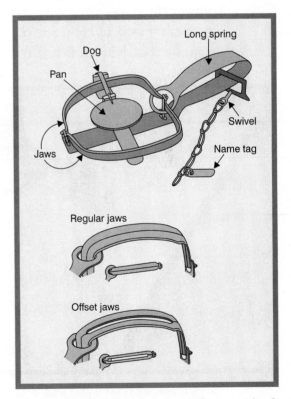

18-13. A single-spring steel trap. (When an animal steps on the pan, it releases the jaws, which are held open under considerable pressure from the long spring. Note that offset jaws can be used to minimize injury.)

18-14. A box-type trap dumps turtles in the box when they walk out on the board for sunning. (Courtesy, Extension Service, Auburn University)

provide the proper environment. Fish, crabs, birds, and other animals may be trapped in this manner for food and other products. Animal collectors use confining traps to gather specimens for zoos, laboratories, and other uses.

18-15. Preparing to set a glue trap.

Glue Traps

Glue traps capture animals with a sticky substance. The animal is held in place for removal of the trap from the area and disposal. The sticky substance may be on "glue boards" or inside plastic or paper box-type frames. Glue traps are used with vermin, such as rats and mice, when there is a strong desire to get rid of the pests.

It is possible to buy cans of glue and prepare your own glue boards. Common rubbing alcohol will remove the glue from your hands. Be careful not to rub your eyes or get the substance elsewhere on your body.

OTHER EQUIPMENT

Equipment is needed to properly fasten traps and handle animals that are caught. Stakes and wires or chains are needed to fasten traps. Various tools are needed to process animals, such as skinning knives, honing stones, fleshing boards, and drying frames.

PROCEDURES

How a trap is used depends on the kind of trap and the animal being sought. Only a few supplies are typically needed, such as bait. Everyone is familiar with putting cheese on a rat trap!

Trap placement is important. Trappers should study the natural behavior of the animal they intend to capture. What the animal eats and where it lives is important. The trap should be properly located for the greatest success in capturing the animal. Animals that live in and around water are trapped on the edges of streams or in the water. Animals that live under logs or in buildings are trapped where they normally travel for food and water.

Fastening a small trap is an important step. If a trap is not securely attached to a stake or tree, the animal might escape with the trap on its foot. Both the trap and animal are lost.

Most traps have something that entices animals into them. Three kinds of materials are used: lures, scents, and baits. Most lures are made from the anal or other glands of the species being trapped. The odor from the gland suggests that another animal is in the area. Scents are typically made from the urine of the target species. Baits are foods that are popular with trapped species. Scraps of chicken, fish, and other meats are used as baits. Fur trappers typically develop their own concoctions based on experience.

Fur trappers generally set out a series of traps called a **trapline**. These are often on stream banks or in wooded areas, depending on the species being trapped. In Canada, snowmobiles may be used to travel long traplines—often as long as 100 miles! Trappers walk shorter traplines. Traps are set in locations based on the habits of the desired animal. Small animals may be skinned at the trap.

18-16. Setting a mole trap in a lawn area to remove damaging moles.

18-17. A trapper setting a steel trap in a muskrat run or trail.

Only the pelt and other desired parts are carried back. The remainder is discarded. Larger animals are carried to a central location for skinning.

Traps should be checked regularly and often. Some people check their traps several times each day. Others check once a day or less frequently. Laws in the states vary. Wisconsin, for example, requires checking most kinds of traps on a daily basis. Non-target animals that get caught in traps should be released. Be careful around animals because they can bite or claw when the trap is being opened. Target animals are humanely killed with a rifle or pistol. Small animals may be killed by stunning with a sharp blow from a metal tool. Young trappers should always be accompanied by an experienced adult because of age restrictions on the use of firearms.

Animals should be properly processed. This varies somewhat with the species. In general, the pelt is removed from the carcass. The meat of the carcass is saved for use as food or bait. The pelt is attached to a stretcher or nailed to a drying board. After drying, it is sold to a buyer.

LIVE TRAPPING

Live trapping is using methods that do not cause more than minimal physical injury. It is an important practice in wildlife management. Traps that enclose or confine animals are typically used. Traps that injure animals are not used. After being captured using live trapping, the animal should be able to be turned loose and live on its own.

BAITED CONFINING TRAPS

Confining traps that use baits, lures, and scents as attractants for animal wildlife are often used. These traps entice an animal into a container of meshed wire, cloth, expanded metal,

18-18. A biologist is preparing to remove ducks captured in a swim-in trap that was baited with grain. (The ducks entered the trap through a narrow funnel, but could not find the small entrance to escape.)

18-19. A small, box-type trap designed to capture small mammals and birds. (Bait is placed in the trap and when the animal enters, a trigger is tripped and the entrance door closes to capture and hold the animal.)

or other material. The entrance is small and has a door that snaps shut once the animal is inside. Other traps are made so it is difficult for the animals to find their way out.

A **bait** is a substance used to lure or entice animals into traps or bite hooks. Most baits are food materials of high appeal to the animal. For example, small pieces of carrot are used in box traps to catch rabbits. Another example is the use of peanut butter to attract squirrels into a box trap.

Career Profile

TRAPPER

A trapper uses mechanical devices to capture animal wildlife. The animals may be used for products, to assure their safety, to remove a nuisance, or for research and education. Trappers work outside in wooded areas or land with water. They work in cold weather and may walk long distances working traps.

Trappers need practical experience with animal wildlife. They need to understand wildlife, how traps work, and ways of providing for the well-being of the animals trapped. Trappers involved with animal safety, nuisance animals, and research and education may need a college education in an appropriate area, such as wildlife management or biology.

Trappers may work for themselves, government agencies, or private companies. The work is found in most all geographical areas, but varies with the nature of the trapping.

This shows a muskrat trapper walking a trapline in the process of moving traps to more productive locations. Cane poles are used to mark trap locations.

Birds are usually captured in large, wire traps called walk-in or swim-in traps. Bait is spread on the ground or water to attract hungry birds. Grain is a common bait material. After birds are accustomed to finding the food and return each day, a trap is put in place and grain poured inside the trap. Most traps have a funnel-type entrance, which allows birds to squeeze through the funnel to reach the bait. Once inside the trap, birds have difficulty finding the narrow end of the funnel to escape. They remain in the trap until removed through an exit doorway.

PROPELLED NETS

A ***propelled net*** is a trap made of nylon mesh that is shot through the air to capture animals. Bait is placed on the ground in a small area. When the animals are present eating the bait, a cannon or rocket fires the net through the air over the animals. The net falls to the ground capturing the animals.

These nets are often made of nylon-mesh material. Nets may be 40 x 120 feet or larger. Careful folding is needed to assure that the propelled net works properly. Cannons or rockets attached to the net are propelled by gunpowder. When fired remotely using a firing wire, the net is pulled by rockets attached to a rope or chain.

Turkey, doves, cranes, ducks, and geese are often captured with propelled nets. As many as 3,000 snow geese have been captured with one net throw. Deer and other animals are sometimes trapped with propelled nets.

18-20. Biologists are loading a cannon to propel a nylon-mesh net over waterfowl lured to the site by grain. (Note the neatly folded net on the ground.)

18-21. A capture net is being propelled by rockets over a group of snow geese. (Note the smoke from the rocket blasts. The net is half extended. The geese are just beginning to try to fly away. About 150 geese were captured during this trapping.)

Box-TYPE TRAPS

Box-type traps are used to catch small and large mammals. These traps are typically made of wood or metal. Bait is carefully placed in the trap. Very small quantities of bait are placed outside the trap to attract the animals. When the small amount of bait outside the traps is consumed, the animal enters the box trap and sets off a trigger device that closes the entrance door. Bear, fox, and other animals are caught with box-type traps.

Other METHODS

A variety of other trapping methods are used. Most of these methods are used to assure that the animal suffers little or no injury.

Helicopters may be used to herd deer into catch pens or corrals. Mesh nets may be set that entangle antelope and other animals.

Capture guns are sometimes used. A *capture gun* uses a dart with a drug that causes the animal to quickly lose consciousness. Unconsciousness

18-22. A snare is being prepared to capture this alligator that wandered onto an industrial site.

may last a few minutes or longer depending on the amount of drug used and size of the animal. The dart is shot so a small amount of the drug goes into the muscles of the animal and is carried throughout the body by the blood circulation system. Deer, elk, bear, and exotic animals that escape from zoos are caught with capture guns.

Trained dogs are sometimes used to capture small animals. Retriever dogs may swim across water and retrieve young, flightless ducklings. The dogs gently hold the ducklings in their mouths until released into the hands of a trained biologist.

REVIEWING

MAIN IDEAS

Trapping is capturing animals using mechanical devices known as traps. People first used trapping to obtain materials for food, clothing, and shelter. Today, sophisticated methods of trapping are used that address animal well-being.

Trapping is used to relocate animals to safe areas, rid areas of nuisance animals, and harvest animal products. Trapping is also important in research and education about animal wildlife. People who trap animals need to follow all legal regulations.

Three kinds of traps are used: exterminating, arresting, and confining. Exterminating traps are often used to control pests. Arresting traps are used to hold animals in strong clamps (jaws) without causing their death. Confining traps capture animals in enclosed areas. Success with trapping requires knowledge of the animal being trapped and proper use of the trap.

Live trapping is often used in wildlife management. Baited traps that confine animals may be set so animals are captured unharmed. Propelled nets and box-type traps are also used. Capture guns may be used to capture animals alive though such guns are not traps.

QUESTIONS

Answer the following questions using correct spelling and complete sentences:

1. How did trapping contribute to the development of North America? What products were desired by French and English traders?

2. What are two alternatives to trapping animal wildlife?

3. What are the major uses of trapping today?

4. What is a nuisance animal?

5. What is a pelt? How is a pelt processed?

6. What general legal regulations apply to trapping?

7. What three major kinds of traps are used? How do the kinds vary?

8. What is live trapping? Why is it important?

9. What are three methods of live trapping?

10. What are four species of animal wildlife trapped for fur?

EVALUATING

Match the term with the correct definition. Write the letter by the term in the space provided.

a. fur
b. pelt
c. trap
d. fur farming

e. trapping
f. nuisance animal
g. arresting trap
h. exterminating trap

i. propelled net
j. capture gun

_____1. Trap made of mesh fabric shot through the air to capture animals.

_____2. Mechanical device for capturing animals.

_____3. Raising animals for their fur and other products.

_____4. Soft coat of hair that covers some species of animals.

_____5. Animal living in a place where it is not wanted.

_____6. Fur and skin of an animal.

_____7. Capturing animals using mechanical devices.

_____8. Type of trap that grips and kills an animal.

_____9. Device that shoots a drug-laden dart.

_____10. Type of trap that grips an animal, but does not cause death.

EXPLORING

1. Determine the regulations in your local area that apply to trapping animals for their products. Contact the local game warden or state agency that regulates trapping. Prepare a report that gives details on trapping, including species that can be trapped, trapping season, restrictions on the kinds of traps, and license requirements.

2. Make a list of the nuisance animal wildlife found in your area. Determine how these pests can be legally controlled.

3. Tour an area where animal wildlife research is underway. Determine how animals used in the research are trapped. Observe the capture of a large animal, such as a deer or bear.

4. Use the Internet and World Wide Web to explore trapping, fur farming, animal well-being, and related issues. Prepare a report on your findings. Here are a few web sites for use in beginning your study:

Fur Industry in America—http://www.fur.org/
The Animal Welfare Institute—http://www.awionline.org/
Trapping Equipment—http://www.animaltraps.com
The Wildlife Legislative Fund of America—http://www.wlfa.org/
International Fur Trade Federation—http://www.iftf.com/

19

Observing Wildlife and Nature

OBJECTIVES

This chapter is about enjoying wildlife species and the natural settings in which they are found. The following objectives are included:

1 Explain nature and nature study.

2 Describe where and when to observe wildlife.

3 Explain what to look for in observing wildlife.

4 Describe how to prepare to observe wildlife.

TERMS

birding
circadian cycle
crepuscular species

estivation
naturalist
nature

nature study
scats
sign

19-1. Wildlife viewing is a fun activity.

WOW! Nature has so many wonderful things to see. Plants, animals, waterfalls, streams, rock formations, and many other wonders are all about us. Taking a little time to see what nature has in store can result in an exciting hobby.

Wildlife and other features of nature can go unnoticed. Sometimes, we take them for granted. We may fail to take the time to observe life processes and how nature provides a healthful environment. With just a little effort, we can greatly increase our enjoyment of nature.

We can enjoy nature without being hunters, fishers, and trappers. Observing nature allows us to enjoy animal wildlife without taking them. We can watch them go about life. In some cases, we may even learn more about our own behavior by observing nature!

STUDYING NATURE

Nature is the natural world around us. It includes both living and nonliving things. Nature is unique because of how the living things relate and adapt to each other as well as to the nonliving features of nature.

A part of enjoying nature is leaving the great outdoors undisturbed for the people who follow. Keeping it clean helps preserve natural appeal. If seriously damaged, an area may never be the same again!

NATURE STUDY

Nature study is observing and learning about things in nature. Since it deals with the

19-2. Nature study may involve finding tree cavities. Cavities are the habitats for nesting wood ducks, owls, and woodpeckers and dens for squirrels, opossums, and raccoons.

19-3. The "talking tree trail" at Jordan Lake in North Carolina is a popular site for observing nature. It has easy-to-play recorded messages about trees, birds, and other wildlife throughout the forest.

19-4. A teal nest is being inspected by a naturalist. (Note the location of the nest in tall grass adjacent to water.) (Courtesy, Matthew Perry, U.S. Fish and Wildlife Service)

19-5. A sign in this wildlife viewing area of Moccasin Creek State Park in Georgia explains the bat house.

world around us, nature study can be carried out in cities as well as remote areas. Cities have gardens, parks, museums, and open areas. The countryside has wooded areas, streams, swamps, and forests. Sometimes, people go into remote areas far removed from cities and modern life. They may hike into valleys or up mountains to get the opportunity to see nature in unique ways.

People who take nature study seriously are naturalists. A **naturalist** is a person who studies nature to learn about living and nonliving things and the relationships between them. Naturalists often have considerable education and experience with nature. They know what to look for and how to do so in a safe manner. Many naturalists keep detailed records of their observations. Some even prepare sketches or paintings of what they see.

A naturalist who recorded his observations in oil paintings and other forms is Walter Anderson. Anderson lived in the Gulf Coast area of Mississippi. He spent most of his life in the coastal outdoors and on several barrier islands in the Gulf of Mexico. It is even reported that he tied himself to a large tree during a hurricane to see firsthand the power and devasta-

19-6. Eggs in a bluebird house are being checked using a stick to hold the house open. Touching the house would leave a scent that might cause the adult birds to abandon the nest.

tion of such a storm. Today, his paintings are widely collected. A museum in Ocean Springs, Mississippi, features much of his work.

THE PUBLIC

Many members of the general public are well aware that observing wildlife is a great way to spend leisure time outdoors. The U.S. Fish and Wildlife Service estimates that 74 million people over age 16 participate in some form of wildlife observation activity. The number is increasing each year.

Nature study can be an inexpensive hobby. No special licenses or permits are needed. Of course, exceptions exist if people go into state or national parks, or other places where fees are charged. People of all ages can enjoy and participate in nature study.

Birding is popular with many people. Just about everyone enjoys seeing birds! **Birding** is the identification and study of birds as a hobby. It is commonly known as bird watching.

WHERE AND WHEN TO OBSERVE WILDLIFE

Most people know what they want to see. They select a location that has it. Some people want to see animal wildlife. Others want to see wildflowers, waterfalls, or rock formations. If what they want to see is available in the local area, little travel will be needed. For example, if a person wants to see squirrels, a local wooded area or park with a squirrel population will be satisfactory. If a species not available locally is the goal, such as polar bears, it is necessary to identify the species habitat and travel to that location.

WHERE TO LOOK

When observing animals, begin by identifying habitats where the wildlife is likely to be found. North America is divided into habitat regions. Each has a diversity of plant and animal wildlife suited to the climate and other features of the region. The major habitat regions are similar to the forest regions in Chapter 14. The regions and examples of wildlife are given here.

Deciduous Forests

Some animal species prefer deciduous forests. These are wooded areas with tree species that shed their leaves in the winter. Deciduous forests cover roughly the eastern third of the United States, extending from the Gulf of Mexico to the Canadian border. The dominant tree species are oaks, maples, hickories, poplars, and gums. These trees produce acorns and other seeds and fruits that wildlife use as food. Areas of pine may be found within the region. Some wetlands are also found within the region.

Common mammal species in deciduous forests include white-tail deer, raccoons, black bear, turkeys, and opossums.

Common bird species include owls, hawks, woodpeckers, vultures, bobwhite, and numerous songbirds.

Common waterfowl in the wetlands areas include cranes, pelicans, and migratory ducks and geese.

Reptiles include alligators, snakes, and lizards.

Wildflowers in deciduous forests include magnolias, dogwoods, redbuds, rhododendrons, jasmine, mountain laurel, and numerous annuals.

19-7. Most national forests have marked trails for watching wildlife.

19-8. Iguanas are often seen basking in the sun.

Coniferous Forests

This region is mostly north of the Canadian border, except for areas of the Sierra-Nevada Mountains and Rocky Mountains. This region blends in with the eastern deciduous forest. The predominant trees are evergreens, such as hemlock, pines, and firs. Aspens (broadleaf species) are found in canyons and areas where more moisture is likely. A few of the animals in the deciduous areas are found here, such as white-tail deer, especially in pockets of deciduous forests among the conifers. Other species dominate as the trees are more scattered.

19-9. The entrance to Baxter State Park in Maine opens over 202,000 acres of wilderness and forest for study.

Common mammal species in the coniferous forests include moose, lynx, timber wolves, snowshoe hares, and flying squirrels. Mountain areas have bighorn sheep, mountain goats, and cougars.

Common birds include blue grouse, mountain chickadees, northern goshawks, bald eagles, ospreys, and some 200 other species.

Common reptiles include snakes, lizards, and turtles, though some are not seen that frequently.

Tundra

Tundra is predominantly north of the coniferous forest region or in high elevations on mountains. The alpine habitat (mountain tundra) supports musk oxen, caribou, tundra wolves, snowy owls, and arctic fox. Millions of migratory ducks and geese are found in the area in the summer. Bighorn sheep and mountain goats are found at high elevations in the Rocky Mountains. A variety of small animals and tender vegetation are found in the tundra.

19-10. Snow geese nest in northern Canada and migrate to the south central and western United States for overwintering.

Pacific Coast

The Pacific Coast includes many species of plant life that support animals. The region extends along the Pacific Coast from San

Francisco to southeast Alaska. High rainfall and moderate climate support extensive wildlife. Major trees include grand fir, redwood, Douglas fir, western hemlock, western red cedar, and Sitka spruce.

Common mammals include black-tail deer, black bear, cougars, and northern flying squirrels.

Common birds include Stellar's jay, red-breasted nuthatch, brown creeper, Oregon junco, common crow, blue grouse, and many other species.

Timber wolves and grizzly bears are found in the northern areas of this region.

19-11. A gull rests on a rock on the California coast.

Deserts

A desert is a dry land area. It is a place where loss of moisture is greater than the amount of precipitation. Water evaporates from the ground at a rate greater than it is added by rain, snow, and in other ways. Two major types of desert are found in North America: shrub-covered desert areas with cooler temperatures and much warmer desert areas often covered

Wildlife Connection

ATTRACTING BIRDS

Many people attract birds to their yards. They use feeders designed for certain kinds of foods and birds. Some people use liquid-type feeders that are filled with a sweetened liquid for hummingbirds. Other people use feeders that allow birds to self-feed on seeds and grain.

Manufactured feeds are often used. These have been made for wild bird species. A feed for songbirds should have a variety of seeds and meet nutritional needs. Common seeds include milo, millet, and sun-flower seed. The seeds may be enriched with calcium, vitamin supplements, and potassium iodide. Bird feed should have at least 10 percent crude protein. Seeds in bird feed that fall to the ground uneaten can germinate resulting in weeds in the lawn. Heating the seed in an oven at 250°F for a few minutes will destroy the ability of seed to germinate.

This shows a small bird feeder being filled with a variety of grains and seeds for birds to eat on demand.

19-12. A Gambrel's quail is looking out from a saguaro cactus in an Arizona desert.

with cactus. The shrub-covered areas often have junipers, pinyon pine, cottonwoods, ponderosa pine, and lodgepole pine. Willows and aspen are found in canyons with more moisture. The hot desert areas have mesquite, creosote bush, cacti, yucca, and native bunch grasses.

Common mammals in the shrub-covered desert include mule deer, black-tail hares (jackrabbits), badgers, coyotes, pronghorn antelope, and white-tail deer.

Common mammals in the hot desert areas include coyotes, jackrabbits, kit fox, and badgers.

Common fowl in cooler areas include golden eagles, prairie falcons, sage grouse, and ferruginous hawks. In addition, ducks, geese, and other migratory birds may spend part of the year in areas of the shrub-covered desert.

Common fowl in the hot desert areas include burrowing owls, Gambrel's quail, prairie falcons, and roadrunners.

Common reptiles in both areas include the Gila monster, sidewinder, and rattlesnakes.

Grasslands

Much of the grassland area, or prairie, is in the Midwestern and western United States. Many native grasses have been destroyed, though some remain. The animal wildlife may also be found in bordering areas of the surrounding desert and wooded land.

Common mammals in the prairie include mule deer, white-tail deer, coyotes, prairie dogs, and black-footed ferret.

Common birds include prairie chickens, horned larks, hawks, sharp-tailed grouse, and many migratory birds, such as ducks, geese, and swans.

19-13. Sharp-tailed grouse are found in grassland areas. (Courtesy, Dan Biggins, U.S. Fish and Wildlife Service)

Tropical

Tropical areas include those in southern Florida and small areas of other southern states and Hawaii. Hawaiian wildlife differs markedly from that of North America.

Most of the tropical area is dominated by hardwood trees, including oaks and cypress. Many of the species found in hardwood areas are found in the tropical hardwoods. The tropical area also includes palmetto and mangrove trees. Much of the area has a high proportion of land area covered with water part or all of the year.

19-14. The American alligator prefers a semi-tropical climate. (Note the habitat of water with lilies and land with grass.) (Courtesy, Dick Bailey, U.S. Fish and Wildlife Service)

Common species in the tropical areas include reptiles, such as alligators, diamondback rattlesnakes, and lizards.

Common mammals include white-tail deer, black bear, bobcats, and cougars.

Common birds include those with long legs that wade in water, such as brown pelicans, egrets, ibises, and storks.

WHEN TO LOOK

"Looking" at the right time is important with many animal wildlife species. Animals follow daily and seasonal cycles.

Circadian Cycles

A **circadian cycle** is a daily living cycle that recurs approximately every 24 hours. The cycle for a particular species tends to be reasonably predictable. It is sometimes known as the "daily biological clock." A diurnal species is one that is active during the day. A nocturnal species is one that is active at night or when it is dark. A **crepuscular species** is one that is active at dusk and dawn, such as deer.

19-15. Many birds can be observed at all hours of the day. (This shows a black-capped chickadee on a small limb.)

Animal species typically feed at certain times of the day. The animals are active and away from their nests or beds at these times. Some are active at night; others, during the day. Many people find it is best to observe animals in the early morning or late afternoon. This is when animals are most active. During midday, after they have found plenty to eat, wildlife animals are resting or caring for their young.

Here are a few guidelines for selected common species:

- Midday—hawks, vultures, and woodpeckers.
- Night—bats, owls, fox, kangaroo rats, and, to some extent, deer.
- Early morning and late afternoon—deer, squirrels, and wild turkeys.
- All day—most songbirds.
- Warm days—reptiles and amphibians (These species are active only when the air and ground temperatures are warm enough. On cooler days, they may be seen sunning on logs, rocks, or other places.)

Seasonal Cycles

Seasonal cycles are based on the time of the year as associated with the temperature and number of daylight hours. Two concepts are involved: hibernation and estivation.

Animals that hibernate become inactive in the winter or colder times of the year. Examples of animals that hibernate include bear, snakes, turtles, salamanders, bats, groundhogs, and frogs. These species may store body fat in the fall in preparation for winter. The mammals often grow thicker coats of fur.

Estivation is the inactivity of animals during warm weather. Animals do so to escape the high temperatures and keep their bodies cool. Lizards and other animals estivate to conserve body moisture and keep cool. Most species that estivate are found in hot desert areas.

19-16. Bird watchers know that blue birds nest in the late spring and early summer. This shows a nest with four tiny eggs.

Migration

Species that migrate are available for "watching" only at certain times of the

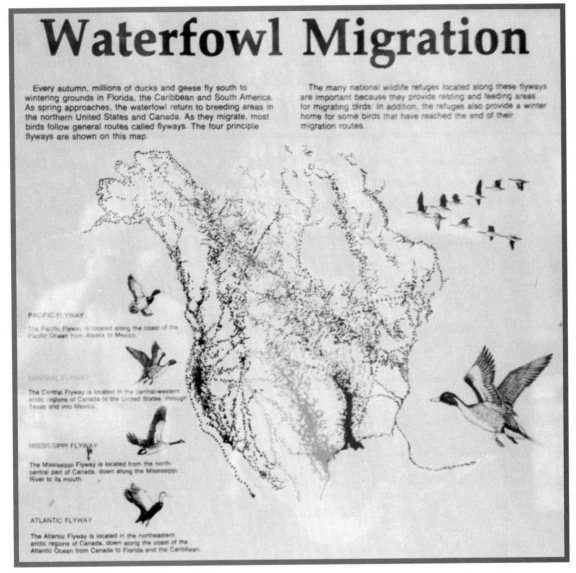

Waterfowl Migration

Every autumn, millions of ducks and geese fly south to wintering grounds in Florida, the Caribbean and South America. As spring approaches, the waterfowl return to breeding areas in the northern United States and Canada. As they migrate, most birds follow general routes called flyways. The four principle flyways are shown on this map.

The many national wildlife refuges located along these flyways are important because they provide resting and feeding areas for migrating birds. In addition, the refuges also provide a winter home for some birds that have reached the end of their migration routes.

PACIFIC FLYWAY

The Pacific Flyway is located along the coast of the Pacific Ocean from Alaska to Mexico.

CENTRAL FLYWAY

The Central Flyway is located in the central-western arctic regions of Canada to the United States, through Texas and into Mexico.

MISSISSIPPI FLYWAY

The Mississippi Flyway is located from the north-central part of Canada, down along the Mississippi River to its mouth.

ATLANTIC FLYWAY

The Atlantic Flyway is located in the northeastern arctic regions of Canada, down along the coast of the Atlantic Ocean from Canada to Florida and the Caribbean.

19-17. A map that shows the major fly-ways of migratory waterfowl in North America.

year. Most bird species migrate. Large numbers of ducks, geese, songbirds, and birds of prey migrate. Most travel south in the winter to escape cold weather. They return north in the summer to nest and raise young. The travel is during the spring and fall.

Bird watchers are well aware of the season of the year and migration of their preferred species. Over half of the birds that nest in the United States overwinter in South and Central America. Some travel 4,000 miles or more in migration.

People sometimes judge the arrival of spring by the return of migratory birds. Robins are the first birds to return in the late winter or early spring. Cold weather in the fall can be predicted by the large flocks of ducks and geese that fly south. During migration, the birds have traditional stopping places. "Watchers" can often see birds at these places as they rest and feed during their long flights.

WHAT TO LOOK FOR

Animal wildlife can be studied by observing an animal or evidence that the animal is in the area. All people know when they see an animal. Unfortunately, many people may not know the species of the animal. This requires study and learning the major characteristics of the animal species. Getting literature that has pictures of animal wildlife in the local area is a good approach. Attending seminars or talking with authorities on wildlife identification is also helpful.

Animals are identified by physical characteristics. Color, size, and other features are used. Birds have feathers; mammals typically have fur. Some have antlers and four legs. Others have two legs and wings. Knowing the preferred habitat is helpful. For example, some like high cliffs and others like tall trees.

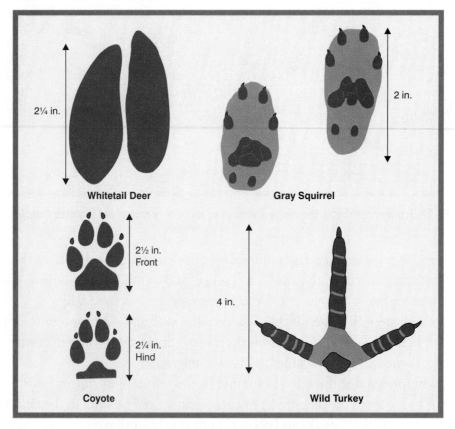

19-18. Examples of footprints of several species.

Signs are often used to determine if animals are around. A **sign** is evidence that an animal has been in an area. Traces were left by the animal. Most animals leave signs unique to their species. Here are a few common signs:

- Footprints—Footprints are the tracks left by animals in mud, snow, sand, or soft earth. People often see tracks before they glimpse an animal. The footprints are evidence that an animal has been in an area.

- Scats—**Scats** are droppings (also known as manure or dung) left by animals. Species typically have unique shapes and sizes of pieces of scats. For example, both deer and rabbit have round scats; however, deer droppings are somewhat larger. (Scats are not the same as owl pellets. Owl pellets are the regurgitated, undigested parts of prey, such as hair and bones.)

- Antlers—Antlers can be used to distinguish between species that have antlers. The shapes and sizes of antlers help distinguish one species from another. For example,

19-19. Comparison of antler shape and size.

19-20. An antler or antler parts on the ground is a sign of a species found in the area.

moose and elk have larger antlers than do deer. Of course, antlers are typically useful in identifying only the males of a species. The females of many species do not have antlers. Antlers are evidence of age. Older animals, for example, have larger antlers.

• Skins—Snakes and other reptiles may leave skins. As they grow, new skins are needed for the larger body. Through molting, the old skin is shed and a new skin is formed.

• Shells—Shells are evidence that an animal has lived in an area. In many cases, shells remain after an animal has died. The fleshy portion of the body deteriorates rapidly, but shells are slow to deteriorate. Oysters, snails, crabs, turtles, and armadillos leave shells. Another form of shell evidence is the shells of eggs after hatching, such as birds and snakes.

• Odors—A few animals leave odors that are easy to smell. A common example is the skunk.

• Feathers and Hair—Animals may leave behind small amounts of the materials that cover their bodies. Birds often lose feathers in daily life or as they molt. The presence of

19-21. The odor of a skunk can be detected quite some distance away.

19-23. A dam across this stream is a sign of beaver in the area.

19-22. A worn or smooth entrance is evidence that an animal has been going into and out of a cavity in a tree.

a feather or feathers indicates that a species of bird has been in the area. Moose, bison, elk, or deer may leave hair on tree limbs or rock edges where they rub.

- Physical Evidence—Animals may scratch in the earth, gnaw on tree bark, build nests, and leave

Career Profile

NATURALIST

Naturalists study nature. They often specialize in the wildlife and natural features of a particular area, such as a swamp or mountain park. The work includes recording information, carrying out practices to promote the well-being of wildlife, and conducting tours and talks about wildlife.

Naturalists vary in education, though all need experience and a good knowledge of the area where they work. Many have college degrees in biology or a related area. Some have advanced degrees.

Jobs are found in parks and refuges. Some jobs are seasonal, such as only during the summer, and the naturalist works elsewhere at other times of the year. Some

naturalists work as volunteers. They have regular jobs doing other work and donate their time on weekends or holidays. This photograph shows a naturalist conducting a group meeting with children. (Courtesy, U.S. Fish and Wildlife Service)

19-24. This small hole was dug in the ground by a gray squirrel.

chewed-up food remains. Squirrels often leave finely chewed husks from nuts on the ground below trees where they have fed. Turkeys scratch in the ground seeking seeds and insects. Beaver gnaw the bark from trees. Many other examples could be given.

• Nests and Homes—Some animals build nests and other forms of homes. Beaver build dams to manage water supply for their well-being. Squirrels and birds build nests for raising young and seeking refuge from inclement weather. Some animals have burrows in the ground, such as prairie dogs and crawfish.

• Color—All animals have distinctive color patterns. With some species, the males and females are different colors. For example, male birds often have much brighter colors than the females. With other species, the males and females are of similar color, such as white-tail deer.

GETTING READY

People can more effectively observe wildlife if they are properly prepared. This includes gaining knowledge of the species as well as the best approaches to view them. Comfort and safety are also important.

19-25. A backyard habitat can be easily constructed as part of the landscape near homes, schools, and businesses.

WATCHING TIPS

People will be more successful in watching animals if they consider what is needed to see the animal. Here are a few tips on getting to see animal wildlife:

19-26. Careful observation will often turn up nests of killdeer eggs in open areas.

1. Move slowly and quietly—Noise frightens animals. Avoid crunching leaves, talking, playing a radio, or other activities that make noise.
2. Sit still—Sitting still makes a person less obvious to an animal.
3. Sneak up on wildlife—Known as stalking, following the tracks or other signs may help locate an animal.
4. Go where an animal is likely to be found—Know the habitats and circadian and seasonal cycles of animals. Animals are also likely to be near food and water.
5. Use bait—Sometimes, food and water can be used to get animals to frequent an area. Deer, turkey, bobwhite, squirrel, songbirds, and other species will frequent places where grain or other food has been thrown out or put in a feeder.
6. Use camouflage—Camouflage is clothing that helps a person blend into the surroundings. Bright colors make it easier for an animal to see a person.
7. Use blinds—Blinds are places where a person can conceal themselves from animals. Thick brush, scrubby trees, tall grass, and other things can be used to form blinds.

19-27. Camping near forests, lakes, and other areas helps in studying wildlife

GOING PREPARED

People often go into woods, meadows, and other places in viewing wildlife. They need to be prepared for a safe and enjoyable experience in the outdoors. Here are a few pointers on having a good experience:

19-28. Only trained biologists should go into areas that are hard to reach, such as this bald eagle nest atop a tall tree. (Courtesy, Mialan Jenkins, U.S. Fish and Wildlife Service)

19-29. It is best not to hold small animals in your hand.

1. Dress properly—Clothing should be comfortable and appropriate for the weather. In cold weather, the clothing should be warm. Long pants and shirts provide more protection.

2. Wear proper shoes—Wear shoes that fit well and are comfortable for walking. The shoes should provide protection against thorns, snake bites, and water. In some cases, special soles are needed for climbing steep rocks or other surfaces. In water, wear rubber boots.

3. Take insect repellant—Mosquitoes, ticks, chiggers, and other insect pests may be present in the area. Use repellant to keep these pests off of arms, legs, and other areas.

4. Take a map—A map helps find important landmarks, as well as keeps an individual from getting lost. Some people also take a compass to aid in finding their way should they become lost.

5. Assess the weather—It is a good idea to check the local weather report before going wildlife watching. Sudden changes in weather can leave a person unprepared. Temperature forecasts help prepare for the outing.

6. Take water and food—Plenty of water should always be on hand. Hot weather requires a supply of good drinking water. It is best to take the water along rather than to drink from streams or water holes. The water could be polluted with animal dung, chemicals, bacteria, or other materials.

7. Take binoculars—Binoculars help see animals close-up, even when they are a distance away.

8. Take a camera and note pads—Cameras are fun to use in recording wildlife for later viewing. Some people enjoy sketching what they see.

9. First aid kit—Take simple first aid items in case of a snake bite or accident.

19-30. Wood duck nesting boxes help attract ducks, as well as help make up for the loss of natural habitat.

10. Communication plans—Leave word with a person who does not go with you as to where you will be. Some people take cellular telephones or radios so they can communicate in case of an accident or other need.

11. Booklets—A small field guide describing plant and animal wildlife, as well as geologic features, will be useful.

12. Back packs and other equipment—Some watchers hike considerable distances. They take back packs with needed items. Be careful not to overload the back pack and make it heavy and tiring for you to carry.

13. Leave an area as you found it—Do not take flowers, rocks, animals, or other living or nonliving materials from trails in parks or wildlife refuges.

REVIEWING

MAIN IDEAS

Everyone can enjoy observing nature. Special skills and equipment are not needed for most activities. The goal is to carefully observe the world around us. With nature study, we better understand our world and the important relationships between living and nonliving things.

People can be more successful in observing animal wildlife if they know where and when to look. Where we look depends on the species we want to see and the habitats where the species are found. Often, we are restricted to habitats in our local areas. Circadian cycles help determine the best time of day to look for particular species. Seasonal cycles help determine the best season of the year for looking for particular species.

In addition to the animals themselves, people can look for various signs of the animals. Signs include footprints, scats, antlers, skins, shells, odors, feathers and hair, physical evidence, nests and homes, and colors.

People need to be prepared for wildlife watching. This includes knowledge of the species and how to get in the best location to observe the species. It also includes taking needed things on our trips to assure safety and success in viewing wildlife.

QUESTIONS

Answer the following questions using correct spelling and complete sentences:

1. What is nature? Nature study?

2. Who is a naturalist?

3. What are the major habitat areas where animal wildlife species are found? Name four species that would be found in each of the habitat areas.

4. What is a circadian cycle?

5. What are examples of species best observed at midday, early morning or late afternoon, all day, and night?

6. Which animals are out when the temperature is appropriate?

7. What is the distinction between hibernation and estivation?

8. What is a sign? What are the common signs of animal wildlife?

9. Why is it important to follow appropriate "watching" tips for animal species?

10. What preparation is needed to enjoy the outdoor experience of observing nature?

EVALUATING

Match the term with the correct definition. Write the letter by the term in the space provided.

a. scats   d. circadian cycle   g. crepuscular species
b. naturalist   e. birding   h. sign
c. nature study   f. estivation

_____1. Evidence that animal wildlife has been or is in an area.

_____2. Droppings (feces).

_____3. Observing and learning about things in nature.

_____4. A person who studies nature.

_____5. 24-hour cycle of an animal.

_____6. Bird watching.

_____7. Inactivity of animals during warm weather.

_____8. A species active at dusk and dawn.

EXPLORING

1. Take a field trip to a park or refuge. Determine the species in the area. Prepare a plan to observe the species. This should include circadian and seasonal cycles, as well as other features, to assure success in seeing the animals.

2. Study the ground in a park, refuge, or wooded area for signs of wildlife. Note any signs present and determine the species that made the signs. Prepare a report on your observations. A good reference is *A Field Guide to Animal Tracks* by Olaus J. Murie and published by Houghton Miflin Company, New York.

3. Learn to use a compass. Get the assistance of a naturalist or forester. Determine the meaning of North and how it is accurately located. Also, use a global positioning system to locate various points in a park or wildlife area.

4. Investigate birding using resources of the Internet and World Wide Web. Prepare a report on what you learn. Here are a few web sites to use in beginning your study:

U.S. Fish and Wildlife Service—http://www.fws.gov/
Birdnet—http://www.nmnh.si.edu/BIRDNET/
Patuxent Bird Identification—http://www.mbr.nbs.gov/bbs/ident.html
Birder and Birding—http://www.birder.com/
Wildlife Watching Supplies—http://www.wildlifewatchingsupplies.co.uk/

Appendixes

APPENDIX A — Common Species of Mammal Wildlife

Common Name/ Scientific Name	Description/Mature Size
Opossum *Didelphis virginiana*	Only marsupial (pouch for young) native to North America; habitat is woodland or farmland near water; found throughout North America; head and body are 13–21 in. long; tail is 9–20 in. long.
Porcupine *Erethizon dorsatum*	Body is covered with some 3,000 modified hairs known as quills; head and body are 18–23 in. long; tail is 6–11 in. long.
Armadillo *Aasypus novemicinctus*	Body is covered with a bony plate and lizard-like skin; head and body are 15–17½ in. long; tail is 13–15 in. long.
Beaver *Caston canadensis*	A flat-tailed mammal that cuts trees and moves earth to build dams across streams or lakes; head and body are 27–38 in. long; tail is 9–12 in. long.
Little Brown Bat *Myotis lucifugus*	A flying, nocturnal (night) mammal that hangs upside down; bats sleep in groups; head and body length is 3–4½ in.; wingspan is 8–10 in.
Broad-footed Mole *Scapanus latimanus*	A mammal that burrows through the soil; head and body are 5–6½ in. long; tail is 1½–2 in. long.
House Mouse *Mus musculus*	A grayish-colored mammal that may invade homes; pesky rodent; head and body are 3–3½ in. long; tail is 2½–4 in. long.
Gray Squirrel *Sciurus carolinensis*	An often-hunted rodent that mostly uses deciduous trees as its primary habitat; head and body are 8–11 in. long; tail is 8–10 in. long.
Eastern Cottontail *Sylvilagus floridanus*	A rabbit that flourishes east of the Rocky Mountains; head and body are 13½–16 in. long; white tail is 2 in. long.
Raccoon *Procyon lotor*	Lives in forested areas near streams; raccoons are not offended by the presence of human activity; head and body are 16–26 in. long; ringed tail is 8–12 in. long.

(Continued)

APPENDIX A (Continued)

Common Name/ Scientific Name	Description/Mature Size
Striped Skunk *Mephitis mephitis*	When threatened, can eject a spray from an anal gland under its tail that has an offensive odor and is temporarily blinding; black with white stripes; head and body are 15–19 in.; tail is 7–10 in. long.
Red Fox *Vulpes vulpes*	Color varies from red to silver and black; preys on other animals; head and body are 20–30 in. long; fluffy tail is 14–16 in. long.
Coyote *Canis latrans*	A nocturnal howler that is now found throughout North America; color is gray on black; head and body are 32–40 in. long; tail is 12–15 in. long.
Gray Wolf *Canis lupus*	A controversial predator that forms social packs and is being re-introduced in some areas; head and body are 40–52 in. long; tail is 13–19 in. long.
Grizzly Bear *Ursus arctos horribilis*	A dangerous animal when surprised; feeds on rodents, fish, moose, caribou, and others; hair coat is yellow to dark brown; head and body length are 6–7 ft.; no tail of consequence.
Black Bear *Ursus americanus*	Feeds on both plants and animals; retreats to dens in winter but does not truly hibernate; head and body are 4½–5 ft. long; babies weigh ½ lb. at birth with mature females (sows) weighing 300 lbs.
Polar Bear *Ursus maritimus*	A powerful bear with webbed toes; white, oily fur; prefer arctic climates; head and body length is 6½–8 ft.; stands 3–4 ft. high at shoulders.
Mountain Lion *Felis concolor*	Goes by other names including puma, cougar, panther, and catamount; a carnivore widely distributed in North America; tawny to gray color, with young having spots; head and body are 42–60 in. long; tail is 24–36 in. long.
Mountain Sheep *Ovis canadensis*	Also known as a bighorn, the mammal has a strong body with horns on both rams and ewes; fur is brown or grayish with a whitish rump; often found in rock terrain; head and body length is 5–6 ft.
Pronghorn *Antilocapra americana*	The swiftest mammal in North America; tan fur with white on belly and rump; horns have a single prong that projects forward; head and body length is 4–4½ ft.
White-tailed Deer *Odocoileus virginianus*	The most abundant hoofed mammal in North America; male has antlers; underside of tail is white, with body having reddish or grayish brown fur; young (fawns) have spots; head and body length is 4–6 ft.; tail is 7–11 in. long.
Mule Deer *Odocoileus hemionus*	With larger ears than the white-tailed deer, mule deer avoid areas with humans; male has antlers; tail has a black tip or is all black; body fur is reddish brown in the summer to grayish in winter; head and body 4½–6½ ft. long; tail 4½–9 in. long.
Moose *Alces alces*	Larger than deer in overall body size, male moose have large antlers that are flattened and pronged; preferred habitat is northern forests around freshwater; body length is 7½–10 ft.; tail length is 2½–3½ in.

(Continued)

APPENDIX A (Continued)

Common Name/ Scientific Name	Description/Mature Size
Caribou *Rangifer tarandus*	Both sexes usually have slightly flattened branching antlers; stocky body covered with brownish fur except for white on neck, rump, and around feet; head and body length is 5½–7½ ft.; tail length is 4–5½ in.
Bison *Bison bison*	Large animals that travel in bands grazing grassland areas; may live 30 years; hump on shoulders; horns on sides of head; shaggy fur on shoulders and front legs; length of head and body is 7–11½ ft.
Harbor Seal *Phoca vitulina*	Adapted to water or land, harbor seals can go to water depths of 300 ft. and stay underwater for 30 minutes; typical habitat is beaches and rock areas along shores of North America except the Gulf of Mexico coast; color ranges from dark brown to gray; body length is 4½–5½ ft.
Manatee *Trichechus manatus*	An aquatic animal that must breathe from the air; bulky body with one pair of front flippers; rare animals found in Florida and coastal areas along Gulf of Mexico; length is 7½–12½ ft.
Common Dolphin *Delphinus delphis*	An aquatic mammal that must breathe from the surface about every 30 seconds; prefers warm seawater; schools often leap in unison; black back, yellow sides, and white underneath; length is 6½–8½ ft. (Dolphins and whales are not fish.)
Killer Whale *Orcinus orca*	Formidable aquatic predators that weigh up to 20,000 lbs.; color is black with a white pattern; large dorsal fin; length is 15–30 ft.

Note: This appendix lists only a few of the common mammal wildlife species. A source listing additional species is *North American Wildlife*. Pleasantville, New York: Reader's Digest, 1996.

APPENDIX B — Examples of Bird Species Found in North America

Common Name/ Scientific Name	Description/Mature Size
Common Loon *Gavia immer*	A water bird, the loon can fly from water but not from land; poor at walking; excellent swimmer; has a large heavy body with pointed bill; body has a black and white pattern; head is black; ring around neck; found throughout much of North America but mostly in Canada and Great Lakes area of the U.S.; length is 28–30 in.
Brown Pelican *Pelecanus occidentalis*	A large, bulky water bird that is a good flyer and has a large bill designed for diving and catching fish in the water; body has gray-brownish color with red-brown neck having a white stripe; head is whitish or yellow; predominantly in southern U.S., especially coastal areas of Louisiana; length is 3½–4½ ft., with a wing span up to 7 ft.; prefers coastal or brackish water. (The brown pelican is somewhat smaller than the American white pelican.)
Double-crested Cormorant *Phalacrocorax auritus*	A large, dark water bird with a thin bill somewhat enlarged at the tip; often stands with wings outspread in freshwater or coastal areas; captures fish by diving into water from the surface; a pest on fish farms yet protected by law from killing; length is 2½–3 ft.
Great Blue Heron *Ardea herodias*	A large, blue-gray water bird with a long neck and legs; head and neck are yellowish white with black on the top of the head; stands motionless in water and spears fish, frogs, snakes, and other birds; prefers freshwater and salt marshes; flies with its head and neck turned back; head and body length is 36–40 in.; wingspan is up to 6 ft.
Great Egret *Casmerodius albus*	Large, all-white water bird with long neck and long, black legs; bill is orange-yellow; prefer wetlands and pastures; frequently lives in mixed colonies with herons, cormorants, and ibses; length is 36–42 in.
Cattle Egret *Bubulcus ibis*	Half the size of a great egret, the cattle egret is white with yellowish areas; often seen around cattle or resting on the backs of cattle to catch insects; preferred habitat is brush areas and open fields; length is 18½–20 in.
Canada Goose *Branta canadensis*	Increasingly popular and sometimes pests, the Canada goose has made a comeback from low populations; dark neck, back, and tail and white underneath (color somewhat influenced by stain of water); preferred habitat is ponds, lakes, bays, and grasslands; nests near edge of water; migrates between Canada and northern U.S. in summer and southern U.S. in winter; length is 22–40 in.
Mallard Duck *Anas platyrhynchos*	The most common duck worldwide, the mallard prefers shallow ponds and marshes in the summer and forest areas in the winter; males are colorful with green heads, necks with a white ring, and body is grayish with white underneath; females are brown overall; found throughout the U.S.; dive head-down (known as dabbling) into water to catch small fish and other foods; length is 16–24 in.

(Continued)

APPENDIX B (Continued)

Common Name/ Scientific Name	Description/Mature Size
Snowy Plover *Charadrius alexandrinus*	A small bird that prefers beaches and open areas near water; pale tan with white underneath and a dark spot behind the eyes; found throughout southern U.S.; length is 6–7 in.
Killdeer *Charadrius vociferus*	A plover that nests on the ground, the killdeer vigorously defends its nest; brownish to reddish with white collar and black neck rings and has white stripe on wings; prefers meadows and other open areas sometimes near water; length is 8½–11 in.
Ring-billed Gull *Larus delawarensis*	One of several gulls, the ring-billed gull prefers lakes, rivers, coasts, and areas where garbage is dumped; has white body with grayish wings, yellow legs and feet, and yellow bill with black ring near tip; length is 17–20 in.
Turkey Vulture *Cathartes aura*	A large black bird with a bare red head; eats dead animals; outstanding flyer; roosts in dead trees; length is 26–32 in., with a wingspan of 6 ft. (The endangered California condor is the largest vulture, with a wingspan of 10 ft.)
Red-tailed Hawk *Buteo jamaicensis*	A predator with a brownish body with barred pattern, lighter area underneath, and reddish tail; strong, hooked bill; found throughout North America; habitat is land and open woodlands; length is 19–26 in.; wingspan is 4½ ft.
Bald Eagle *Haliaeetus leucocephalus*	The bald eagle has a dark colored body with a white head and white under tail; found throughout much of North America with populations increasing; feeds on dead animals, fish, and waterfowl; nests high in trees and on cliffs; length is 35–40 in.; wingspan is 7½ ft.; protected as a national symbol.
Ruffed Grouse *Bonasa umbellus*	A bird with a fan-shaped tail; blackish with mottled browns and grays; male displays courtship behavior marked with drumming the air with its wings producing thumping sounds that can be heard some distance away; prefers mixed or deciduous forests; range is primarily in northern U.S. and Canada; length is 16–19 in.
Northern Bobwhite *Colinus virginianus*	A popular bird for sport hunters, bobwhite are found east of the Mississippi River and a few areas in the west; relatively small birds with mottled reddish-brown bodies and white and dark areas on the head; preferred habitat is brushy areas, open areas on farms, and open pine forests; usually form groups known as coveys; length is 8–10 in.
Ring-necked Pheasant *Phasianus colchicus*	A popular bird for sport hunters, the ring-necked pheasant is a relatively large bird with distinct color and plummage; male has a long tail; the color is brownish and somewhat mottled; heads of males have distinct green, black, and red feathers with a white collar; length is 22–35 in.

(Continued)

APPENDIX B (Continued)

Common Name/ Scientific Name	Description/Mature Size
Wild Turkey *Meleagris gallopavo*	A large-size bird with a long tail; colors are brownish, grayish, with reds and blacks mixed in; male struts during the breeding time producing a profuse display of feathers; turkeys can fly well for short distances but often prefer to walk or run; habitat is deciduous woodlands in hills or bottomlands; length is 3–4 ft.
Mourning Dove *Zenaida macroura*	A small streamlined bird; tail is long and pointed; body is grayish brown with black spots; white underneath; habitat includes woodlands, brushy areas, farms (particularly harvested grain fields), and parks; length is 10–12 in.
Great Horned Owl *Bubo virginianus*	One example of several owl species in North America found in nearly all areas except the far northern areas of Canada; predator that feeds on other birds, such as ducks and grouse, and medium-size rodents; large widely-spaced ear tufts give the great horned owl a distinct appearance; color is mottled brown, with darker colors on the back and lighter colors underneath; has strong beak and claws; prefers woodlands, canyons, and bottomlands; length is 18–24 in.
Ruby-throated Hummingbird *Archilochus colubris*	The smallest bird, with very rapid wing movement that makes a humming sound and allows the bird to hover without landing; long, pointed beak takes nectar from flowers for food; grayish-green color, with male being red under throat and female being dingy white; found from the prairie states east in the U.S.; length is 3–3½ in.
Pileated Woodpecker *Dryocopus pileatus*	A bird with a pointed red crest on its head; body is mostly black except for white on the neck and underside; pecks on trees, poles, or other usually dead wood structures producing a hammering sound; preferred habitat is mature forests; found over much of the U.S. except the southwest; length is 14–18½ in.
Blue Jay *Cyanocitta cristata*	A medium-sized bird with distinct blue colors barred with black and white underneath; has pointed, blue head crest; a noisy and sometimes pesky bird; found over the eastern three-fourths of the U.S.; prefers woodlands, parks, and farm areas; length is 9½–12 in.
American Crow *Corvus brachyrhynchos*	A large, glossy black bird with a distinctive "caw" sound; known as intelligent but are often pests with crops; bill, feet and legs are black; length is 16–20 in.
Purple Martin *Progne subis*	Because they are known for eating large numbers of insects, houses are often put up to attract purple martins; the male appears solid blue-black and the female has a whitish color on the belly; found throughout the U.S. except areas of the Rocky Mountains; prefers woods and open areas near water; length is 7–8 in.

(Continued)

APPENDIX B (Continued)

Common Name/ Scientific Name	Description/Mature Size
Northern Mockingbird *Mimus polyglottos*	Found through much of the southern and eastern U.S., the northern mockingbird is known for imitating or mocking other birds; color is gray on top and white underneath; preferred habitat is scrubby growth or woodland near water; length is 9–11 in.
American Robin *Turdus migratorius*	A bird with special appeal because it is one of the first to return in the spring; dark gray with reddish color underneath on its breast; prefer open forests, farmlands, and residential or park areas; length is 9–11 in.
Red-winged Blackbird *Agelaius phoeniceus*	Only male of the species is black and it has a spot of red and yellow on its wings; female is brown with streaks; preferred habitat is swamps and open farmland; found throughout most of North America; length is 7–9½ in.
Northern Cardinal *Cardinalis cardinalis*	The northern cardinal is found in the eastern half of the U.S.; male is near solid red with black around the eyes and under the beak; female is tan with some red on the crest and wings; preferred habitat is thickets and brushy areas near woodland but often seen in parks and residential areas in late winter and spring; length is 7–8½ in.
English Sparrow *Passer domesticus*	Also known as the house sparrow, the English sparrow was brought here from Europe and is found throughout most of the U.S.; female is brownish on top and grayish underneath and male is grayish and reddish with some black; preferred habitat is farms, residential areas, and cities; length is 5–6 in. (Many species of sparrows are found in North America. Most are of a completely different family than the English sparrow.)

Note: This appendix lists only a few examples of birds found in North America. Materials from the Audubon Society or other sources can be used to help identify bird species found locally.

APPENDIX C — Examples of Reptiles Found in North America

Common Name/ Scientific Name	Description/Mature Size
American Alligator *Alligator mississippiensis*	The alligator is the largest reptile in North America; preferred habitat is freshwater or brackish water in swamps, ponds, bayous, and rivers; primarily found in Florida, Texas, and Louisiana; after mating the female builds a nest near water where she lays 20–60 eggs that hatch in about 10 weeks; color of young is black that turns gray-black as an adult; feeds on frogs, insects, birds, small mammals, and other animals that come near; humans should be cautious around alligators as they can quickly inflict severe injury or consume pets, such as dogs; length is 6–15 ft.
Snapping Turtle *Chelydra serpentina*	Usually seen floating in ponds, often just below the surface; eat aquatic plants and animals; female usually comes on land to lay eggs; head and legs so large compared to shell size that they cannot be fully retracted into shell (carapace); found in eastern two-thirds of the U.S.; brown shell often covered with algae or mud; shell is in segments that have points or knobby ridges; can be aggressive; preferred habitat is quiet mud-bottomed ponds, rivers, etc.; length is 8–12 in.
Slider Turtle *Chrysemys scripta*	Primarily found in the southeastern U.S.; often seen on logs or rocks basking in the sun; can quickly slide into the water (hence, its name slider); carapace is olive to brown with yellow stripes and bars; may have red or yellow stripe or patch behind eyes; eats small aquatic organisms; prefers shallow areas of freshwater with weeds; length is 5–11½ in.
Banded Gecko *Coleonyx variegatus*	Found in tropical and subtropical areas, including the southwestern U.S.; though most geckos climb, the banded gecko lives on the ground and hides in rocks during the day; active at night; preferred habitat is hillsides and canyons; has eye lid that shuts (most geckos do not have eye lids); pinkish or cream yellow with brown bands and spots; length 4½–6 in.
Eastern Fence Lizard *Sceloporus undulatus*	Most widely found lizard in North America; rough, raised scales cover body; gray to brown with dark crossbars; male may have bluish patches on throat and belly; prefers dry woodlands, prairies, and brush lands; length is 3½–7½ in.
Common Kingsnake *Lampropeltis getulus*	Usually considered a beneficial snake because it kills rats and other pests by wrapping around and choking them before eating them; glossy brown to black smooth scales cover the body; may have cross bands, stripes, or speckles; habitat is varied and includes woodlands, marshes, swamps, rocky hillsides, grasslands, and deserts; length varies from 3–6½ ft.

(Continued)

APPENDIX C (Continued)

Common Name/ Scientific Name	Description/Mature Size
Common Garter Snake *Thamnophis sirtalis*	Found throughout most of North America except areas of the Southwest; gives birth to live young; feeds on fish, worms, and small animals; molts as it grows, shedding all of its skin at once, beginning head first and moving toward the tail; typically black or dark with three yellowish stripes lengthwise; yellow stripes may have black spots or red blotches; habitat is grasslands, woodlands, suburban parks and gardens, and often near water; length is 1½–4 ft.
Cottonmouth *Agkistrodon piscivorus*	Also known as a water moccasin, this poisonous pit viper uses sensory pits between each eye to locate and strike warm animals; long, hollow fangs are folded back in the mouth until being extended for striking and injecting venom; gives birth to live young, which are poisonous from birth; strong, stout body with wide, flat head; pit below and in front of eyes; eyes have vertical pupils; brownish with dark, ragged bands; mouth white on inside; habitat is swamps, slow streams, ditches, and shallow ponds in the southeastern U.S.; length is 2–6 ft.
Copperhead *Agkistrodon contortrix*	A poisonous pit viper, the copperhead has orange, pinkish, or copper color with red-brown cross bands; gives birth to live young; habitat is rock outcrops and areas of forests, swamps, and flood areas in the southeastern U.S.; length is 2–4½ ft.
Western Diamondback Rattlesnake *Crotalus atrox*	Venomous pit viper with a device on tip of tail that creates a rattling or buzzing sound as shaken by the snake; black and white bands encircle the tail; body has hexagonal or diamond-shaped blotches of grayish-black; two diagonal stripes on cheeks; habitat is dry prairies, brush deserts, and rocky hill areas of western U.S.; length is 3–7 ft.

(Note: Other rattlesnakes are found in the southern and eastern U.S., with the timber rattlesnake being dominant.)

Note: Many other species of reptiles are found in North America. This appendix lists a few species to show the diversity of reptiles.

APPENDIX D — Examples of Amphibians Found in North America

Common Name/ Scientific Name	Description/Mature Size
Spotted Salamander *Ambystoma maculatum*	Found in the eastern half of the U.S. in wooded areas around water; lays eggs in freshwater, often under edges of rocks; thin, moist grayish-black or dark brown skin with two irregular rows of orange or yellow spots; have four legs with four clawless toes on each foot; length is 5½–9¾ in. (Note: Many kinds of salamanders are found in all areas of North America except the deserts and Rocky Mountains.)
Eastern Newt (Red Eft) *Notophthalmus viridescens*	A salamander-type of amphibian that lacks the side grooves of salamanders; eggs laid in water in spring and larvae remain aquatic through summer at which time gills are lost and the adult (known as an eft) moves on land; after about three years, the adult returns to water to mate and lay eggs; color varies, with aquatic adult being olive-green to dark brown with a yellow belly having black dots and land adult being reddish brown with red markings on back; habitat is moist woodlands, quiet ponds, and lakes with weeds; length is 2½–5½ in.
Common Toad (Woodhouse's Toad) *Bufo woodhousei*	The common toad is one of several toad species found in North America; wide-bodied and with warts on a thick skin, the common toad has a line down the middle of the back; dark spots are on a brownish to grayish background; the adult toad lives away from water areas on drier land than frogs; at breeding time, toads gather at quiet bodies of water with mating occurring in water as the female produces long strings of eggs that are fertilized by the male; the male has a large vocal sac that is inflated for calling a female mate; the adult eats insects (a long tongue catches them) and plant materials; length of body is 2½–5 in.
Green Treefrog *Hyla cinerea*	The green treefrog is one of 13 species of treefrogs found in North America; a green treefrog has a thin, smooth, moist skin that is yellow to green with a white or yellow stripe on each side starting just beneath the eye; eats live insects; can perch on leaves because of light weight; male sings loudly; mates in water, with eggs hatching into tadpoles, which transform to adults in two months; colors change in response to temperature and other environmental conditions; may be seen in trees or on structures; length is 1¼–2½ in.
Bullfrog *Rana catesbeiana*	Commonly found in ponds, bayous, or lakes; large frog with smooth skin, with ridge extending from head down body to back; color is greenish to grayish-brown and black with irregular spots; often observed with eyes extending above water level; spends time on banks and jumps into water when frightened; eats insects and other small animals including fish eggs; male makes deep mating solo calls (other frogs often join in a chorus), especially in the spring; masses of eggs are laid in water and hatch into tadpoles that mature into adults; a bullfrog can live in any body of freshwater; found throughout the U.S. except for dry areas and Rocky Mountains; large legs are a desired food; length is 3½–18 in.
Northern Leopard Frog *Rana pipiens*	Found throughout most of the northern U.S. and southern Canada, the northern leopard frog is green or brown with rounded spots on its back; light-colored stripe on jaw; prefers brackish marshes, damp meadows, and weedy edges of small streams; one of 21 frog species found in North America; length is 2–5 in.

APPENDIX E — Examples of Fish Found in North America

Common Name/ Scientific Name	Description/Mature Size
Spiny Dogfish Shark *Squalus acanthias*	Found in saltwater off shores of North America in both the Atlantic and Pacific Oceans, the dogfish shark migrates northward as the water warms; prefers water that is 42°–60°F; no anal fin; two dorsal fins; five gill slits; typically a silverish color with light splotches; has venomous spines on its dorsal fins; length is 1–15 ft., with 21 ft. being maximum. (Note: Many other shark are found in the offshore saltwater areas of North America. Most can cause serious injury to humans.)
Big Skate *Raja binoculata*	The big skate appears to have a flat body but has a somewhat narrow body with structures on each side known as wings; a saltwater species, skates produce a tough case with one or more eggs, which hatch in water; yellowish-brown with splotches of lighter colors; 1½–8 ft. long, with 8 ft. being the maximum length.
Rainbow Trout *Oncorhynchus mykiss* (formerly *Salmo gairdneri*)	An appealing species found in cool, flowing clear streams; body has greenish color at top with speckles and a pinkish color on the sides with white underneath; streamlined fish for adapting to a moving water environment; spawns in spring and summer; not found in warm areas of southern U.S.; desired sport fish protected by law in many states; length is 18–24 in.
Channel Catfish *Ictalurus punctatus*	Found throughout the eastern two-thirds of the U.S. and the southern part of Canada; greenish to brown or silverish with spots; deeply lobed tail fin; barbels about the mouth; prefers warmwater streams or ponds; mating is in spring, with the female producing large numbers of eggs in a mass that are fertilized by the male; eggs hatch in seven days or less; young are tiny fry that grow into fingerlings and adult fish; the most popular farmed fish in the U.S.; a popular sport fish; typical mature length is 18–20 in.
Bluegill *Lepomis macrochirus*	A popular freshwater sport fish, bluegills are often stocked in farm ponds; frequently referred to as one of the sunfishes; deep body often the size of an adult hand; has sharp spines at front of dorsal and anal fins; color ranges from greenish-gray to bluish and orange underneath; brightly colored areas are found on the gill covers; typical length is 4–12 in.
Largemouth Bass *Micropterus salmoides*	The largemouth bass is the largest and best known of the sunfishes and a popular sport fish; characterized by a large mouth, spines at dorsal and anal fins, deep, rounded body with a blunt head and large mouth; color is grayish-green to brown with white underneath; spawns masses in ponds or lakes; found throughout the U.S. and southern Canada; length is up to 32 in.

(Continued)

APPENDIX E (Continued)

Common Name/ Scientific Name	Description/Mature Size
Striped Bass *Morone saxatilis*	Found throughout many areas of the U.S., the striped bass is a popular sport fish; silverish with dark stripes extending from gill cover to tail fin; often live in temperate streams connected to oceans and swims up freshwater rivers to spawn; many have adapted to freshwater only; often used in breeding programs with other bass, such as the white bass *(Morone chrysops)* to produce hybrid striped bass; length is up to 60 in.
Northern Pike *Esox lucius*	A carnivorous fish found in most areas of North America except the Southwest and West Coast; greenish to grayish with lighter splotches; head has long, pointed jaws with many teeth; prefers lakes, slow-moving rivers, and other water areas where plants are abundant; length is 2–4 ft.
Yellow Perch *Perca flavescens*	The yellow perch is valued as a sport fish; characterized as a finfish with scales, small mouth, and brownish-yellowish color; prefer clear streams and lakes; found throughout the eastern and northeastern U.S., Pacific Northwest, and southern Canada; length is typically 8–20 in.
Fathead Minnow *Pimephales promelas*	The fathead minnow is a popular bait fish when fishing for largemouth bass and similar species; usually grown on bait fish farms in the southern and central U.S.; typical length is 1–3 in.

Note: Only a few species of fish found in North America are included here. Since local areas may have different species, refer to materials from the state wildlife or game departments. A reference for cultured species is *Aquaculture — An Introduction*, available from Interstate Publishers, Inc.

APPENDIX F
State Fish and Game Departments

Alabama Department of Conservation and Natural Resources, 64 N. Union Street, Montgomery, AL 36130, telephone: (205) 242-3486

Alaska Department of Fish and Game, P.O. Box 25526, Juneau, AK 99802, telephone: (907) 465-4100

Arizona Game and Fish Department, 2221 W. Greenway Road, Phoenix, AZ 85023-4312, telephone: (602) 942-3000

Arkansas Game and Fish Commission, 2 Natural Resources Drive, Little Rock, AR 72205, telephone: (501) 223-6300

California Department of Fish and Game, 1416 Ninth Street, Sacramento, CA 95814, telephone: (916) 653-7664

Colorado Division of Wildlife, 6060 Broadway, Denver, CO 80216, telephone: (303) 297-1192

Connecticut Department of Environmental Protection, 79 Elm Street, Hartford, CT 06106-5127, telephone: (203) 424-3011

Delaware Division of Fish and Wildlife, 89 Kings Highway, P.O. Box 1401, Dover, DE 19903, telephone: (302) 739-5295

Florida Game and Fresh Water Fish Commission, 620 S. Meridian Street, Tallahassee, FL 32399-1600, telephone: (904) 488-1960

Georgia Wildlife Resources Division, 2070 U.S. Highway 278 SE, Social Circle, GA 30279, telephone: (404) 918-6401

Hawaii Department of Land and Natural Resources, Box 621, Honolulu, HI 96809, telephone: (808) 587-0400

Idaho Fish and Game Department, 600 S. Walnut, Box 25, Boise, ID 83707, telephone: (208) 334-3700

Illinois Department of Conservation, Lincoln Tower Plaza, 524 S. 2nd Street, Springfield, IL 62701-1787, telephone: (217) 782-6302

Indiana Department of Natural Resources, 402 W. Washington Street, Room W255B, Indianapolis, IN 46204-2748, telephone: (317) 232-4200

Iowa Department of Natural Resources, E. 9th and Grand Avenue, Wallace Building, Des Moines, IA 50319-0034, telephone: (515) 281-5145

Kansas Department of Wildlife and Parks, 900 S.W. Jackson Street, Suite 502, Topeka, KS 66612-1233, telephone: (913) 296-2281

Kentucky Department of Fish and Wildlife Resources, 1 Game Farm Road, Frankfort, KY 40601, telephone: (502) 564-3400

Louisiana Department of Wildlife and Fisheries, P.O. Box 98000, Baton Rouge, LA 70898-9000, telephone: (504) 765-2800

Maine Department of Inland Fisheries and Wildlife, 284 State Street, Station 41, Augusta, ME 04333, telephone: (207) 287-2766

Maryland Department of Natural Resources, Tawes State Office Building, 580 Taylor Avenue, Annapolis, MD 21401, telephone: (410) 974-3987

Massachusetts Executive Office of Environmental Affairs, Leverett Saltonstall Building, 100 Cambridge Street, Room 2000, Boston, MA 02202, telephone: (617) 727-9800

Michigan Department of Natural Resources, Box 30028, Lansing, MI 48909, telephone: (517) 335-4623

Minnesota Department of Natural Resources, 500 Lafayette Road, St. Paul, MN 55155-4001, telephone: (612) 296-6157

Mississippi Department of Wildlife, Fisheries and Parks, P.O. Box 451, Jackson, MS 39205, telephone: (601) 362-9212

Missouri Department of Conservation, P.O. Box 180, Jefferson City, MO 65102-0180, telephone: (314) 751-4115

Montana Department of Fish, Wildlife, and Parks, 1420 E. 5th, P.O. Box 20071, Helena, MT 59620, telephone: (406) 444-2535

Nebraska Game and Parks Commission, 2200 N. 33rd Street, P.O. Box 30370, Lincoln, NE 68503-0370, telephone: (402) 471-0641

Nevada Department of Wildlife, Box 10678, Reno, NV 89520, telephone: (702) 688-1500

New Hampshire Fish and Game Department, 2 Hazen Drive, Concord, NH 03301, telephone: (603) 271-1438

New Jersey Division of Fish, Game and Wildlife, CN 400, Trenton, NJ 08625-0400, telephone: (609) 292-2965

New Mexico Department of Game and Fish, P.O. Box 25112, Sante Fe, NM 87504, telephone: (505) 827-7911

New York Department of Environmental Conservation, 50 Wolf Road, Albany, NY 12233, telephone: (518) 457-3446

North Carolina Wildlife Resources Commission, Archdale Building, 512 N. Salisbury Street, Raleigh, NC 27604-1188, telephone: (919) 733-3391

North Dakota State Game and Fish Department, 100 N. Bismarck Expressway, Bismarck, ND 58501, telephone: (701) 228-2633

Ohio Department of Natural Resources, Fountain Square, Columbus, OH 43224, telephone: (614) 265-6565

Oklahoma Department of Wildlife Conservation, 1801 N. Lincoln, P.O. Box 53465, Oklahoma City, OK 73152, telephone: (405) 521-3851

Oregon Department of Fish and Wildlife, 2501 SW 1st Avenue, Portland, OR 97207, telephone: (503) 229-5410

Pennsylvania Department of Environmental Resources, Public Liaison Office, 16th Floor, MSSOB, P.O. Box 2063, Harrisburg, PA 17105-2063, telephone: (717) 783-2300

Rhode Island Department of Environmental Management, 9 Hayes Street, Providence, RI 02903, telephone: (401) 277-2080

South Carolina Department of Natural Resources, Rembert C. Dennis Building, P.O. Box 167, Columbia, SC 29202, telephone: (803) 734-3488

South Dakota Game, Fish and Parks Department, 523 East Capitol, Pierre, SD 57501-3182, telephone: (605) 773-3387

Tennessee Wildlife Resources Agency, P.O. Box 40747, Ellington Agricultural Center, Nashville, TN 37204, telephone: (615) 781-6500

Texas Parks and Wildlife Department, 4200 Smith School Road, Austin, TX 78744, telephone: (512) 389-4800

Utah Department of Natural Resources, 1636 W.N. Temple, Suite 316, Salt Lake City, UT 84116-3193, telephone: (801) 538-7200

Vermont Department of Fish and Wildlife, 103 S. Main, 10 South, Waterbury, VT 05671, telephone: (802) 241-3700

Virginia Department of Game and Inland Fisheries, 4010 W. Broad Street, P.O. Box 11104, Richmond, VA 23230, telephone: (804) 367-1000

Washington Department of Fish and Wildlife, 600 Capitol Way, N., Olympia, WA 98501, telephone: (206) 902-2200

West Virginia Division of Natural Resources, 1900 Kanawha Boulevard E., Charleston, WV 25305, telephone: (304) 558-2754

Wisconsin Department of Natural Resources, Box 7921, Madison, WI 53707, telephone: (608) 266-2621

Wyoming Game and Fish Department, 5400 Bishop Boulevard, Cheyenne, WY 82006, telephone: (307) 777-4600

Glossary

A

Abiotic factors—nonliving things found in an eco-system; examples include air, water, and soil.

Acorn—dried fruit or seed of a wide number of oak tree species.

Aesthetic value—benefits derived from the value people place on wildlife for beauty and appeal.

Air pollutant—any material that degrades air when released into it.

Albinism—inherited characteristic in which offspring have a color that parents do not; inability of an organism to produce pigment.

Alpine tundra—areas in mountains above tree lines, characterized by low temperatures and perma-frost.

Ammunition—any powder, shot, or bullets used in shotguns, rifles, or pistols.

Anatomy—the study of the form, shape, and appear-ance of animals.

Angiosperm—a plant that has enclosed seeds.

Animal well-being—using practices that provide the best environment and situation for animals.

Annual—plant that lives one growing season or year and dies.

Aquaculture—production of aquatic organisms; fish farming.

Aquatic wildlife—wildlife species that live in water.

Arresting trap—kind of trap that grips an animal without causing death.

Arthropoda phylum—the phylum in the animal kingdom that contains all species with external skele-tons and bodies divided into segments.

Asexual reproduction—producing new organisms without sexual reproduction.

Atmosphere—air that surrounds Earth.

B

Bag limit—the maximum number of animals that a hunter, fisher, or trapper can take in one day or sea-son.

Bait—live or dead material put on a hook or trap to entice an animal to bite or enter.

Banding—placing a band around the leg of a bird to identify it for study.

Barbel—a slender appendage that extends from the mouth area of some species of fish; serves as a sense organ.

Berry—fleshy fruit with seed usually embedded inside; often formed on small bushes, vines, or forbs.

Biennial—plant that has a two-year life cycle.

Biodiversity—the variety of living organisms that naturally exist in an area.

Biological magnification—process in the food chain where pollutants increase to concentrated levels.

Biome—a large area with a distinct combination of plant and animal life.

Biophage—a wildlife animal that eats living plants and animals.

Biotic factors—the living organisms found in an ecosystem.

Biotic pyramid—graphical way of showing a food chain.

Bird—an egg-laying vertebrate that has feathers, a pair of wings, and a pair of legs.

Birding—bird watching; identification and study of birds as a hobby.

Birth rate—number of young produced per unit of population over a given time.

Bivalve mollusk—species with hard shells covering the body; shells are hinged into two parts that can be opened by the animal; examples include clams, mussels, and oysters.

Bony fish—species of fish with internal skeletons made of bone; have swim bladders.

Botany—the science of plants.

Bowhunting—using a bow and arrow as a hunting device.

Browse—leaves, stems, and shoots of trees, shrubs, and vines used as food by some wildlife species, such as deer.

C

Canopy—the upper part of a tree comprised of limbs and foliage.

Career—the general sequence of occupations and jobs in a person's life.

Career pathway—a group of occupations involving similar interests and education needs.

Carnivore—an animal that eats the flesh of other animals.

Carrying capacity—maximum numerical level at which a wildlife population can live comfortably in an area.

Cartilaginous fish—species of fish having skeletons made of cartilage; do not have swim bladders and must keep moving to stay afloat.

Cartridge—ammunition manufactured for use in a rifle or pistol.

Capture gun—gun that shoots a dart laden with drugs to quickly cause an animal to become unconscious without causing other harm to the animal.

Choke—a constriction at the muzzle (end of barrel) of a shotgun.

Chordata phylum—the phylum in the animal kingdom containing all species with vertebrae.

Chromosome—tiny, twisted, thread-like structure made of protein and DNA; found in cells.

Circadian cycle—daily living cycle that recurs approximately every 24 hours.

Circulation—movement of substances within an organism.

Circulatory system—network of vessels that move blood throughout the body of an organism.

Citizenship—how people support their government and the ideals for which it stands.

Climate—the weather that is generally present in a location.

Climax stage—final stage in habitat growth.

Cloning—producing organisms without sexual union.

Commercial forest—where trees are grown to be harvested for wood products.

Commercial fishing—capturing wild fish from oceans and inland waters for use as human food and in making other products.

Commercial value—deriving money from wildlife.

Community—all living things in an area that live together in some sort of harmony.

Confining trap—kind of trap that captures an animal in an enclosure.

Conifer—evergreen trees with needle-like leaves.

Consumptive use—taking or harvesting wildlife so the organism is killed. (see nonconsumptive use)

Controlled burning—using fire to remove unwanted debris and enhance new plant growth.

Controlled hunting—a practice used to keep wildlife populations from exceeding carrying capacity.

Cotyledon—seedling leaves; structure in a seed that becomes the leaves of a new plant.

Cover—the vegetation or other material useful to a wildlife species in a habitat.

Crepuscular species—animal species that are active primarily at dusk and dawn.

Crown—the top part of a tree with limbs, leaves, and, perhaps, flowers and fruit.

Crust—surface of Earth.

Death rate—number of deaths per thousand population each year.

Deciduous—plants that have leaves in the summer and lose them in the fall.

Declining populations—populations that have no gains and lose numbers from one year to the next.

Degradable pollutant—a pollutant that can be decomposed, removed, or consumed. (see nondegradable pollutant)

Desert—an area of dry climate; moisture loss is greater than precipitation.

Dicot (dicotyledon)—plant species with seeds having two cotyledons; leaves have a network of veins.

Digestion—the process that changes food so it can be absorbed by an animal; occurs in the digestive system.

Dioecious—plant species in which male and female kinds of flowers are produced on separate plants.

Disease—any condition that disturbs normal body functions or structures.

Diurnal species—animal wildlife species that tends to be active only during the daylight and rests at night.

Domestication—process of bringing living things under the control of humans.

Dominance—when one or a few wildlife species control the habitat conditions that influence other species.

Dormant—condition of a perennial plant that sheds its leaves in the winter; a time when a plant is resting.

Earth science—study of the environment in which wildlife organisms live, grow, and die.

Ecological value—value of wildlife based on the role of each organism in nature.

Ecology—the study of ways organisms interact with their environment.

Ecosystem—the sum of the living and nonliving characteristics of an environment.

Ectotherm—an animal species that adjusts its body temperature to that of its surroundings; a species that does not maintain a constant body temperature.

Edge—the area where two habitats meet.

Elimination—process by which waste materials are expelled from the body.

Endangered species—wildlife species in immediate danger of extinction.

Endangered Species Act—Federal law passed in 1966 setting regulations about endangered species of wildlife and listing species that are endangered or threatened.

Endangerment—threatening a wildlife species so its numbers are very low or so the species goes out of existence.

Endotherm—animals that have the capacity to maintain a constant body temperature.

Engine emissions—materials released into the air by an engine.

Entrepreneur—a person or group of people who start and own a business to meet a particular consumer demand.

Equinox—day in fall and spring when the Sun is directly over the equator; day and night are of the same number of hours.

Escape cover—vegetation sufficiently dense to allow an animal to escape danger.

Estivation—inactivity of animals during warm weather to escape heat and conserve body moisture.

Estuary—land area where a stream flows into an ocean.

Excretory system—body system that rids the body of wastes.

Exterminating trap—kind of trap that grips and kills an animal.

Extinction—the disappearance of a wildlife species from Earth.

Extinct wildlife—species no longer living on Earth.

Featured species—a species in a habitat that is promoted through improved conditions.

Fee lake—small lake or pond where people are charged a fee to fish.

Fertilization—union of male and female sex cells in sexual reproduction.

Fertilizer—any substance used to add plant nutrients to the soil or other growing medium.

Fingerling—small fish ranging from 1 to 8 or 10 inches long.

Firearm—a tool that propels a projectile (bullet) by burning gun powder.

Firearm safety—preventing accidents and injury by using a firearm in a responsible manner.

Fisheries—the study of fish and related aquatic species.

Fishing—capturing fish with seines, nets, hooks, or other means.

Fishing hook—curved piece of metal for holding bait and sticking into and holding fish.

Fishing lure—artificial bait with one or more hooks; it is pulled through the water with the notion that a fish will mistake the lure for food and will strike as if to eat it.

Fishing season—time of the year when it is legal to catch certain species of fish.

Fishing tackle—equipment used in fishing.

Float—cork or other material lighter than water that adjusts the depth of the hook and bobs up and down to indicate a bite.

Follower—an individual who adopts the ideas, goals, or tasks of a leader.

Food—any substance that nourishes an organism; provides energy for growth, movement, and life processes.

Food chain—the sequence in a community in which wildlife animals get their food.

Food fish—fish captured or raised for food; typically 1 to 2 pounds for cultured fish.

Food web—the interconnection of food chains.

Forb—small broadleaf plant.

Forest—place where trees and other plants grow in a community that is ever changing.

Forester—a college-trained individual who works with forests.

Forest Service—an agency of the U.S. Department of Agriculture that oversees 156 national forests.

Fruit—a fleshy structure formed by a mature ovary of a flowering plant.

Fry—newly hatched fish; known as sac fry if yolk sac is still attached.

Fur—the soft, fine hairy coat that covers mammals.

Fur farming—raising animals for their fur and other products.

Game species—species hunted for sport or food.

Game value—placing value on wildlife species as game organisms.

Gene—a unit of heredity; found on chromosomes in each cell nucleus of an organism.

Genetics—study of how traits are passed from parents to offspring.

Geology—study of the solids parts of Earth's surface.

Germinate—sprouting of seed.

Gestation—period of development of an embryo and fetus in the reproductive tract of a female.

Girdling—cutting a small trench around the circumference of a tree trunk; results in death of tree.

Global warming—gradual increase in the temperature of the earth's surface due to concentrations of certain gases in the atmosphere.

Greenbelt—strip of grasses, shrubs, and other plants that serves as a cover leading from existing habitats to newly established habitat areas.

Growth—the process of an organism increasing in size by adding cells, by the cells getting larger, or by replacing cells.

Habitat—the physical area in which a wildlife species lives.

Habitat community—all of the living organisms in an area and how they interact with each other to establish a certain environment quality.

Habitat degradation—reducing the quality of the habitat in an area.

Habitat destruction—land use activities that result in loss of wildlife habitat.

Habitat management plan—a written document describing the needs of an area to improve a habitat for a featured species.

Hazard—something that causes danger or risk that may harm people, other living things, or property.

Health—the general body condition of an animal.

Healthy population—populations that have the capability of increasing or maintaining stable numbers from year to year.

Herbage—the succulent non-woody leaves and stems of herbaceous plants.

Herbicide—a chemical product used to control weeds.

Herbivore—an animal that eats only foods derived from plants.

Heredity—the acquisition of traits by offspring from their parents.

Home range—the space an animal normally uses for living.

Hunter orange—a bright, fluorescent color that helps other hunters see people who are wearing the color; safety material worn on the body and/or head to prevent accidental shooting.

Hunting—killing game for food or pleasure.

Hunting license—written document that indicates that a person has paid a fee and met other conditions to be entitled to hunt certain species of game animals.

Hydrology—study of the water found in the areas of Earth.

Ingestion—eating or taking in food.

Insecticide—a chemical product used to control insect pests.

Integumentary system—body system that covers and protects the internal organs and gives shape to the body; the skin.

Internode—the space on a plant stem between two nodes.

Interspersion—plots in different stages of growth mixed within an area.

Invertebrate—species of animals without an internal skeleton; an exoskeleton of hard material covers the body.

Kingdom—first and broadest classification of species in the scientific classification system.

Lacey Act—Federal law that regulates the shipment of illegally killed animals.

Landowner rights—the authority of landowners to control who enters their land.

Leadership—the ability to influence others to achieve worthy goals.

Legume—a plant that improves soil fertility by fixing nitrogen from the air in nodules on the roots of the plant.

Life processes—essential functions of a living organism in order to remain in the living condition.

Life span—period of life of an organism.

Lime—soil additive used on soils that are high in acid; compound containing calcium.

Limiting factor—a factor in a habitat that restricts the potential for growth or survival.

Line—string or other fiber material with a fish hook on one end with the other end attached to a pole or other device.

Live trapping—using methods of trapping that do not cause more than minimal physical injury to an animal.

Locomotion—movement of an animal from one place to another.

Malnutrition—lack of proper food.

Mammal—animal species with backbones; the females produce milk to feed their young.

Marksmanship—the ability to hit a target with the shot from a gun.

Marsh—low-lying land area that is wet and, sometimes, covered with water grasses, sedges, and rushes.

Mast—nuts, seeds, and fruit from trees and shrubs that serves as food for some wildlife species.

Metabolism—the internal process by which an organism gets energy from food.

Metamorphosis—a series of changes through which the young of some species develop as they mature.

Meteorology—study of the atmosphere.

Migration—moving from one climate region to another for a particular purpose; most common with birds, though some mammals migrate.

Mollusca phylum—the phylum in the animal kingdom containing all species with hard outer shells that are not divided into segments.

Molting—losing outer shell, feathers, or skin during the growth and maturation process.

Monocot (monocotyledon)—a plant species that produces seed with one cotyledon; leaves have parallel veins.

Monoculture—a large area that grows predominantly one species of plant.

Monoecious—plant species in which separate staminate and pistillate flowers are produced on the same plant.

Monogastric—an animal with a simple stomach having only one compartment.

Mortality—death rate of animals.

Mulch—material placed on land to prevent direct exposure of the soil to water or wind.

Muscular system—body system that creates bodily movement, support, and locomotion.

Mutation—change in the DNA and resulting organism that is not inherited from parents.

Muzzleloader—a firearm that is loaded through the barrel; not a modern firearm.

Natality—number of new animal organisms born in an area each year.

National Park Service—federal government agency that oversees operation of national parks; located in the Department of the Interior.

Native forest—a forest where the species are voluntarily growing; comprised of species that are naturally present in the area; contrasted with a tree farm where the trees of certain species have been planted.

Natural selection—process of organisms with favorable traits being stronger and surviving longer than those without the traits.

Naturalist—a person who studies nature.

Nature—the natural world around us.

Nature study—observing and learning about things in nature.

Nectar—a sugary secretion of flowers.

Nervous system—body system that conducts impulses from the brain to the muscles and from the muscles back to the brain.

Nesting cover—vegetation that covers the ground and conceals nesting birds against danger.

Nocturnal species—species that tend to be active at night, such as owls and bats.

Node—place on a stem where a leaf or leaves are attached.

Nonconsumptive use—watching or using wildlife organisms so they are not destroyed or killed.

Nondegradable pollutant—a polluting substance that is not easily broken down through natural processes.

Nongame species—species that are not hunted for food or sport.

Nonpoint source pollution—pollution from sources that cannot be readily identified.

Nuisance animal—an animal that is living in a place where it is not wanted; a pest animal.

Nut—a mature, dry fruit enclosed in a shell.

Nutrient—chemical substances in food that support life.

Oceanography—study of the water found in oceans.

Omnivore—an animal that eats both plant and animal foods.

Old-growth forest—area where trees have never been cut; an ancient forest.

Overpopulation—having a number of wildlife species that exceed the carrying capacity of their habitat.

Ovule—the female reproductive cell.

Owl pellet—a bolus of undigested material, such as hair and bone, that is regurgitated by an owl from its digestive tract.

Parasite—an organism that lives in or on another organism (known as a host) and derives food from the host.

Parasite burden—the presence of parasites without causing particular harm to an organism.

Pelt—fur and skin of an animal.

Perennial—plants that live more than two years with alternating vegetative and reproductive stages.

Personal skill—a quality of an individual that helps him or her relate to other people; common courtesy.

Personal trait—an observed quality of an individual that expresses the nature of the person; how people relate to each other.

Pest—a plant, animal, or other organism growing where it is not wanted.

Pesticide—material used to control pests.

Photosynthesis—process by which plants convert nutrients to food or simple sugars; occurs in the presence of chlorophyll and sunlight.

Phylum—the second division in the scientific classification system.

Physiology—study of the functions of parts of the anatomy of an organism.

Point source pollution—pollution that is discharged at places that are readily identifiable.

Pollen—the male reproductive cell.

Pollination—the transfer and union of pollen with an ovule or ovule structure.

Pollutant—any substance that causes pollution.

Pollution—act of releasing harmful substances into the environment.

Population—number of organisms.

Population density—number of wildlife organisms in an area; measure of how crowded the organisms are in their habitat.

Population status—overall health condition and numerical count of a wildlife population.

PPE (personal protective equipment)—equipment worn to protect individuals from hazards, such as goggles to protect the eyes or ear plugs to protect hearing.

Predation—the capture and consumption of one animal by another.

Predator—an animal species that hunts and uses other animals for food.

Prey—animals used as food by predators.

Primitive hunting device—a device with less power and capacity to kill; includes bows and arrows, crossbows, and muzzleloading guns.

Propelled net—kind of trap made of a mesh blanket that is shot through the air to capture animals.

Pruning—removing limbs, buds, fruit, and other plant structures to obtain a desired shape or growth condition.

R

Rare species—wildlife species that exists in small numbers.

Regrowth forest—wooded areas where trees have grown following cutting.

Renewable natural resources—resources that produce more of themselves if conditions are favorable.

Reproduction—process by which organisms give rise to new organisms of the same species.

Reproductive potential—ability of a population to increase.

Reproductive stage—the time when a plant is producing flowers, fruit, and seed. (see vegetative stage)

Research—the investigation of problems using scientific methods; seeking answers to questions.

Respiration—process by which an organism provides its cells with food and oxygen.

Respiratory system—body system that takes in oxygen and gives off carbon dioxide.

Revolution—movement of Earth in space around the Sun.

Rifle—a firearm with a spiral or rifle bore inside the barrel.

Ripe—a condition of fruit in which the amount of juice and sugar increases as maturity nears.

Rodent—small, gnawing monogastric animals with four large incisors; examples are rats and squirrels.

Rotation—turning of Earth on an imaginary axis; one rotation is 24 hours or a day.

Ruminant—an animal with a stomach divided into compartments.

S

Safety—exercising care to reduce risk and be free of harm and danger.

Saprophage—a wildlife animal that eats dead animals or plants.

Savanna—a grassland area with scattered trees; soil fertility is low.

Scats—animal droppings; often used as signs to identify animals present in an area.

Scientific method—an organized way of asking questions and seeking answers; used in research.

Scientific name—the name of a species based on its genus and species; written in italics or underlined with the first letter of the genus written as a capital.

Scientific value—value of wildlife for research and study.

Season length—number of days that a species can be hunted, fished, or trapped in a year.

Secretion—production within an organism of substances needed for life processes.

Seed—container of new plant life; formed in the ovaries of plants following fertilization.

Seedling—a young tree 15 to 18 inches tall.

Sensation—ability of an organism to feel or otherwise gather information and respond to its environment.

Sexual reproduction—union of sperm and egg to create a new organism.

Shell—container that holds shot, powder, and other parts needed in the ammunition of shotguns.

Shelterbelt—rows of trees and shrubs planted to reduce wind currents and drifting snow.

Shooting hours—time of the day when hunting can take place.

Shot—the pellet of lead, steel, or other metal used in a shotgun shell.

Shotgun—a firearm that fires several small pellets in a pattern at a target or game.

Sign—evidence that an animal is currently or has been in an area.

Silviculture—managing forest tree stands to increase productivity.

Sinker—small weight on a fishing line near the hook to cause the hook to move downward in the water.

Skeletal system—bony framework that gives the body shape and protects the organs.

Snag—standing, dead tree that serves as habitat and perches for some species of birds.

Soil—top few inches of Earth's crust that supports the growth of plants.

Soil aeration—adding air to the soil.

Soil conservation—using soil in a way to prevent loss and damage.

Soil degradation—lowering the quality of soil to grow crops and support wildlife; damaging the soil.

Soil erosion—washing, blowing, or wearing away of the soil.

Soil pollutant—any material that gets into the soil and degrades its quality.

Soil texture—the proportion of sand, silt, and clay found in soil.

Space—area or territory around an organism.

Species richness—the number of different species found in an area.

Sport fishing—capturing fish for relaxation and enjoyment; may be used for food or trophies.

Stock enhancement—improving the number and quality of fish in a natural lake or stream; raising and releasing fish into a lake or stream to increase the fish population.

Story—the horizontal layer of vegetative growth in a forest.

Succession—natural and progressive change as one community replaces another.

Supervised experience (SE)—the planned application of skills learned in class; may be in school labs, placed on jobs, own and care for animals or crops, and other ways; also known as supervised agriculture experience (SAE).

Swamp—land area where water stands on the surface during times of the year.

Taiga—areas in cold climates where large conifer forests grow.

Terrestrial wildlife—wildlife species that live on land.

Territory—the space of an individual animal within a home range.

Thermal pollution—raised temperature in some component of the habitat of wildlife, such as water, soil, or air.

Threatened species—wildlife species that is likely to become endangered in the future.

Trap—mechanical device used to capture animals.

Trapline—a series of traps, often along stream banks or in wooded areas.

Trapping—capturing animals using traps.

Trapping season—time of the year when it is legal to trap animals; time when pelts are most valuable and yield the highest grade.

Tree—a woody plant over eight feet tall with a well defined stem and a definite branching top.

Troposphere—layer of the atmosphere that is closest to Earth.

Trunk—main stem of a tree connecting the crown and roots.

Tundra—vast, treeless arctic areas or areas above treelines in mountains.

Understory—vegetation that grows beneath trees in a woodland.

Univalve mollusk—species of animals whose bodies are covered with a hard exoskeleton shell; the shell is a single, coiled structure; species are also known as gastropods and include snails, conchs, and limpets.

Urban forest—areas in cities where trees and other species found in forests grow.

Vascular plants—plants that have specialized cells forming structures to transport food, water, and minerals.

Vegetation management—using practices that promote the growth of desired plant species.

Vegetation survey—determining the kinds and amounts of vegetation present in a wildlife area.

Vegetative stage—the time when a young plant is rapidly adding new tissue and storing food.

Vertebrates—animals with backbones.

Vertical stratification—the physical arrangement of a community into layers.

Wasteful exploitation—not using wildlife wisely; killing too much game and not eating it; cutting trees and not using them.

Waterfowl—bird species that prefer to live around or in water.

Water pollutant—any liquid or solid material that gets into water and alters its natural state.

Weather—current condition in the atmosphere including temperature, moisture, wind, and atmospheric pressure.

Wildlife—all plants, animals, and other living things that have not been domesticated.

Weathering—the process of gradual conversion of rock into soil.

Wild flowering plant—a plant that produces flowers and grows wild without human effort; flowers are not necessarily attractive.

Wildflower—a plant that grows wild and has attractive or interesting flowers and other features.

Wildlife animal—an animal that has not been domesticated.

Wildlife conservation—wise use of wildlife resources.

Wildlife management—the art and science of manipulating a wildlife system to achieve a desired goal.

Wildlife plant—a plant that has not been domesticated.

Wildlife population—number of individuals in a group of organisms that occupy an area.

Wildlife population survey—counting the number of wildlife organisms in an area.

Wildlife productivity—rate at which mature wildlife organisms are produced.

Wildlife Refuge System—a system of some 400 wildlife refuges in the United States.

Woodland—land that has some covering of trees in various stages of maturity, species, and condition.

Woodlot—a woodland area on a farm.

Work habits—traits of individuals as related to job performance.

Zygote—product of fertilization in sexual reproduction; becomes an embryo.

Bibliography

Allaby, Michael. *The Concise Oxford Dictionary of Ecology*, 2nd Ed. New York: Oxford University Press, 1998.

Anderson, Stanley A. *Managing Our Wildlife Resources*. Englewood Cliffs, New Jersey: Simon and Schuster, 1991.

Benyus, Janine M. *The Field Guide to Wildlife Habitats*. New York: Simon & Schuster, 1989.

Boggess, Ed and Perry Loegering. *Wisconsin Cooperative Trapper Education Program Student Manual*. Madison: Wisconsin Department of Natural Resources, n.d.

Bolen, Eric G. and William L. Robinson. *Wildlife Ecology and Management*. Upper Saddle River, New Jersey: Prentice Hall, Inc., 1995.

Bookhout, Theodore. *Research and Management Techniques for Wildlife and Habitats*. Bethesda, Maryland: The Wildlife Society, 1994.

Corson, Walter H. *The Global Ecology Handbook*. Boston: Beacon Press, 1990.

Hall, Steve, ed. *Texas Hunter Education Manual*. Austin: Texas Parks and Wildlife, 1998.

Jaynes, Richard A. *Handbook of North American Nut Trees*. Geneva, New York: W.F. Humphrey Press Inc., 1995.

Judd, Mary K., Diane Schwartz, and Todd L. Peterson. *Wildlife and Your Land*. Madison: Wisconsin Bureau of Wildlife Management, 1995.

Kircher, Harry B., Donald L. Wallace, and Dorothy J. Gore. *Our Natural Resources and Their Conservation,* 7th Ed. Danville, Illinois: Interstate Publishers, Inc., 1992.

LaTourette, Joe. *Wildlife Watcher's Handbook.* New York: Henry Holt and Company, 1997.

Lee, Jasper S. and Michael E. Newman. *Aquaculture: An Introduction,* 2nd Ed. Danville, Illinois: Interstate Publishers, Inc., 1997.

Lee, Jasper S. *Natural Resources and Environmental Technology.* Danville, Illinois: Interstate Publishers, Inc., 2000.

Leopold, Aldo. *Game Management.* New York: Charles Scribner and Sons, 1948.

Owen, Oliver S., Daniel D. Chiras, and John P. Reganold. *Natural Resource Conservation,* 7th Ed. Upper Saddle River, New Jersey: Prentice-Hall, Inc., 1998.

Payne, Neil F. And Fred C. Bryant. *Techniques for Wildlife Habitat Management of Uplands.* New York: McGraw-Hill, Inc., 1994.

Porter, Lynn, Jasper S. Lee, Diana L. Turner, and Malcolm Hillan. *Environmental Science and Technology,* 2nd Ed. Danville, Illinois: Interstate Publishers, Inc., 2003.

Rolfe, G. L., John M. Edgington, I. I. Holland, and Gayle C. Fortenberry. *Forests and Forestry,* 5th Ed. Danville, Illinois: Interstate Publishers, Inc., 2003.

Scalet, Charles G., Lester D. Flake, and David W. Willies. *Introduction to Wildlife and Fisheries.* New York: W. H. Freeman and Company, 1996.

Smith, Robert L. and Thomas M. Smith. *Elements of Ecology,* 4th Ed. Menlo Park, California: The Benjamin/Cummings Publishing Company, 1998.

Stutzenbaker, C.D. *The Mottled Duck.* Austin: Texas Parks and Wildlife Department, 1988.

____. *North Carolina Hunter Education Manual.* Raleigh: North Carolina Wildlife Resources Commission, 1996.

____. *North American Wildlife.* Pleasantville, New York: Reader's Digest, 1996.

Index